# GALAPAGOS
## Islands of Birds

Bryan Nelson

# GALAPAGOS
## Islands of Birds

*With a foreword by H.R.H. The Duke of Edinburgh*

 *William Morrow & Company, Inc., New York*

# Dedication

I offer this book to my mother and her sister,
companion for seventy unbroken years, my aunt
Emily; to the memory of my father who died
whilst we were in the Galapagos; and to June,
who made the whole thing practicable.

# Contents

# List of Plates

Between pages 74 and 75

1 A tidal creek at the head of Darwin Bay. Juvenile frigates (white heads), adult male frigate and adult white booby in foreground
2 Our Darwin Bay camp. This low coral beach is occasionally breached by extra high tides
3 Red-footed boobies soon found our tent
4 The mocking birds, alert and thieving, were a constant delight or irritation
5 A young sea-lion looks amazed at the sight of a native on Hood Island
6 Our tame Darwin's finch – a large-billed *magnirostris* male from Tower
7 June with red-footed booby in the crow's nest
8 Carl Angermeyer makes a good barber on *Beagle II*. Here he practises on the author
9 *Beagle II*, the vessel of the Charles Darwin Research Station
10 H.R.H. The Duke of Edinburgh with the author on Hood Island

GALAPAGOS HERONS
11 Adult yellow-crowned night heron
12 Small Galapagos blue heron stalking prey
13 Great grey heron, much like our own

RED-FOOTED BOOBY
14 Brown and white forms of the red-foot
15 White form. Teamwork in defence by mother and chick
16 Male, left, 'advertises' (a sexual display) to female. Notice this species' short legs
17 Reciprocal aggression between members of a pair. Bird on right showing synchronous wing-flailing and evoking threat from mate

Between pages 170 and 171

GANNET
18 A fierce territorial fight. No boobies fight to any comparable extent
19 The gannet's ecstatic meeting ceremony

viii

# Figures in the Text

by John Busby and the author

# Foreword

## By H.R.H. The Duke of Edinburgh

In *Galapagos: Islands of Birds* Bryan Nelson has achieved a rare combination; he has written a book full of important information and valuable scientific discussion in a lively and entertaining style.

I found the book particularly interesting as I had the pleasure of visiting Tower and Hood and meeting the Nelsons at their camp on Hood Island, albeit on the last day of its occupation. Although the author makes light of their long period of isolated existence, it ranks as a major achievement in itself. I think he is also particularly fortunate to have found a wife and helper willing and able to put up with that kind of life, and at the end of it all to appear as neat and tidy as the day she left civilisation.

If, on occasions, his descriptions of life sound almost idyllic, I would strongly advise anyone who has ideas about rushing off to live on a desert island to think three and preferably four times about it and then to consult June Nelson.

The Galapagos Islands hold a special fascination for all naturalists. I suppose it is partly because of their association with Darwin and partly because of their extraordinary list of animal populations that they inevitably prompt speculation about the 'hows' and 'whys' of evolution. Dr Nelson has quite a lot to say about this fascinating subject as a result of watching and recording many of the islands' animal inhabitants. It is books of this kind which emphasise what a fundamental redirection of human thought was initiated by Darwin with the publication of *The Origin of Species*.

The objective study of wild populations within their environment is yielding more and more remarkable information. However, I find it difficult to believe that every feature of structure and behaviour is equally important for the purposes of survival. In some species quite wide margins of difference in physical features or behaviour patterns seem to be tolerated, whereas in other cases a very slight difference or aberration can spell greater success or complete extinction in a particular environment. The difficulty seems to be to assess the relative survival value of any particular feature without an exact knowledge of all the environmental changes through which a particular species has developed, and without being able to distinguish accurately which features of colour and habit have given rise to greater breeding success.

There seems to be one hangover from the pre-Darwinian days which still recurs to haunt many ethologists today. It was not unnatural for the philosophers of old to make a sharp distinction in humans between the purely physical processes of life and the apparently totally different operation of the brain; the growth of a fingernail and the ability to invent a limerick were considered to be two quite unrelated processes. They probably are, but in animals, without the same ability of conscious and deliberate thought, the processes of the brain must surely form an integral part of the physical process as a whole. To a large extent the animal brain must resemble a 'printed circuit', in that a particular combination of inputs produces a given output every time. The answer to the questions 'Why does a bird grow feathers?' and 'Why does a bird have a migratory instinct?' is the same: it is part of the whole physical process of a successful species. Without both these features it would have become another failure or, at any rate, a different sort of bird.

This to me is the wonder and fascination of the evolutionary concept, that the process of natural selection has controlled the very minutest details of every feature of the whole individual and the group to which it belongs.

This book, and a more specialist one about the Boobies and Gannets of the world which I hope is to follow soon, will provide many new pieces for the giant jig-saw puzzle of life which the natural sciences are slowly putting together; Dr Bryan Nelson has made a valuable contribution and I am sure he would consider that ample reward for all his discomforts, painstaking observations and detailed records.

*Buckingham Palace*                                               PHILIP

# *Preface*

Any Galapagos chronicler is immediately handicapped by the brilliance of Charles Darwin and William Beebe, who have immortalised these enchanted islands. Fortunately, they were both biologists of breadth and vision; for all Darwin's ability to spend years investigating barnacles and for all Beebe's declared passion for the particular problem, the tiny thread, the square yard of jungle, they both, literally and intellectually, crossed continents. Their time in the Galapagos was measured in hours, though the range of their curiosity was vast. I, on the other hand, sat down for a year on two of the lesser islands and tried to unravel the life histories of the sea-birds.

This book is a series of their portraits, painted broadly with spring balance, binoculars, camera and field notebook. It cannot be a work about the archipelago and in the main it will not be anecdotal, simply because it is not the tale of a single happening – not a 'first walk on Santa Cruz' or a 'visit to a crater lake', with all their wayward encounters, but an attempt, as complete as time allowed, to see what made my subjects tick. I would like to think it contains enough completely new material to interest the serious naturalist and biologist, though it has not been my aim to burden the account with supporting details nor with the references to existing literature which are essential to a scientific paper. Yet the setting is the incomparable Galapagos Islands and who could depict them and their inhabitants solely in the clinical language of science.

It becomes more and more difficult to find a Garden of Eden. My wife and I were lucky enough to spend a year on two of the uninhabited Galapagos islands, Tower and Hood – about as gardenlike as a lava desert – but for a year we were Adam and Eve; there was nobody else on earth, so far as we could tell. Many friends who are not biologists have said they might muster the energy to read what we found and did, if written without jargon. This is my attempt.

Sea-birds, Galapagos wildlife and desert island camps are my themes in order of priority, preferring accuracy to a good story, but ordinary words to technical terms. Whether the hybrid produced by the union of formal biology, particularly behaviour and ecology, with island-living-cum-nature-minstrelsy, turns out neither fish nor fowl, the reader must judge. I hope that any merit the book has lies in the facts, which were gathered with substantial effort in the field, rather than the fancies which, later, armchair comfort induced. Finally, I hope that the contribution made by the sea-birds of the Peruvian Guano Islands, especially the piquero, will persuade the reader to overlook my licence in including them.

B.N.

# *Acknowledgements*

A few people will know the real extent of my debt to my wife, field assistant, cook, secretary, companion and critic rolled into one, and that, not in the comfort of a modern home within reach of car, gadgetry, supermarket and diversions, but first for three years on the windy old Bass Rock and then in the heat and restrictions of life on an uninhabited and waterless Galapagos island.

In Ecuador we fell deeply in debt to Dr and Mrs Roberto Gilbert-Elizalde, who were incurably kind and hospitable; John Lacey, who did far more than duty required; and Rolf and Aricelli Blomburg, who enabled us to see Quito. We wish also to thank helpful Ecuadorian officials, from the Minister of the Interior to the Naval Commander on San Cristobal and the Air Force Captain on Seymour. In the Galapagos Dr David Snow and Barbara gave invaluable guidance, assistance and hospitality; David was then Director of the Charles Darwin Research Station. All the Angermeyers, but especially Carl and Marga, Mrs Horneman and the dear old Rambecks, were unfailingly kind and hospitable. Edgar Pots did me the greatest service in repairing my camera so that I could take photographs on Hood and showed numerous other personal kindnesses. Miguel Castro was, as always, a tower of strength on the few occasions when we were together in the field. Later in the day, Roger Perry, fourth director of the Station, accepted me as a doubtful legacy bequeathed by David Snow and was immensely helpful. Dave Balfour of the *Lucent*, the *Beagle*'s crew, Julian Fitter and Richard Foster, cheerfully bore the many chores which arose because of us.

In Peru, Ing. Gamarra and the officials of the Corporacion Nacional de Fertilisantes, especially Señor Cabrera and Ing. Onego Foridencia and the *guardianes* of Guañape Norte, showed such kindness that one can only hope that they would receive its equivalent if ever they visited Britain. Mr Griffis of the *Peruvian Times* and Mr

xix

Spire, first Commercial Secretary at the British Embassy in Lima, also spent time and thought arranging contacts. Later, Col. Ian Grimwood very kindly provided access to information on the 1964–1965 crash of guano birds.

Perhaps more prosaically, but essentially, I acknowledge my large debt to the United States Frank M. Chapman Foundation, without whose generous aid towards travelling and equipment this expedition could never have taken place. Dean Amadon, its chairman, was a model of prompt, brief and understanding action. The Carnegie Trust provided a zoology scholarship, which in conjunction with the Chapman award financed the work, and is gratefully acknowledged. R. Cushman Murphy helped by correspondence, but especially through his classic *Oceanic Birds of South America*, to which I, in common with all others interested in sea-birds, owe a big debt.

I am deeply privileged that His Royal Highness The Duke of Edinburgh has consented to write the foreword to this book and so further the cause of conservation in the Galapagos.

I am most grateful to my friend John Busby for the time and care spent on the drawings. Although, necessarily, guided by photographs and my requests, his free and artistic interpretation of his subjects will delight everybody. My own drawings were traced directly from negatives and are purely functional. Major Aubrey Buxton kindly provided the photograph of the Duke of Edinburgh and has helped enormously in other ways.

Last, but in some ways most of all, I must acknowledge my debt to Prof. Niko Tinbergen, F.R.S., and Dr Michael Cullen, for it was they who encouraged my interest in sea-birds and provided the basis for most of whatever I understand about animal behaviour. The time, effort and skill which they devote to their fledglings' scientific well-being is invaluable. It is essential that I do not imply their necessary agreement with anything I say in this book!

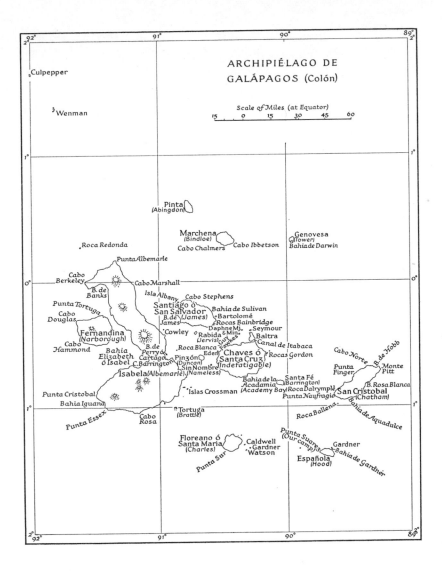

ARCHIPIÉLAGO DE
GALÁPAGOS (Colón)

Scale of Miles (at Equator)

15    0    15    30    45    60

2°  92°                    91°                    90°                    89°  2°

Culpepper

Wenman

1°                                                                          1°

Pinta
(Abingdon)

Marchena                    Genovesa
(Bindloe)                    (Tower)
Roca Redonda        Cabo Chalmers  Cabo Ibbetson   Bahia de Darwin

Punta Albemarle

Cabo
Berkeley          Cabo Marshall
0°       B. de                                                              0°
Banks         Isla Albany   Cabo Stephens
Punta Tortuga                Santiago ó        Bahia de Sulivan
Cabo                        San Salvador       Bartolomé
Douglas                     B. de (James)      Rocas Bainbridge
James      Cowley   Daphne Mj.      Seymour
Fernandina            Rabida & Min.  Baltra
(Narborough)          (Jervis)  Guy    Canal de Itabaca      Cabo Norte  B. de Hobb
Cabo         B. de   Roca Blanca  Fowler              Punta        Monte
Hammond      Perry & Eden    Chaves ó  Rocas Gordon    Finger       Pitt
Bahia   Cartago         Santa Cruz
Elizabeth  C. Barrington  Pinzón  (Indefatigable)                 B. Rosa Blanca
ó Isabel          (Duncan)  Sin Nombre                 San Cristobal
Isabela (Albemarle)  (Nameless)                        (Chatham)
Bahia de la   Santa Fé
Punta Cristobal              Academia  (Barrington)
Bahia Iguana     Islas Crossman  (Academy Bay) Roca Dalrymple
1°                                  Punta Naufragio            Bahia de Aquadulce  1°
Punta Essex   Cabo            Roca Ballena
Rosa    Tortuga
(Brattle)
Floreano ó      Punta Suare
Santa Maria   Caldwell  (Our camp)      Gardner
(Charles)  Gardner                Bahia de Gardner
Watson   Española
Punta Sur          (Hood)

2°  92°                    91°                    90°                    89°  2°

# *Preliminaries* *I*

Two bleached skeletons rested side by side on a strip of black Galapagos lava lonely in the Pacific. One domed skull held the nest of a tiny black Darwin's finch. The male habitually alighted on the inviting row of lower teeth, in a mouth prised open as the muscles dried and contracted. This was mainly my fantasy, but there were some gloomy prophecies too, and it had happened in the past.*

Here, it was 12 October 1963 on the Bass Rock, Scotland. The Galapagos boxes, ten stout wooden ones, stood in orderly rows, lids open, on the coconut matting between the gleaming brass in the silent engine house. Her Majesty's Commissioners of Northern Lights would have been shocked, but there was no other place big enough to shelter our gear from the rain. City dwellers, poor devils, were already resigning themselves to wet pavements, cold, fog and indoor comforts. On the Bass the autumn gales blustered, whipping the Forth into white caps and whining desolately in the stays and wires of the famous lighthouse. Most of the gannets, the real owners of the Rock, had already deserted their nests. Now they would be careening over the bleak North Sea, cutting impassively into the teeth of the wind or, with a small inflection of the wings, hurtling before it. Winter seas, however stormy, do not trouble a gannet; he is truly oceanic, impervious to the icy salt water and quite able to tame the wind. The other sea-birds, kittiwakes, puffins, guillemots, razorbills and fulmars, had long since left the Rock, which was bowing its basaltic shoulders to take the winter storms that we, escapists, would evade on our new island.

It is a great sight, the Bass in a good going gale; permanence against destruction, defiance against brute force. The Bass is a natural fortress, the finest of Scott's 'emeralds chased in gold'. It was a fastness millennia before a Scottish king, possibly Malcolm II, built

* Remember Lorenz and Nuggerwood (see Chapter 3).

there a garrison post that, outwardly little decayed, still seems to grow naturally from the rock itself. It stood invincible for centuries, a thorn in the English flesh (they first tried to take it in 1548 or 1549) and a symbol of independence intolerable to the Plantagenet Edward, the 'hammer of the Scots'. Now, even the keepers are often English and I suppose it is too inaccessible for university students to paint 'home rule for Scotland' on the great east face. Oddly enough, the first thing we saw on Tower in the Galapagos was the defacement of the cliffs by great white letters; the names and dates of visiting yachts whose crews wanted them to be remembered; the evidence of their desire for immortality still jolts those who sail eagerly into Darwin Bay, expecting to find this lonely island as nature left it.

Among the sweet shavings, with the sun slanting through the dusty windows, and outside the rock pipits singing an autumnal song, we worked away at our ten chests, made of half-inch deal with the corners protected by old cans flattened and cut into shape. Each measured 36″ × 20″ × 20″; it had taken me and two lighthouse keepers, or perhaps two keepers and me, a fortnight of planing, sawing and hammering to convert a stack of cheap timber into something useful, but it would have cost five times as much to have had them made professionally. Incidentally, the best way to get a perfectly fitting lid, with sides, is to make a closed box and then saw through at the required height. Lighthouse keepers detest flimsy jobs and like weight and strength, but I stupidly failed to imagine that often enough a single skinny porter would have to manhandle these heavy, obstinate boxes across greasy gangplanks.

The Bass had seen many a sea chest, from those holding the public records of the Church of Scotland along with gold and silver plate belonging to the Earl of Buccleuch, brought there to escape Cromwell, to the fortnightly provisions for the keepers, delivered fair weather and foul by the vessels of the Lighthouse Service. Food, cannonballs, heraldic plate, treasure, kings, ecclesiastics, papal bulls and who knows what else going on to the Bass; dead gannets, oil, feathers and the products of men's minds and hands going off – a queer traffic.

No chests, though, had ever left the Rock as ours did, bound for a far remoter island, also the haunt of sea-birds but baking on the

Equator in the Pacific – the Galapagos island of Tower or Genovesa. Stowed on the Bass, disinterred on Tower some 5,000 miles, ten weeks and much sweat later. It seemed unreal stacking away our battered paraffin oven, for instance, with the thought of next setting it up for baking day in the Galapagos. The very age and battered conditions of our things established a continuity between the old life and the new and brought a trivial satisfaction that was not entirely thrifty. Our years on the Bass were in fact extremely useful, not only in helping us to estimate the food we needed but more vitally in reassuring us that we could stand each other in prolonged and isolated confinement. We can honestly say that it was not in the least difficult, but perhaps that was only because we had plenty of interesting work to do. People often remark that 'tests' of this kind must either make or break personal relationships but to my mind they need not do either. Frank and 'Bobby' Darling spent several happy years on remote, uninhabited Scottish Islands, often under harsh conditions. Yet they parted afterwards. The special circumstances come and go and may leave little mark.

The chests symbolised the self-contained life we were to lead on Tower; they held the essence of our venture – notebooks, cameras, films, clothes, tools, tents, cooking and eating equipment and materials for a crude solar still, together with tinned and dried food. There were gaps to hold 60 lb of butter, 70 lb of margarine and lard and 20 lb of bacon, from Selfridges in London. We went to some trouble to obtain these provisions, fearing to rely on the ship's chandlers in Ecuador. Then we heard that good tinned butter was available not only in Ecuador but actually on Santa Cruz at Academy Bay. 'Don't drag extra hundredweights to the Galapagos – sell it and buy more there,' said someone. When we got there we found everybody smearing oil on their bread and no butter within 600 miles.

Lists proliferated endlessly, amidst calculations about the amount of dried yeast, dried egg, dried vegetables and spaghetti for a year's camping. Large items like flour were easy; we made a rough calculation on the basis of our Bass experience and then doubled it. Knowing that replacements would be entirely out of the question we took plenty of spare parts for lamps, primuses and oven, and twine, canvas, ropes, sail-maker's needles, darning needles, solder, tools, etc. Even the alcohol for pre-heating our lamp and primuses lasted the full term. Our friends from the *Kismet* (see Chapter 8) used to hold a daily vote to decide the fate of that day's alcohol – was it to burn wastefully, as a flame, or economically in the internal machinery of their bodies. They soon got used to cold food.

Instead of shipping all our supplies from England, we found Elias Mayorga, the most reliable ship's chandler in Guayaquil, the Pacific port for the Galapagos. After many sickly-warm bottles of the local pilsner consumed in the stifling heat of the market-place, seething with the usual indescribable, dirty but fascinating throng of humanity common to all the Central and South American ports we visited, we came to an amiable understanding that cost us some 17,000 *sucres* (£300) and Elias Mayorga and Sons some forty-nine boxes of very mixed food. Two people eat a lot in a year. If you are interested in exactly how much, there is an appendix with the full list at the back of this book. But we could have survived on much less.

We were going to all this trouble, lugging a year's food and equipment to a remote desert island, for one main and, we hoped, good reason. It was to study three species of colonial sea-bird – three kinds of booby belonging to the same family as the gannet. You may think it was an abominable waste of time, effort and money; I still think it was a good enough reason. We learnt a lot, as I hope the following pages will show, and there is good biological precedent for that!

People who have little to do with academic research often ask how expeditions of this kind arise; who pays for them and why? There is often a clear hint of criticism, born understandably from the contrast between the daily grind to which millions are committed and the apparently carefree, idyllic and above all unproductive existence on an uninhabited island.

Film-makers, photographers, more or less professional writers and broadcasters, shoe-string university vacation expeditions and a handful of individual adventurers form one heterogeneous assemblage of odd-corner wanderers, liable to turn up almost anywhere. But nowadays few people pay out of their own pockets for extensive travels in the interests of biological work. Relatively long-term studies are usually supported by a university or a grant-giving body. Darling, whose popular books did much to stimulate the imagination of aspiring young biologists, once wrote that if his work was worth-while the money would be forthcoming, if not he would 'go down the nick and good riddance'. This is less true than it was when he penned it in 1939, simply because there is more money stirring. Still, it is not to be had for the asking. The work has to seem worthwhile to the body concerned and it is usually assessed, in outline, by people highly experienced in the relevant subject. Nor does one expect to live in luxury. Our total living grant for the period October 1963 to May 1965 was £600, though it was officially intended for only a year. In addition we received our return fare to the Galapagos and some film and equipment from a generous American foundation. We counted ourselves lucky to combine our work with our natural bent and this is perhaps the greatest good fortune of all. Field scientists are particularly lucky in that their work often takes them to wild and beautiful places, whereas a physics or chemistry building is much the same anywhere. Despite this, the biological sciences are by no means top heavy with field workers. The glamour and comfort of the laboratory perhaps counts as well as other worthier reasons.

A persistent critic, however, might well argue that field scientists working on pest control, agriculture, forestry and wild life manage-ment are one thing; field scientists working on purely academic problems connected with sea-birds are quite another. The simple responsibility to put something practical back into one's society becomes even more relevant where this society, as ours, is permissive.

*Figure 1* Oystercatchers

Culture, however, is 'practical' and an understanding of birds and beasts has, since pre-history, been part of culture. However, we must away to our islands and birds, leaving the complexities of modern societies and their trends to those competent to deal with them.

The little we saw of Ecuador suggested that this, the second smallest South American country with some four and a half million people, has immense potential. It is certainly a country of unbelievably dramatic contrasts. To me it was chiefly the lucky custodian of the wonderful Galapagos Islands, a sort of international guardian. But it is also the country of Quito, its magnificent capital city 9,375 feet in the Andes beneath the eternal snowfields of Chimborazo and Cotopaxi, the wild domain of the great Andean condor, and the country of the steaming Guayas plain, filled with cacao, rice and the overwhelming Ecuador bananas, millions of them. The Guayas lowlands are flatter than anything I have ever seen. There, the railway tracks converge to a shining point in the far distance and the massive, leafy growth of the boring monocotyledons restricts one's entire horizon to a blank wall of vegetation. In some areas nothing, absolutely nothing, rears its head high enough to form a landmark above the banana jungle and the thousands of Ecuadorian Indians living in their banana-leaf thatched dwellings in the plantations are as securely cloistered as a monk in his cell. On our return from the Galapagos we plunged down on to this alluvial plain by the dizzy Quito–Guayaquil railroad which drops 9,025 feet in forty-nine miles from Guamote to Bucay.

The Galapagos Islands are reached by sea from Guayaquil, the second city of Ecuador which, its citizens say with some rancour, makes the money for Quito to spend; the football derbies between them are intense affairs. It is as ugly, dirty and commercial, as Quito apart from its smells is romantic and medievally charming. Nevertheless it has some attractive corners and is a friendly place. Guayaquil's Malecon hugs the dirty, fast-flowing Guayas river, from which pirates used to sack the ancient city, probably before sailing out to the Galapagos. The thick yellow water, like wool suds, swirls past banks littered with rotting banana stems and less wholesome detritus among which the human flotsam pokes and rummages and lights smoky little fires to boil tea-water in rusty old cans. Water-borne diseases are mercifully beyond the understanding of many Ecuadorians who submerge themselves ablutionally in the filthy river and even rinse out their mouths with it. Barges inch their way upstream against the current or sweep grandly down with it. The waterfront is irresistible, thronged with craft and lined with ramparts of green bananas and a motley collection of remarkable cars and lorries. An air terminal is like an overgrown bus station but docks, water-fronts and harbours are stirring places – tangles of tropic-rusted, storm-battered or paint-new liners, filthy tramps, trawlers, lobster boats, yachts and dinghies. Airports smell of nothing but fuel and that warm human compound of scent, tobacco and bodies, but docks regale the nostrils with resin, fish, vegetable matter, mud, effluvia, the hot and nauseating engine-room smell – a whole library of evocative odours.

We haunted the busy waterfront. Again and again in Ecuador it seemed that the sheer impact of people far exceeded that of any European crowd. They overpower by noise, colour and boisterousness. It would often be better if they were a little more inhibited; but if the authorities won't provide public lavatories . . .

A chance friendship enormously smoothed a potentially troublesome passage through Guayaquil. Dr Roberto Gilbert was to us, as D'Arcy Thompson to British Zoology, a bright light in a dark night. He was also the owner and eminent surgeon of the private Clinica Guayaquil and chief surgeon in the General Welfare Hospital, a third-generation surgeon of Guayaquil. His great-grandfather was a British sea-captain. Nearly everybody from (fortunately) the Chief of Customs downwards, seemed to have surrendered a gall-stone, an appendix or some other detachable portion of anatomy to Dr Gilbert. In 1964 he made world news by transplanting a hand from a fresh corpse on to a sailor maimed by a premature hand-grenade explosion. Unfortunately the graft was eventually rejected, but the operation was a prodigious technical feat and a generous attempt to save the man's hand. Deferential to a man, the trades-people of Guayaquil greeted Dr Gilbert with affection as he penetrated the clogged back streets in his immaculate surgeon's gown, pursuing some elusive article on our behalf.

I hoard odd fragments in my Galapagos junk box, amongst them a dried-out iguana, an albatross embryo, some sea-lion teeth and a treasured letter from the Ecuadorian Minister of the Interior, procured for us on the day of our departure to the islands by Dr Gilbert in person. These were the early days of the military junta that deposed President Arrosemeana in 1963, and the Town Hall was thick with heavily armed soldiers and buzzing with people. The Minister was engaged in the central chambers of this rather forbidding building, but Dr Gilbert forced his way through, with charming smiles and eloquent Spanish, whilst I trailed to heel trying to look like a cross between his bodyguard, patient and colleague but more resembling an anxious greyhound. Surviving a succession of exuberant Latin-American embraces, he interrupted the Minister in conference and got him to sign an astonishing letter which read: 'I hereby request all civil and military aid to be put at the disposal of Her Britannic Majesty's special envoys Dr and Señora J. B. Nelson.' Bureaucracy wears a double face in Ecuador. It can be as obstructive as the most infuriating British brand, but the tangle is far more easily cut by those who know how, or how much. It has taken ours a long time to perfect its intransigence.

It was Dr Gilbert who spotted the *Cristobal Carrier* at the eastern end of the Malecon, wallowing at her berth on the muddy river Guayas. At that moment our equipment lay in a garage in Guayaquil, our year's supply of food in Mayorga's store, our personal belongings and cameras were at the Pension Helbig (which we strongly recommend to frugal Europeans visiting Guayaquil), our dinghy floated in a creek up river and various items, such as four fifteen-gallon polythene water-containers in stout wooden cases and a few sacks of flour and sugar, sat on the roof of the Clinica. The *Carrier* does not permit loading of passengers' cargo until a few hours before sailing, in which time we had to co-ordinate the collection and loading of this heterogeneous mass.

John Lacey, the British Consul, was a great help. When my first letter arrived, briefly stating our intention of living on Tower, the Consulate made some pungent comments. As British subjects within his territory we could have created technical problems if it became necessary to ship the dead bodies home, or at least to the mainland; there is no deep freeze in the Galapagos, none on the *Carrier* and only monthly sailings. However, once convinced that we were sane and responsible, he gave endless assistance.

A lorry and the inevitable agent tackled our logistical problems. In Guayaquil one hails a lorry in the same way as a taxi. Ours was falling to pieces; the wheels were secured by lashings of wire and the cab had been gradually replaced by old boards; it had no front screen or windows. On level ground it thrashed itself to a juddering fifteen m.p.h. after interminable passages through the worn gears. We ground our way to the waterside and the *Carrier*, picking up from various depots en route. By this time our entourage included two lorries, two cars and a van, with a labour force of thirteen, including the British Consul.

The old *Carrier*, swarming with people, was tenuously linked with the broken slats of the so-called wharf (for the use of which one pays forty *sucres*) poised above the swirling, muddy river. The bare, leathery feet of the stevedores pattered across to the hold up a long gangplank with a steep slope and an unfriendly tilt. Traffic was strictly one way and anyone wanting to get aboard scurried to join the upstream flow before the lights changed. Coca-Cola and cement seemed to be the principal exports. The cement worried me; it looked just like our flour with which it was being loaded simultaneously; dusty porter followed dusty porter and it didn't need much imagination——

As I rushed around trying to keep tabs on the stream of boxes, sacks and cans, particularly the alcohol for pre-heating the primuses, I saw a well-built fellow, bronzed and bearded, with the hint of a swagger and a flashing smile. He was bandying words in Spanish with one of the crew and gold fillings gleamed with each smile. Later we sailed a few times with Carl Angermeyer in *Beagle II*, and drank excellent coffee in his interesting house built from blocks of lava. We also met his brothers Gus and Fritz and the Angermeyer wives, Marga, Carmen and Señora Gus (the relationship between the wives of Carl and Fritz make Carl his brother's stepfather*). The Angermeyers set out in their own yacht from Hamburg in 1936, five young brothers looking for their idea of the good life and

* They are mother and daughter.

escaping from the increasingly oppressive climate of a Germany where Hitler and his brownshirts were screaming ever more ominously. After their fair share of adventures they finished up on Santa Cruz in the Galapagos. Three of them are still there and have built their own trim fishing-boats and lava-rock houses. Carl no longer fishes; he has developed a distinctive style of oil painting capturing the tortured volcanic landscapes and cacti which are the chief glory of the Galapagos scene. They do not yet command the prices which some grade A lunatics pay for a Warhol picture of a Campbell's soup tin or a plastic giant hamburger. Fritz, the master boat-builder, is the deep one of the trio, with smouldering eyes. He makes every word count. Gus, the cheerful extrovert, has almost completed an autobiography which will discredit the shamelessly untrue articles by which some unscrupulous free-lance journalists and photographers have profited at the Angermeyers' expense.

At the *Cristobal Carrier* I envied the sangfroid of the stranger, whilst I rushed around like a disoriented ant. So much faceless junk was being swallowed up by the gaping hold that I felt any article marked a shade ambiguously would be irretrievably buried. The cargo-master checked in the precise number of items against the owner's name and only that number could be claimed at the other end. If anything slipped past him we had problems later. In fact we lost our only crate of stewed steak due to just such a discrepancy between the 'in' and 'out' count – a serious loss since our other main meat supply for the year, bully beef, was inedible and we dumped the lot in Darwin Bay less than three weeks after our arrival on Tower.

The official blurb from Cetuga Co. Ltd, the concern running the *Cristobal Carrier* on a roughly monthly schedule from Guayaquil to the Galapagos, describes her in generous terms. The 'well-stocked bar, spacious dining-room, large after-deck, good refrigeration system, powerful light plants, radio station and hot and cold water' were rather 'within the meaning of the word'. She was, I think, a war surplus landing craft from the U.S. government, modified by the Ecuadorians. Practically flat-bottomed and square-ended, with a high prow as the sole concession to the regular crossing of six hundred miles of open Pacific, the first good storm would undoubtedly finish her. Fortunately her route lies in a storm-free track. Fair and square on the aft three-quarters of the deck, with its sides sheer to the gunwales, sat what looked like a decrepit cricket pavilion. This was the 'special class' accommodation. Forward lay the main hatch and open fore-deck, piled with stems of bananas and miscellaneous cargo such as tree trunks. In the extreme stern, partly shaded by a tattered, loosely flapping tarpaulin, a patch of deck was graced by two enormous stems of bananas. The only route down from the special quarters threaded through the wheel-house and a small hatch and down an iron ladder on to the ship's deck, where the under-privileged 'first class' passengers survived. Below there, I understand, one could take a chance with the cattle.

For special class passengers the voyage is quite pleasant. The cabins are small but adequate and the food is at least ample, even if garlic stew makes an unusual breakfast for an Englishman. Fresh air is free and one can sit under the tarpaulin eating excellent Ecuadorian bananas, spotting the waved albatrosses, swallow-tailed gulls, red-footed, blue-footed and white boobies, Hawaiian, Madeiran and Galapagos storm petrels, Audubon shearwaters, bosun and man o' war birds that become commoner as one nears this remote archipelago where they all breed. One night a Galapagos storm petrel landed with a thud in our cabin and subsequently others flopped on to various parts of the ship, doubtless attracted by the lights as migrants flutter against lighthouses. They are delightful little birds, velvety black with white rumps, forked tails and delicately segmented tube noses and a pleasantly musky scent. Flying fish leap in small, silver showers, porpoises appear from time to time, sharks, mantas and other large fish cruise through the clear water and all the while the port-holes dribble and the diesel engines burble, driving the boat at a fair five knots to the famous 'Archipelago de Colon'. Still, I should hate to be aboard the *Carrier* if ever it did hit rough weather. There was no lifeboat, neither could I see a single life-jacket.

The first landfall is Chatham or San Cristobal and with three raucous blasts the carrier slipped into Wreck Bay at five one morning. The settlement includes the naval command buildings, a bust of Charles Darwin and an office and representative of the Cetuga Company. A fine sweep of golden sand runs to meet a nice rickety wooden pier and the wooden houses spill down to the water's edge, unspoiled by concrete or tarmac frontage or road. The village 'pub' squats companionably under the equivalent of the spreading chestnut tree. San Cristobal, the capital island, holds some 1,400 people in its 166 square miles (highest point 2,350 feet), though most of the interior is a still unexplored wilderness of scrub, lava and cacti. A relatively good road connects Wreck Bay with Progresso, the village up in the hills, and soon reaches the green zone, at about 800 to 1,000 feet, marking the region of higher rainfall and luxuriant growth. Wild oranges grew plentifully at the side of the trail and were well worth eating. On the way down we were startled by the thudding of hooves and loud yelling as a wild-eyed bull, led by the nose, thundered along behind a mounted Ecuadorian. The islanders control their horses with one-sided reins; a very uncertain-looking method to my eyes.

We disembarked the following morning in Academy Bay, on the Island of Santa Cruz or Indefatigable. When the Angermeyers arrived in 1938 there were only a handful of European settlers, mainly Norwegian, farming in the fertile hills. The settlement at Academy Bay did not then exist. Hardly anything now remains of the famous 1920's influx of Norwegians. They came expecting to find a lovely, fruitful archipelago and were cruelly disheartened by the harsh surroundings. The Rambekhs still live and work on Santa Cruz and can reach back into the '20s, but most of the present-day Europeans came after that. One of the originals, an old Norwegian whose name, as far as I could gather, was 'Old Moo', lived alone in the hills and was found dead in his house during our year on the islands. He had laboured for over thirty years, virtually bound to his homestead for fear of theft, his only pleasures a few paperbacks from Norway and his vile, home-grown tobacco. He left, in the circumstances, quite an amount of money, yet he had lived an austere, almost miserly life. It seemed strangely and sadly illogical to come to the Galapagos to enjoy the simple, easy life and then exist more harshly than ever, to end up dying alone in the hills, with thirty years' earnings hidden in the earth like the parable talents. In addition to the Ecuadorian population, Santa Cruz now holds a number of European families well-known to visitors. Mrs Horneman's visitors book reads like a meeting of the International Ornithological Congress.

The Charles Darwin Research Station, created on paper in 1959, has been well established on Santa Cruz since 1960, when Raymond Lévêque, its first Director, succeeded in setting up the first buildings and clearing a track to the village, both considerable feats in the Galapagos. The only serious drawback to its site seems to be the lack of a natural harbour. The *Carrier* cannot come in close, nor is there a direct channel from the deep water to the Station pier. Instead a tortuous one marked by white posts winds between spiteful little black reefs. One comes ashore in a wide semi-circular sweep, with an eye to the pursuing Pacific rollers. For transporting cargo the Station used a raft, buoyed up with empty petrol drums and powered by a 40 h.p. Johnson outboard. It had no sides and our gear went ashore with quite a swell running. I could see a pendulum increase in the amplitude of pitch or roll gently and inevitably sliding the boxes over the edge, exactly as it once ditched a cargo I ferried across to the Bass. However, nobody else seemed worried.

Flying may be convenient, but there is a stricter reality in sea travel; distance means something and changes are assimilated gradually. The last lap to Tower Island promised to be the best of all. Five or six trips from the pier to the *Lucent* and she looked like a Thames barge, with sacks of flour, now bursting open, sacks of sugar, the Bass boxes, tents, ropes, crates and drums; a load ill-designed for a yacht with hardly any deck space. It seemed a pity that we had no hens, canaries, rabbit hutches or white mice to top the pile. The *Lucent* was a converted Cornish fishing-boat, well over half a century old, iron-wood heavy and straight-stemmed. She was handled by Dave Balfour, an Englishman bound for Australia, with his friend Roger Jamieson, the *Lucent*'s skipper. They had dropped in at Academy Bay one day in July 1963 and soon afterwards Roger found himself on his way back to England, commissioned to find a suitable research and patrol boat for the Charles Darwin Station. David meanwhile stayed in Academy Bay as temporary boatman for the station or to be chartered by visiting scientists. He was a splendid character. Like most of the people who casually drop in at Santa Cruz, and they are surprisingly many, he loved the sea and lived happily aboard the *Lucent* pottering around in a pair of tattered canvas shorts, a beard and the sun. Life is a lottery in more ways than one. In ninety-nine cases it produces a normal humdrum person with comfortably limited horizons and luxury goods ambitions, whilst in the hundredth it turns up somebody like Dave Balfour, who surrenders a good job to adventure in out-of-the-way places. Unfortunately, for its control, happiness is too subjective to let us establish a cause and effect relationship between it and any particular way of life. Are we happy because we behaved in a certain way, or because we are so built that we could behave so? Clearly a lottery.

Towards dusk on 27 December we slipped past Carl Angermeyer's veranda with its tame iguanas, along the east shore of Santa Cruz and northwards towards Tower. There was plenty of life around us. A spectacular shoal of yellow-tailed mullet thrashed into motion a large patch of the ocean's surface and attracted several brown pelicans, which threw themselves clumsily into the sea, jabbing and scooping with their enormous mandibles. All around vast numbers of grey phalaropes flitted over the surface, continuously alighting and taking off, a 'stippling of living creatures' as Beebe described them. On board, the ship's grey-striped cats prowled and climbed. Behind, like a frisky colt, bounded a Galapagos-built, flat-bottomed dinghy holding our paraffin refrigerator. We sat in the well chatting and drinking coffee whilst the light faded. Sandy, a New Zealander employed by the Station, was with us. Like many others he had drifted into the Galapagos with no intention of staying. Thirteen years later he was still there. He had been in the North African desert campaigns during the war; later he was shipwrecked and spent a year on Cocos Island in the Pacific, whence he thumbed a lift to the Galapagos *en route* for New Zealand. People seemed to regard a mere ten or twenty years in the Galapagos very casually, as though it were a month or two. Time is put in its proper place, until you desperately want something, and then it is a different matter.

Soon the moon rose and shed a beautiful silver light over the sea and the whole venture became alive again. Six weeks of intermittent travel, organising and hanging around had taken the edge off it. Our aim was to arrive at Tower with the dawn; we were travelling by dead reckoning and Tower is low and easily missed. Currents are dangerously strong in Galapagos waters and the next landfall on a northerly heading was the coast of Mexico; north-west it was somewhere off the Russian coast, if we missed the Aleutian Islands. It was a relief to see the faint line of Tower breaking a nondescript sea in the grey dawn. It didn't look at all exciting. I tried to pierce

15

the greyness and make out more details; there was only a blackish line of cliffs, broken in places, and fringed on top by the thinnest fuzz of dry scrub. Seven months suddenly seemed rather a long time. Meanwhile the outward bound stream of red-footed boobies appeared overhead, stationing themselves on winnowing wings and peering down curiously, they were going fishing.

Two hours later we dropped anchor in the calm of Darwin Bay, a beautiful circular bay about a mile across, cliff-girt on all sides but the south where the sea enters—actually a volcanic crater with the southern wall broken down. Dried scrub silvered the tops of the igneous cliffs and stretched away inland. Colour was muted, even drab; black, browns, buffs and silver. At the head of the bay and quite invisible from outside lay a dazzling little coral beach backed by a small patch of dense green shrub. This beach, no more than sixty yards long, about thirty yards wide and hardly clear of high tide, was to be our camp site for seven months. In that period the world could have erupted into nuclear war, the pound been devalued or the trade unions learnt some sense, and we might never have known. It all seemed quite irrelevant. I savoured that moment. There lay our beach, imagined a thousand times, the improbable attainment of a long-held desire to live on, not just visit, a deserted bird island in the tropics, and of all islands for the biologist, the Galapagos. I recalled Beebe's emotions when he first anchored off Indefatigable: 'In my turn I had come to the Galapagos and another dream of my boyhood had become real.' When he visited Tower, Beebe pitched his tent in the exact spot on which we lived for half a year. His photograph shows that only extremely small changes have taken place in the vegetation in forty years. But there was no time, everybody was bustling and I couldn't day-dream, even though I can never again sail up to live on my first desert island.

The eastern half of Darwin Bay is an abyss whose depths are still unplumbed. Towards the beach, probably above a shelf near the rim of the crater, the water suddenly becomes shallow, with one or two nasty reefs just clear of low tide. For a few hundred yards off the beach the bottom is mixed sand and rock, at an average around four to six fathoms, often much less. Dave anchored four or five hundred yards out, leaving enough leeway to manœuvre if the *Lucent* dragged anchor towards the cliffs. We breakfasted in bright sunlight, to the screaming of the red-billed tropic or bosun birds performing their aerial courtship and the frantic screeches of red-footed boobies attacked by the great frigate birds which piratically force them to regurgitate their fish. These were to become the background to everyday life. Now and then Dave looked doubtfully at the beach, guarded by breakers which roared in before smashing against the jumble of boulders at the cliff base. My landing luck, notorious among the keepers of the Bass, had stuck to me across half the world. As we later found, such days were extremely few and far between. We took a trial run with the 'fridge' and a few odds and ends. On this very first run the dinghy's seagull outboard went on strike and for seven grilling hours we toiled back and forth with one oar and a piece of driftwood lashed to a thick bamboo pole. I soon discovered that I was not as fit as David. Getting the heavy stuff from the yacht down on to the bobbing dinghy was hair-raising for me. David prophesied disaster on every trip and with such heavy loads we might easily have been swamped, but he read each 'big un' right. Operations began about eight a.m. and by four p.m. we were through. The beach looked indescribable. The other two were in haste to get away before dark, so they shook hands, wished us luck and departed. We strained our ears for the rattle of the anchor chain

*Figure 2* Galapagos grey heron

and then the strong note of the diesels. There it was; they were away. It was a moment of strongly contrasting emotions; that dwindling speck, now finally beyond recall, was our last link with human beings probably for months. We had no radio communication; no boat worth mention; we were not an official expedition with several members and an expedition doctor; we were on our own. Well nearly; it happened that a small fishing-boat from San Cristobal arrived for its annual three weeks' fishing on the day we arrived. We felt cheated and spent our first night on Tower sulking behind a barricade of boxes, fatigued, in utter chaos and, I must admit, with a slight sense of anti-climax.

# The Galapagos and Tower Island

Robinson Crusoe was brought here by his buccaneer
rescuers and must have rejoiced that his luck had not
cast him upon these inhospitable shores.
William Beebe, *Galapagos: World's End*

From a distance remote oceanic islands of fair size and height look
much alike, rising mysteriously from the vastness of the sea, jagged
peaks hazy and slightly menacing. It looks impossible to live on
them. So look the Galapagos Islands, straddling the Equator
between latitudes 1° 40′ N. to 1° 26′ S. and across longitudes 89° 16′
to 92° 1′ W.; less than 3,000 square miles of land scattered over
23,000 square miles of ocean. They are all volcanic, made of basaltic
lava; granite has yet to be found in them. It is still not known
whether they are a single land mass, now partly subsided so that the
peaks and higher ground alone remain above the sea forming
apparently separate islands, or whether some or all were formed and
uplifted independently; possibly there were at one time more inter-
island connections than now exist. Although all but two or three are
now volcanically dead they show clear signs of age differences. The
lava on Tower was in many places razor sharp, easily shredding
tough rubber-soled boots, whilst Hood was well weathered, its
smooth red slabs and boulders kind even to bare feet. Narborough
has perhaps the most hostile lava of all; fearsome clinker screes
resulting from the stupendous eruptions, one of which (14 February
1825) was vividly described by Benjamin Morrell, quoted by Beebe
(pp. 401–5). Theoretically I suppose it is possible that some islands
were actually formed before others or were merely uplifted at
another period – differences in weathering would result either way.
Published estimates of the age of the Galapagos range wildly, but the
most recent, argon-dated geological evidence gained by the 1964

Galapagos International Scientific Project tentatively put the age of Hood Island, one of the oldest, at about 2,000,000 years, although 3,000,000 is a more usual figure and fossils have indicated a much greater possible age. It seems no two sources agree on the number of islands in the group. Besides the thirteen to sixteen large or reasonably sized ones (define your size and thus your number) there are about another fifty-five rocks and islets.

Some spots in the Galapagos are just like their counterparts on any of a thousand pan-tropical oceanic islands; a mangrove swamp fringing a muddy lagoon, like Turtle Bay on James Island, is a mangrove swamp fringing a muddy lagoon anywhere. But the name Galapagos, though it actually refers to the giant tortoises, means to most people a weird, fire-seared landscape of lunar aspect, where crested dragons (marine and land iguanas) festoon the tortured black outcrops and millions of red crabs scuttle over the algae-slimed, wave-beaten shores. Again, the Galapagos Islands mean primal, undisturbed paradises where birds treat man with the same fearlessness they bestow on cattle. And to a degree, unfortunately decreasing, this is still true. The Galapagos have always had, and it is fervently to be hoped will always have, this aura of magic, of unreality. Crazy things happen there and it is still very possible to feel a strong emotional kinship with animals because of their trust and curiosity. Beebe returns again and again to this theme, fearing that if he fails to convey the out-of-this-world quality of the Galapagos he fails to convey their essence. Of Tower he writes: 'wherever I went I was the centre of an admiring, or at least curious group of birds, and whenever I squeaked or chirped I added more to the ensemble. A pair of red-footed boobies overhead was having some terrible family disturbance. Squawk after squawk rang out and attracted no attention whatever . . . I reached up and seized the foot of one of the boobies, and both forgot their matrimonial woes and concentrated on me. My ear could detect no difference in their squawks – they were as rasping and raucous as before, but in a few seconds every small bird within hearing was at hand . . . peering down at me with concentrated interest.'

In the grimmer reaches of the islands one could hardly imagine a more desolate landscape; cinders, ash, mournful lava streams re-create the beginnings of the earth. There is plenty of fresh-looking evidence of molten lava and ash storms on all islands; even on far-away Tower our canvas was in no time thickly coated with fine black ash, doubtless wind-borne. But only Albermarle (eruptions in 1953 and 1957), James and Narborough have recently been active. The possibility of eruption was not one of our worries on Tower.

The archipelago lies on a raised platform 1,000 fathoms or more above the level of the surrounding ocean bed, near enough to the coast of Ecuador, over 600 miles east, and to Central America, about 1,000 miles north-east, to raise the question of a possible former land bridge with the mainland. This perhaps seems particularly necessary to explain the advent of giant tortoises. However, the generally accepted view is that the Galapagos were never connected with the mainland; the intervening sea is too deep, though a sub-marine ridge extends east from the Galapagos to connect with the Carnegie ridge and another goes north-east to connect with Cocos ridge running from Costa Rica to the region north of the Galapagos. Whether or not these ridges were ever above sea level for all or part of their length, it seems clear that the present plant and animal life of the islands can be accounted for on the supposition that they drifted, swam or flew there. It is surprising what mixed cargoes of plants and animals can survive such a journey among the branches of trees and other debris swept out to sea. Darwin himself teased the famous botanist Hooker by demonstrating that many plants which the latter thought incapable of germinating after prolonged immersion in sea water, could in fact do so. Heyerdahl proved that the currents favour such an assisted passage and the evolutionary time available for it is sufficiently great to allow thousands of misses for every hit. If there had been a land link within the last two or three million years it is almost certain that many ubiquitous invertebrates that are found on the mainland would occur also in the Galapagos from which, in fact, they are absent. Thus, Dr Leleup, a Belgian zoologist, told me that many primitive leaf-mould beetles are entirely missing from the Galapagos but are common in equivalent habitats in Ecuador. The hit-and-miss character of the fauna is also apparent in many other spheres, for instance the almost total lack of endemic ground predators, the absence of amphibia (there are no frogs, toads or newts in the Galapagos), the very limited number of species of snakes, which comprise but a single genus, and the relatively few genera of other reptiles. Quite apart from the restricted avifauna, these are all conditions incompatible with the former presence of a land bridge, which would have opened up the Galapagos to colonisation from the rich amphibian, reptilian and mammalian sources of the South American continent. So their by no means hospitable shores received, as they still receive, birds with seeds and small organisms on their feet and floating detritus with its cargo of insects, spiders, resistant seeds of all kinds and occasionally a rat or two of the species that gave rise to the endemic rats later largely eliminated by their imported competitor, the highly successful black or house rat.

The two main sources of current-assisted invaders seem to have been Central America, from which the Panamanian current sets south, and the areas of Chile and Peru washed by the Humboldt before it turns westward into the Pacific, carving its way through the warm equatorial seas with its vast volume of colder water before lapping the shores of the southern Galapagos Islands. The cold-loving fur seal and Galapagos penguin must have travelled north with the cold water. The Galapagos penguin still strongly resembles the Humboldt penguin from which it is probably descended. The seal found in the warm waters of Darwin Bay is merely a race of the southern fur seal, happy in the freezing waters of the Antarctic. The Galapagos flora has Central American affinities, although apparently two cacti (*Brachycereus* and *Jasminocerepus*) have their nearest relatives on Punta Salinas in Ecuador. Much of the invertebrate fauna is probably Central American in origin and also Curio's recent discovery of the remains of *Megalomys*, a rodent from the West Indies, extends the sphere of Central American influence (see Abs, Curio, etc., 1965).

Once they arrived the survivors found themselves in an environment probably far different from the one they left. Now their chief assets were invisible – the stock of genes which encoded possibilities as yet unused, but now perhaps essential for the survival of the species. Natural selection got to work, putting a premium on some abilities and a penalty on other tendencies. Slowly the size, shape, colours and habits of the animals were changed by complex interactions between them and the environment and slowly the unique Galapagos fauna arose. There are now, for example, 86 per cent endemic Galapagos bird species or races, peculiar Galapagos forms evolved in their own miniature world. These are not particularly large innovations; the Galapagos fauna is neither drastically new nor exceptionally primitive, but contains many examples of small adaptive changes evolved in isolation.

So this remote and sombre collection of defunct volcanoes had been slowly evolving its wonderful fauna for thousands or perhaps millions of years undisturbed by man, when the first tentative biped set foot on its barren shores. The main light shed on the prehistoric conquest of the Galapagos comes from Heyerdahl's Norwegian archaeological expedition, which set out in the belief that a visit to these islands had been well within the range of balsa rafts belonging to prehistoric men. The Norwegians based this on a species of cotton found in the Galapagos and wrongly thought to be endemic, which had in fact been raised and cultivated by aboriginal cultures on the north coast of Peru. Therefore it might have got to the Galapagos via these Amerindians. The expedition discovered a site in James Bay, Santiago Island, and other occupation areas on Santa Cruz and Floreana. The remains of 131 aboriginal pots were discovered and it was concluded that the Galapagos were visited repeatedly in pre-European times, though not continuously settled. (Eibl-Eibesfeldt suggests that the buccaneers, attracted by Indian ware, carried off a quantity from the mainland and broke them during carousals on the islands.) Legend,* however, attributes the first successful exploration of the Galapagos to the Inca Tupac Yupanqui, grandfather of the unfortunate Atahualpa whose treacherous execution by Pizarro in 1533 ended the Incan empire. Tupac Yupanqui rather confuses things by having returned with Negroes and copper, neither of which he could have obtained in the Galapagos, so he must at least have been elsewhere, whether or not he ever reached the islands. Two years later (1535) Tomas de Berlanga, the Bishop of Panama, made history by (accidentally) reaching the archipelago and committing his impressions to the King of Spain and to posterity; to him belongs the inspired comment: 'It seems as though God had sometimes showered stones.' From about that time the decline of these unique islands began, under successive waves of buccaneers,

---

* Accepted and promulgated by the Inca historian Sir Clements Markham, (1892) but challenged by Lothrop, although on the fallacy that balsa rafts were unable to make such sea-crossings.

whalers and adventurers. Live goats were probably put ashore in 1684–85, and the Viceroy of Peru subsequently sent out dogs to kill off the goats. In 1789 Alonso de Torres sailed to the Galapagos under the auspices of Charles III of Spain and renamed all the islands. The first organised attempt at colonisation came in 1832 when General José Villamil took possession in the name of Ecuador, renaming the group Archipelago de Colon.

All these visits made substantial inroads into several Galapagos species, notably the tortoises, land iguanas, flamingoes and fur seals. When Darwin paid his memorable *Beagle* visit in 1835 the islands had already gone through severe exploitation, mainly of tortoises and seals. The first half of the present century probably saw the extinction of some island forms of tortoises and land iguanas and the near extinction of fur seals and flamingoes. By then the settlers and their introduced animals were the main threat. In 1954 Eibl-Eibesfeldt was deeply concerned by the alarming destruction and exploitation evidently openly pursued, and his subsequent appeal to the International Union for Conservation of Nature and Natural Resources bore considerable fruit. Under the auspices of the Charles Darwin Research Station* the scientific investigation and conservation of Galapagos wild life is now being tackled and some valuable progress has been made in helping the hardest hit species, notably tortoises, to recover or at least helping to create conditions in which they can eventually do so.

'Our' island, pin-pointed on the map long before we set out and returned to in fancy ever since we left, is Tower or Genovesa, forming with Wenman and Marchena the northernmost group in the archipelago. It lies within sight of the 'dead' island of Marchena where Lorenz and Nuggerwood met their gruesome end in 1934.†

* The Charles Darwin Research Station is administered by a Director, responsible to a committee under U.N.E.S.C.O., and a small staff including a Field (Conservation) Officer, a Station Manager, Captain and crew of the *Beagle* and about ten local people working for the Station (maintaining the buildings, etc.). The Station includes a laboratory, weather station, Director's house, several small dormitories for visiting scientists, together with ample storage buildings and equipment and a good and growing library of literature and unpublished records about the Galapagos. There is also a Galapagos herbarium and a collection of Galapagos fauna. Soon, for those interested in Galapagos wildlife, there will be no substitute for a visit to the Galapagos themselves. The station jeep can run between the station and the village, but not far up into the hills; for that it is *à pied*, with or without pack animals.

† The Baroness settled on Floreana with Alfred Rudolf Lorenz, Robert Philippson

Hood, which was our second island, looks out to Floreana where Lorenz and others landed with the 'mad' Baroness Eloisa Bosquet von Wagner in 1932. Tower is low, scrubby, hot and arid, not exactly a rest home or an escapist's paradise. Its six and a half square miles do not seek to delight the intruder – it recognises no visitors since they defaced its most majestic bay by scrawling on the cliffs – with changing moods and landscapes. Most of it is a gently sloping expanse of low trees and scrub, silvery dry and apparently stone dead, their living tissues deeply buried in the hoary limbs. Take away the scrub and the rough, red-brown, ankle-cockling lava and you are left with a crater lake, two or three sandy beaches, an acre or two of green shrub and the crumbly cliffs. On the south-east horn a magnificent cinder plain stretches into the distance, hiding beneath its crusty surface a teeming colony of thousands of Galapagos storm petrels. There is an expanse of clinker on the south-west corner that no product of blast furnace could beat, a sea of sharp-edged lava, buckled, jagged and lying higgledy-piggledy as though millions of slabs had been smashed and bulldozed into heaps. Crossing this toilsome, sulphurous stuff with a load in the stifling midday heat, with nothing but desolation around, one feelingly agreed that Tower well lived up to one of its Spanish names – *Quita sueno*, nightmare island. Return, however, to the bonny white coral beach, backed by the mermaid's lagoon at the head of Darwin Bay and the nightmare relaxes into a pleasant dream.

From the summit of Tower, looking south-west, it seems as though the whole island has slipped sideways into the sea, plunging the southern rim of the Darwin Bay crater far beneath the surface. From the northern edge of the bay the island gradually rises in a series of terraces to the summit. First come the parallel reefs that menace the approach to the inner bay and at high tide lurk barely beneath the surface, then the rocky shore and then two cliff faces separated by flat-bottomed rift valleys. The faintly conical summit of Tower marks the rim of a second huge crater, this one entirely circled by more or less sheer cliffs, terraced with broad and flat

---

and Felipe Valdevieso. Lorenz and Trygive Nuggerwood (a Norwegian) vanished in the latter's sloop (the *Dinamita*) en route from Academy Bay on Santa Cruz, to Wreck Bay, on San Cristobal, in July 1934. Their bodies were found side by side on Marchena in November.

ledges, and filled with extremely brackish water. From here the long, narrow peninsula which is the western arm of Darwin Bay curves steadily round towards its opposite partner on the eastern side of the bay. Both 'horns' are the sites of extensive birds colonies; the eastern one with its several thousand pairs of Galapagos and Madeiran storm petrels and the western horn with a white booby colony and many great frigate-birds. Swallow-tailed gulls breed in substantial numbers on the eastern horn and lava gulls on the western one. Audubon shearwaters, red-billed tropic birds and black noddy terns also frequent the cliffs of the eastern horn.

The northern side of the island is difficult to negotiate. Except for broken ground approaching either horn it is almost cliff-bound. Opuntia and cereus cacti, palo santo trees and prickly shrubs grow densely right to the cliff edge, forcing frequent detours inland to find a penetrable spot. Along the north cliffs large numbers of Audubon shearwaters glide and angle, stiff-winged among the swallow-tailed gulls, red-billed tropic birds and black noddies. The shearwater population of Tower is certainly substantial, at least several thousands, whilst there are over a thousand black noddies, perhaps many more, well spread around the island.

Except for a thin coastal strip, a bare area on each horn of the bay and the inland crater, the whole of Tower is covered with sun-silvered shrub and succulent cacti. The 'rains' fall between January and May, which is also the hottest season – February is about the hottest month. On Tower, one of the driest islands, they are often no more than a few heavy showers with more frequent short periods of mist or drizzle – the *garua*. Our only really heavy shower quickly turned itself off when June had soaped herself and was standing on the beach ready for the rinse. Even this small rainfall brings out the leaves. We awoke on 18 February, ten days after the first heavy showers of the year, to find the island misted over with green – nothing more than a hint, but so fresh and lovely. It lasted about three weeks, then all was dead and dry as before. Leafing and flowering were thus extremely compressed, and for this short period the air held a wonderful delicate fragrance which came from tree-like bushes covered with yellow flowers, probably cordias. Later, the berries of a tree – I think bursera – gave out a pungent aromatic odour so strong that we could easily smell it on the breath of our tame ground finch who ate the seeds and then came to us for water. In the rare 'wet' years the island stays green longer and may be verdant as late as July.

Our Tower camp sat squarely on the dazzling white coral beach at the head of Darwin Bay. Coral is relatively rare in the Galapagos, partly because of the cooling influence of the Humboldt; these small colonial coelentrates cannot grow in water colder than about 21° C. Reef-building corals also need shallow water, so that the deep off-shore waters of most Galapagos islands are not suitable. The most coral we saw was off the west coast of Tower. It also grew profusely in fairly deep water out in Darwin Bay and chunks of it rolled in with the tides, forming the substantial bank which was our camp site. Each piece had been worn smooth and round, hardly like coral except for the telltale pores in which the living polyps had been housed. Animal skeletons also weathered to just such a whiteness and it took a sharp beachcombing eye to pick out the skulls of tropic birds, boobies, sea-lions and fish that turned up.

We lived spaciously in a safari ridge tent 12′ × 8′ × 7′ at the ridge, of heavy tropical canvas with fly sheet and veranda. It stood up magnificently to the bleaching and weakening effect of the fierce sun; our store tent of ordinary canvas became so fragile after a few months' insolation that even the small Galapagos ground doves put their feet through the roof. Before us the waters of the bay rolled up to our very door, from which we could literally toss crumbs into the sea at high tide. Turnstones and wandering tattlers twinkled over the sand in the wake of retreating waves and expertly judged the speed and distance of each pursuer, turning and running deeply into it before it began its backward drag. The tattlers were migrants from Alaska; Arctic tundra to equatorial lava. Around the time of the Alaska earthquake the extra high tides actually flowed between our tents, fortunately without entering. Behind our camp an idyllic little lagoon filled and emptied with each tide, changing a patch of drab yellow sand into a shining pool. The crystal clear water entered through deep cracks along the seaward edge, always leaving, even at lowest tide, a tiny deep pool in which a few colourful orange-bellied fishlets waged ceaseless territorial war. The lagoon was a delightful swimming pool free from the sharks and mantas which often wandered into the bay, and infinitely more beautiful than the

D

most exotic man-made structure. More prosaically, it was handy for rinsing clothes, which meant tossing them in, letting two or three tides stir them around and then extracting the surviving socks and shirts from the dark crevices into which they had been carried by the currents.

We never quite knew how to treat the sharks. One learns implicit dread of sharks from every sea-tale, but the ones that regularly came close inshore on Tower, occasionally even to the extent of beaching themselves when chasing fish in the shallows, were mainly harmless black sharks and white-tips, about four or five feet long, the black sharks perhaps a bit larger. Despite the many shark stories, the most objective and experienced opinion seems to be that even the species largely responsible for attacking inshore bathers (the grey, mullet or river shark) almost always attack by mistake, seeing a sudden movement and going for it. Once they have drawn blood they rarely, if ever, return to the attack, apparently being inhibited by the unfamiliar scent or some other disturbing factor. The literature is full of instances of bleeding victims rescued from the tainted water without further molesting by the shark, thus apparently disproving the popular belief that sharks will attack man if there is blood in the water. It probably depends on whose blood! This is all very well to know in theory, but it doesn't remove one's apprehensions in fact, or it didn't in our case as we swam out to our rowing boat a few yards offshore. Yet there could hardly be a more shark-blasé population than that of the Galapagos. Tens of people, including toddlers, were bathing at Wreck Bay on San Cristobal, yet I saw sharks only a few score yards further along the coast. The fishermen from the San Marco dived into the sea after gutting, even though a few minutes earlier the water had been boiling with a dozen black sharks fighting for the fish heads and guts. The lobster fishermen from the Villamil and Floreana swam and dived every day for months on end all round the Galapagos without any shark accident. Yet Eibesfeldt thought we had been foolish to take the risk and he should know.

Giant mantas often came into the shallows of the bay and flapped and glided just a few yards from the tent. They are a quite astonishing size; a manta once swam beneath our boat, undulating gently, and its fins stuck out for feet on either side. One afternoon a herd of dolphins, evidently pursuing a shoal of fish, moved regally across the bay in a series of graceful, curving dives one after the other, their great dorsal fins emerging and disappearing in hypnotic rhythm. They fed for several hours, methodically quartering the bay, whilst excited crowds of red-footed boobies winnowed above, probably attracted by the fleeing shoal. We soon discovered a small colony of twenty or thirty fur seals on the east side of the bay at the foot of the cliffs. After persecution fur seals vanished from several islands. Eibl-Eibesfeldt states that between 1816 and 1897, 17,845 Galapagos fur seals were taken, and in 1923 Beebe saw only two in the entire archipelago. This Tower colony marked a big increase over anything seen there for years. Fur seals are easily distinguished from sea-lions, particularly when dry, by their blunter faces, thicker set bodies and much longer fur, which unlike the sea-lion's often hangs in wet spikes. This group was restricted to a jumble of rocks and caves at the base of a small stretch of cliffs. They loved dark recesses, from which they peered, whiskery faces flat against the rock.

Tower was kind to us. Day after day the sun shone and the waters of Darwin Bay sparkled. When we returned, jaded, from the far ends of the island or across the bay to our modest camp the white coral beach and green tent, pin-points in the distance, beckoned hospitably. It was never cold, never wet and the area is virtually free from gales. Our American visitors from the *Kismet*, replete on lobsters and home-baked 'bread' and sitting by the beach fire in the soft, warm air, wouldn't, they said, have exchanged it for any spot in the world. But they were there only for a day.

Apart from the seals and sea-lions we were the only mammals on Tower. We felt very much a part of the fauna and in no time attracted hangers-on, mainly mocking birds, ground doves, Darwin's finches and lava gulls. The mocking birds were endlessly amusing. They are thin and agile, like a small, spare, sandy-coloured blackbird, with a long, slightly down-curved bill which they use for a great variety of purposes, and long legs which carry them along at an astonishing speed. The highly cursorial mocker frequently runs rather than flies, and covers great stretches at a smart sprint using its wings as balancers, like a miniature ostrich. In fact its legs (and beak) are longer than those of the mainland forms, though this is often the case with island representatives of a species, and need have no connection with increased running habits.

The mockers have survived in the extremely harsh environment of a low-lying Galapagos island not by specialisation but by adaptability and incredible sharpness. Any strange object – a shoelace on your foot or anything with a hole in it – is quickly noticed and investigated. Their beaks are ideal for poking into holes and crevices, from which they extract lurking insects. The hole in the top of our can of cooking oil fascinated them and they eagerly queued up to poke their beaks into it even though they could never reach the oil; moreover, the same individuals came back day after day to make the same futile attempt before hopping down and running briskly away with a knowing air. Holes and cracks usually mean a point of entry, say into a sea-bird's egg which may be too hard for them to crack. Black spots painted on shells provoked intense attempts to get inside.

We were astonished by the things they would eat and drink. Birds are relatively economical in their water requirements, saving a considerable amount by excreting uric acid instead of dilute urine. Mockers are further adapted for life in arid regions, but despite this the Galapagos environment eventually severely taxed their physiological endurance and they avidly sought all possible forms of liquid. They gathered enthusiastically around the stinking contents of ancient albatross eggs, probably more than a year old, which we broke open for them on Hood Island, and even ate sea-lion faeces. They were passionately fond of fruit; swallowed lumps of beetroot; drank vinegar as though it were nectar and would sell their souls for fat. If we averted our eyes from, much less turned our backs on the breakfast table, they jumped up and gobbled the butter, laying their slim beaks sideways to get bigger mouthfuls. Often a tug at the hand alerted us to the forty thieves stealing butter from our bread. This applied only to the Hood mocking birds, which had evidently acquired a strong taste for fat, perhaps from feeding so much on spilt albatross oil. They used to gather around an adult albatross feeding its chick and scrape up any oil that fell (albatrosses feed their young by regurgitation, squirting an oily substance direct from their stomach into the chick's mouth – see Chapter 9). On Hood mockers flocked like bluebottles onto the goat meat which we hung from the veranda pole. By pivoting from the hip joint and bracing their neck muscles they dealt hammer blows and managed to tear sizeable fragments from the carcase. In the most blatant case of opportunism I saw, a mocking bird noticed a spot of blood on the cloaca of a blue-footed booby which had probably pierced its rectum whilst excreting an undigested fish bone. The mocker ran beneath the booby's tail and cheekily pecked at the blood on the cloaca rim until it actually lacerated the tissue and pulled off fragments (fig. 3). The booby

*Figure 3* Mocker pecking at cloaca of blue-footed booby

just stood there, shifting uneasily, wincing with every poke from the mocker and dropping spots of blood onto the excreta-whitened boulders, but never looking down to see what was the matter. Fosberg, reporting his 1964 visit with the Galapagos International Scientific Project, gives an account of this habit in the (presumed) *Geospiza difficilis* of Wenman Island. 'A pair of Darwin's finches . . . were bothering a red-footed booby that was sitting on its nest. One finch would light on the tail of the booby and walk up and reach under the tail coverts to pick at something – I suppose lice. . . . The beaks seemed bloody. Examination of the booby's tail showed that the roots of the main feathers were pecked open and bleeding. The finches were supping the blood. This went on a good twenty minutes. . . . That evening at dinner the ornithologists were talking in some astonishment about the finches pecking at the elbows of the wings of the masked boobies on the tops of the cliff edges, causing them to bleed and drinking the blood. So I had less hesitation about telling my own story.' Fosberg then discusses the literature about this intriguing habit. Beck, quoted by Gifford, probably referred to this behaviour on Wenman, and also said that whenever he shot a finch several others would gather about it and pick up the blood. Harris said, further, that 'the *Geospiza* are carrion-feeding birds, eating from the dead carcasses of seals; also observed them feeding on the boobies, standing on the feet and backs of the boobies for that purpose.' Drowne said that 'he noticed some finches climbing on a booby's back and pecking the feathers – probably in search of parasites'. All these observations, Fosberg points out, refer to Wenman. We certainly never saw it on Tower or Hood. Specialised feeding techniques, even among members of the same species, are extremely noticeable in the Galapagos and new forms will no doubt arise in the future as they have in the past.

Blood-drinking shows how eagerly these passerine inhabitants of the arid islands seek liquid. But pride of place must surely go to the mockers which drank a warm and concentrated solution of Dettol; they shook their heads violently after every sip but still returned for more. Birds that will drink warm Dettol must indeed be short of water; their internal parasites must have received a nasty shock.

One prying individual fell head first into a narrow jar of beetroot vinegar and by bending itself into a U just managed to get its head out. We rescued a shivering and bedraggled scrap of bird, all skin and bone, and June warmed it next to her body. It didn't seem very happy so we put it in the oven; that dried it out nicely and it became a special favourite, tamer than any of the others. It was easy to recognise since its feathers long remained stuck together, exposing tracts of pink skin, and it was incapable of flight for some weeks.

The mockers on Tower were quite polite – a special island characteristic, which future visitors might like to treat as diagnostic – but the Hood mockers really besieged us. They used to come from at least a mile away, probably much farther, and thirty or forty pestered us from dawn till dusk. One or two bold individuals, which we could recognise, behaved exactly like mischievous children. When we tried to keep them out of the tent by blocking every conceivable entry, they would squirm and scuffle violently to squeeze through any crack, unshakably convinced that they were missing something. However quiet things seemed, a few moments' inattention inevitably brought trouble from a slyly entered mocker. Their concerted predations, particularly when June was baking, drove a normally placid female into a state of frenzy. Only the bright-eyed mockers dared defy her shouts and gesticulations and, having knocked over the fermenting yeast and scuffled devastatingly through the bowl of flour, finish off by excreting into everything before taking to their heels.

Galapagos mocking birds show a great deal of variation between islands. They are weak fliers and even a few miles of sea forms an effective barrier. The mockers of each island, thus effectively isolated, have become distinct in size, proportions and, I suspect, in many behaviour traits also. The Tower mocking birds are the smallest and the Hood ones the largest; we were astonished to see the difference in size between birds from these two islands (see p. 244).

Mockers show intriguing social behaviour. They often feed in groups, ranging over at least a mile or two in a collective territory. At the boundaries group members sometimes combine in display against other groups. They stretch themselves upright and then violently flick their drooping wings and jerk their long tails, which

*Figure 4* Mocker displaying

sometimes stick up vertically (fig. 4). There is much running to and fro and harsh, loud calling. Occasionally two birds clash, rolling on their sides and thrusting at the opponent with straightened legs, using their strong feet to grip. The others run around excitedly.

Within each group there is a peck order similar to that in domestic hens, in which one or two dominant individuals are able to displace lower order birds from food. Inferior birds approached by a dominant member turn their backs to it and raise their tails vertically, cheeping harshly and repeatedly – appeasement behaviour which is clearly effective in protecting them from attack. If they don't face away they often receive a sharp peck on the head. It greatly amused us to see the way in which a mocking bird would run up from behind, bend round and peer earnestly into the face of another to recognise it before attacking or submitting as appropriate. They have rather striking facial patterns with slight individual differences, and obviously recognise each other by these marks. From behind they occasionally and understandably made a mistake and an inferior bird pecked its superior, who turned, stood stock still for an instant as though unable to believe its eyes and then tore after the fleeing subordinate which by this time had realised its error and wisely taken to its heels. Once a dominant bird displaced others from food by actually lifting them aside by the scruff of the neck like so many twigs, instead of pecking them in the usual way. It was, in fact, treating them like obstructing inanimate litter and using the appropriate behaviour pattern.

The value of peck orders seems perhaps clearer in the mocking bird than in many species. They live in an extremely harsh habitat; they are small, thin and ferociously active, which means they could not long survive starvation. Much of their food is in the nature of windfalls – anything edible, such as a deserted egg, a dead booby chick, spilt fish or oil. One can easily see the advantages both of the collective territory and the peck order. First, the territory is thoroughly scoured by its highly active group. One bird spots food and begins eating; others come running to investigate and this, in turn, attracts yet others. We could draw mocking birds to any spot simply by attracting one or two; the others ran madly to follow them, as farmyard hens run to join their feeding fellows or gannets stream to join a fishing flock. Then if there is plenty all the mockers get some; if not the dominant birds get it all by exercising their peck order priority. This system obviously means that the stronger birds are constantly in a favourable position, able to benefit from the finds of the weaker members of their group as well as from their own efforts. If anybody dies it is the most expendable members of the community. There is clearly no suggestion of altruism here; the inferior birds are not sacrificing their own interests for the good of the species, but are forced to give way to the stronger members.

Conversely there is no kind and considerate treatment from the superior birds. Some anecdotes of birds and animals helping the unrelated underdog are hard to reconcile with this kind of observation. Yet no two species are organised exactly alike and whilst ailing, wounded or deformed individuals are in some species the butt of persecution, there may be others in which the behaviour patterns associated with parental care are extended to adults which somehow provide the right stimulus. However, it is easy to mistake the meaning of a bird's action and most of us have to contend with a strong tendency to anthropomorphise. But there is also the other side of the matter; books like Miss Howard's *Birds as Individuals* give detailed anecdotes which apparently defy interpretation along normal lines. Such, for instance, is the case of her male blackbird A which, though normally territorially vigilant, temporarily relaxed his hostility during drought when his neighbour B had young to feed but he himself had not, and allowed B to gather food in his territory. A then accompanied B to his nest and supervised the feeding of the young with the food gathered in his own territory. How male B allowed male A to his nest, the very centre of his territory, is a mystery to me. In such instances one must either churlishly doubt the accuracy or honesty of the observer or allow that there is a great deal more individual variation, even in normally rigid systems, than we usually assume.

Despite the arid surroundings the mocking bird populations of Tower and Hood were extremely high. Even in the interior we estimated at least a pair for every two acres, which for Tower would give a population of about 1,600 pairs; the large number of insects probably form an important part of their diet. The coastal ones frequently foraged in the littoral zone. They sang mainly in the morning and evening and the Tower mockers sang far more sweetly

than those on Hood, superior in tone and phraseology. Their breeding success must be extremely low in some years. We did not see a
single fledgling on Tower; the few nests we found all failed. On
Hood, during the whole of our stay, we found only old nests and no
young being fed out of the nest. Probably they have no regular
breeding season and may miss unfavourable years altogether.

Mocking birds and Galapagos ground doves were sworn foes on
Tower, at least around our camp. Doves came literally from miles
around; we had twenty-three feeding together outside the tent, even
though they are normally a solitary species. One could watch individuals take off and fly into the far distance and we reckoned that we
drew our camp followers from at least two miles away. The doves
were as stupid as the mockers were smart. They are plump and
rounded, about eight inches long, an attractive deep reddish-brown
smartly flecked with cream on their backs and with startling blue
rings around the eyes giving them a foolish, staring expression. They
potter around pecking industriously in the dove way. At first they
tried to dash larger pieces of food into fragments, but eventually
acquired the habit of gulping pieces as large as they could swallow,
frantically scratching their craw when the food stuck. Fights over
food were common, even when it was littered everywhere around
them. One dove would leave its own piece and rush over to challenge another eating exactly the same stuff. Rivals faced each other
with head and body tilted forwards whilst making backward movements with the feet – a clear indication of their mixed tendency to
attack and flee (fig. 5). All the while they pecked at the ground. This
was 'displacement feeding', one of the 'irrelevant' acts often performed by an animal stimulated by conflicting drives. We may
scratch our head, or pull the lobe of an ear when similarly disturbed.
Often, the dove's displacement feeding became real feeding, probably because they had put themselves into the right position for
feeding, performed the right preliminary actions and then, having
spotted a fragment of food, willy nilly completed the chain of actions
and fed properly. Posturing frequently led to actual attack. Each
bird tried to get above its rival and pecked furiously at its crown,
plucking out feathers galore. The underneath bird tried to fend off
blows by raising a wing and the whole struggle involved tremendous
fluttering and scuffling. Soon we had a strange collection of doves,

*Figure 5* A Galapagos ground dove displacing a rival from food

some lacking crown feathers and others with their remaining ones congealed into two or three spiky tufts like a Mohawk Indian. These tufts fascinated other doves, which pecked away at them until they provoked another fight. Mated pairs tended to forage together and the male would then allow the female to take food from beneath his nose.

Mocking birds frequently scattered a bunch of feeding doves, dashing up with a fine flourish. However, it was mainly bluff and whenever a dove assumed its high intensity threat posture, fluffed into a huge ball, tail fanned, wings drooped or raised vertically and head lowered, the mocker ran away, though it always gave the impression that it had suddenly remembered something more important and couldn't spare the time to thrash the dove. The large-billed ground finch, no bigger than a sparrow but with a huge thick beak, rarely interfered with either dove or mocker, though it was usually master of both.

The doves had an amusing habit of sun and rain bathing (fig. 6). A sudden shower immediately stimulated all the doves to drop whatever they were doing and keel over, raising one wing vertically so that the undersurface caught the rain. Our own feral pigeons

*Figure 6* Dove rain-bathing

rain-bathe by spreading their wings so that the upper surface catches the drops.

The dove's most improbable piece of behaviour, however, was certainly its courtship twist. As human dances become steadily more ludicrous and primitive (or is it merely more realistic?), descending from the sophisticated Viennese waltz beneath the chandeliers of the Archducal ballroom to the functional twist in any old place, it is some comfort to see doves making even bigger fools of themselves. Two courting doves seize hold of each other's beak, puff out their chests and violently twist each other's head round as though cranking a car. Their astonished round eyes, brightly encircled with cerulean blue, stare foolishly, and the dance terminates, perhaps to avoid cervical dislocation, with the partners facing each other breathlessly before the male returns to his more dovelike flicking and bowing and the female to her apparently disinterested, but really displacement, feeding.

Mockers, doves and finches formed an amusing trio. There are three species of Darwin's finch on Tower – *Geospiza magnirostris*, *G. difficilis* and *G. conirostris* – though only the first two are common. The famous feature of these finches is that starting from common stock they have evolved into thirteen distinct species each with their own special features, such as size, shape and strength of beak, and body proportions, which have eventually fitted their owners particularly well, though not exclusively, for certain diets. *Magnirostris*, for example, like our hawfinch, can crack seeds which other species cannot; and there is an insectivorous ground finch, *Certhidea olivacea*, with a warbler-like beak. Perhaps most remarkable of all, the woodpecker finch, *Cactospiza pallida*, and also the Mangrove finch, *C. heliobates*,* has evolved the ability to use twigs or cactus spines as tools, holding them in its bill to probe insects out of cracks. It then drops the instrument and picks up the grub or insect with its bill. According to Eibl-Eibesfeldt, who has studied the woodpecker finch both in the Galapagos and in captivity, they will even choose and shape twigs to their requirements by breaking off a piece and trimming it.

Since the publication of Lack's famous *Darwin's Finches* it has been believed that on islands where the 'specialists' occurred the more generalised species nearest to them in bill size and diet would tend not to occur. In competition for food with the special forms most closely related to them they would be that little bit less successful. Thus the finch with the next biggest bill to *magnirostris*, *G. fortis*, tends to take the place of *magnirostris* on islands where this is absent. This exclusion by competition certainly seemed to work on Tower. There were no *fortis*, but there were both *magnirostris* and *difficilis* – that is, no medium-sized bill, but both very large and very small ones, specialising in different foods. *Fortis* could have eaten either type of food, but could exploit neither of them so completely as the specialists.

A two-year-old *magnirostris* male, with a beak like a hawfinch and a stumpy little black body and black feet, became delightfully confiding. He wore yellow and blue rings put on by Curio and Kramer, two German scientists interested in these finches, so we knew him for certain. We soon discovered that he was excessively fond of almonds, which he would take from our fingers and then perch on our hand to eat. He would ask for nuts by gently nipping a finger and quickly became adept at this, even trying to catch our fingers as we typed, or in the early morning, when we were still in our sleeping-bags, rather half-heartedly nipping a nose or lip. He flew straight from his territory into the tent, looked round, found a hand to fly

* See Curio and Kramer (1964).

to and nip and then cocked his head expectantly. Besides almonds he always expected a drink of water which for some reason, probably because his first drinks came from it, he would take only from a silver spoon. As soon as he had finished he flew swiftly out of the tent and away to a big opuntia cactus on the cliff, where he immediately gave his simple though rather attractive territorial song 'too-lu, too-lu'. By coming to our tent he was trespassing in the territory of a coal-black adult male and his behaviour clearly showed his fear.

These finches make domed nests of fibres, roots and twigs, usually in a cactus or a bursera bush. The male seemed to do most of the feeding of the young after they had fledged, but perhaps the brood split up, the female taking half into an area outside our observation. The juveniles look rather curious with a strikingly pale, flesh-coloured lower mandible, extremely conspicuous when they beg for food. It may act as a marker, particularly in the rather gloomy places, beneath shrubs and cacti, where these birds habitually feed. The adult pops morsels into the fledgling's mouth with a very deft and pretty action, first making a quick forward bob as though bringing the fragment of food up from his crop.

When we returned to Tower in November, four months after leaving it, a tiny black figure flew down to meet us on the beach, crest feathers raised in obvious excitement, and there were the colour rings to prove that our almond-loving friend was delighted to have us back. To our great relief, Miguel Castro had a piece of chocolate with which to reward the friendly little finch, but alas no almonds.

*Figure 7* Mockers

The *Sulidae*, gannets and boobies, are a compact sea-bird family in the large order Pelecaniformes (pelicans, boobies, gannets, cormorants, darters, tropic birds, frigates) whose total coherence is not universally accepted, though there can be no doubt of the ordinal relationship between the first five mentioned. The order is an ancient one, foreshadowed in the cretaceous era and a sulid fossil is known from the oligocene epoch.

Sulids have feet webbed between all four toes, lack a brood patch and external nostrils, produce small broods (often a single chick) of naked and helpless young. All are plunge divers, largely fish eaters and to a variable extent nest in colonies. They are divisible into the allopatric gannets, often included in the same genus, *Sula*, as the boobies, but probably better separated into the genus *Morus* and the true boobies, genus *Sula*, some of which overlap in distribution.

Gannets (three species or races, status debatable) comprise the North Atlantic gannet *Sula bassana*, the South African or Cape gannet *S. capensis* and the Australasian gannet *S. serrator*, and are typically birds of more temperate latitudes. Boobies are typically pan-tropical, though the Peruvian *S. variegata* and the blue-footed *S. nebouxii* are cool water species. There are six clearly marked species of booby, red-footed *S. sula*, white, masked or blue-faced *S. dactylatra*, brown *S. leucogaster*, Abbott's *S. abbotti*, Peruvian and blue-footed. However, regional variation in the brown booby especially and polymorphism in the red-footed booby have given rise to considerable confusion and several races or even full species have been created by taxonomists.

This book covers the red-footed, white, blue-footed and Peruvian boobies.

Where several species occur in the same area, boobies, especially when immature, may be difficult to recognise at sea. Red-footed and male blue-footed boobies are distinctly the smallest, but size is of little use for the remainder. Long distance confusion could arise (1) between adult white and the white form of the red-footed boobies, (2) between adult brown and juvenile white or juvenile blue-footed boobies, (3) between several juveniles and between the intermediate or immature forms of red-footed boobies and immature white boobies or even adult blue-foots. Each species is described and illustrated in the appropriate chapter, and figured in an identification plate (p. 292), but useful comparative pointers in some of the above cases are (1) smaller size of red-foot than white and less black on the tail (the comparatively less amount of black on the red-foot's wings when compared with the white booby is not so diagnostic as some books aver; black is not confined to the primary quills of the white form of the red-foot). (2) Juvenile white boobies are brown above with brown head and neck, but the white of the underparts extends up on to the throat instead of terminating in the sharp pectoral band of the adult brown booby. Juvenile blue-footed boobies usually have a white nape patch breaking the dark upper surface. (3) Juveniles are all pretty dark, often with paler or even white undersurfaces (see p. 292). (4) The common intermediate form of the adult red-footed booby – with white tail – is distinctive, but the more variable patterns assumed by white form birds in transition to full adult plumage may cause trouble, though at closer range the red feet and blue bill are distinctive and the long wings give its flight a characteristic 'jizz'. Adult blue-foots, brown above and white below, should be easily identifiable by the white patches on nape and lower back, both of which are conspicuous in flight, long before the spiky brown head or blue feet can be seen. The Peruvian, which overlaps with the blue-foot off Peru, has pure white head and underparts and dark back with white markings. The adult brown body is very dark above and on head and upper breast and pure white on lower breast and abdomen. Abbott's booby is distinctively long-necked in flight with long, narrow wings and conspicuous black and white mottling in the middle of the back and on the thigh.

The hardest crusts always fall to the toothless.
Greek Cypriot proverb.
Lawrence Durrell, *Bitter Lemons*

If there are two birds most typical of Tower, they are perhaps the red-footed booby and its piratical persecutor the frigate-bird or man o' war. The dead, scrubby surface of Tower Island hides a vast number of red-footed boobies. Just how many we had no idea, though there had been guesses of around one, two, perhaps even five thousand pairs. Apart from the rare Abbott's booby which breeds only on Christmas Island in the Indian Ocean, the red-foot is unique among boobies in its arboreal nesting habit. Its distribution in the

*Figure 8* Boobies fishing

pan-tropics is largely governed by this fact, although it has been known to nest on grass culms where there were no bushes. When one recalls that the Galapagos are the only specks of land in several hundred thousand square miles of Pacific and that of these only Tower and Wenman are really suitable for red-foots, it is small wonder that a good many nest there. If they are to exploit that vast area of warm Pacific they must concentrate on Tower. Normally their colonies are not large, never attaining anything like the numbers at an average gannetry, let alone a Peruvian booby colony. However, the dried scrub which covers Tower holds around 140,000 pairs or about ninety pairs in every 10,000 square yards, probably the world's largest red-footed boobery. I give the figures so, because that is how we laboriously collected them. In principle it is simple enough to mark out squares with hundred-yard sides, in several areas chosen to represent the variations in habitat such as height above the sea, distance inland and the density of shrubs, then count the number of nests in each square and multiply up to get the total population of the island. In practice it was different. Having chosen our area and fixed a starting point we could not then bias the results by deviating from the indicated line just because a ravine or tangle of scrub got in the way. After laying out the first hundred-yard line it was essential to turn through an exact right-angle to begin the next hundred yards and then through two more before setting out on the trek to join up with the starting point. In dense scrub and over extremely jagged ground and without the aborigine's well-developed sense of direction this was not as easy as it may sound. Once, we not only failed to join up, we could not even locate any of our other three sides though they were outlined in bright orange corline. For good measure I also mislaid the other half of the human

E

population when June set off through the brush to locate one of the sides and vanished. It took us the best part of an hour to find each other again. Then there was the problem of counting the nests in the 10,000 square yards – a good day's work. However, the result calculated for the whole island was a population figure far exceeding any we, or apparently anybody else would have guessed. One notoriously tends to underestimate bird numbers but nobody could have suspected such a gross error.

Red-footed boobies are small as the family goes; in fact the male is the smallest booby of all, about twenty-eight inches long with a wing span of almost five feet, which is slightly longer in proportion to body length than in other boobies. The female red-foot is larger than the male, weighing on average 100 gm more (1050 gm against 950 gm).* Both sexes show the family's brightly coloured face; a blue beak runs into red facial skin, whilst a bright blue-green ring surrounds the large, brown eye and a neat black velvet patch under the chin adds a weightier touch. Juvenile red-foots are easy to distinguish from adults by their darker brown plumage, polished black bill and face parts and blackish feet. The bill gradually becomes blue, probably in the second year of life, though at one stage it is faint blue, stained, particularly at the tip, with bilberry juice colour. The feet become dark khaki, then the orange colour of ripening tomatoes and finally the deeper red of the adult. Which brings to mind an odd paragraph in Beebe's description of the red-foot: 'The bill was greenish-yellow shading into blue at the tip, the base of the bill and narrow forehead pink, set off by jet black pigment behind. The skin around the eye was bright blue-grey, the eye itself cadmium-yellow, framed by eyelids of clear forget-me-not blue.' Perhaps he mixed up his notes on the red-footed and brown boobies.

Red-foots do not need to walk about on the ground and they cannot do so with any facility. Their legs are now very short, proportionately much shorter than in other boobies and even though they are set reasonably well forward red-foots cannot walk like other boobies. They shuffle awkwardly along the ground like shearwaters. The anatomical changes probably occurred during or after the red-foot's change in nesting habitat, possibly from cliffs and steep slopes to trees and bushes. Their feet are extremely flexible and

* 450 gm in 1 lb.

44

prehensile, ideal for clasping the twigs among which the booby is surprisingly agile and dexterous; in Murphy's lucid phrase 'a lively twig-hopper'. The mere idea of a booby nesting in a tree seems silly until one sees a red-foot, but then a tree-nesting tern seems even more improbable and the fairy tern manages to incubate its egg and rear its young in the fork of a tree with virtually no nest.

Like our tawny owl and arctic skua, red-footed boobies are dimorphic, occurring in two distinct colour forms, although these are far more dissimilar than in most examples of dimorphism; they are so different that one would certainly take them for two totally distinct species. There are also a number of intermediate forms, so no wonder the taxonomic history of the red-foot is a tangle of sub-species and presumed species. On Tower the commonest form by about twenty to one is more or less entirely brown, often noticeably paler or buffish on the head and ventral surface. In the red-foot's range as a whole this morph is apparently relatively rare; most of the so-called brown forms have at least some white on the belly and tail. The other kind, which is probably most typical of the species over its world range and in some areas, such as the Caribbean, makes up nearly all the population, is white with black primaries and secondaries which show in flight as black tips to the wings and black trailing edges. The white forms often have a variable yellowish tinge on the head and neck and are never as dazzling white as the gannet or, particularly, the white booby. While the two colour forms do interbreed, white ones seemed to choose white mates (though our figures for this were inconclusive). In the clubs where non-breeding birds gather there were both kinds. In the Galapagos a common intermediate form is brown all over except for two white scapular patches, but in several regions most red-foots have brown backs and white bellies and tails. This form has sometimes been assumed to be intermediate between juvenile and fully adult plumage, but it is probably permanently intermediate between the brown and white forms. Then there are far subtler and more variable Galapagos intermediates, with white or cream markings on the forehead or some other highly localised area. The two main morphs are often called 'phases', though this is a poor term implying a transitoriness which may not exist. Finally, all red-footed boobies, without exception and regardless of the type of parent, begin their independent life as brown juveniles and the white-to-be birds take about two to three years to gain full adult plumage, becoming very pale beneath whilst still brown above. During their variable transition period they add further complications to the confusing range of forms. Both brown and white forms sport the blue bills, reddish skin on their faces and red feet and legs, all adding a touch of colour to the brown ones and rendering the white quite exotic.

This most intriguing situation of red-foot colour forms certainly calls for some comment, though there is little enough factual information to go on. If I understand the situation correctly, there are several apparently possible ways of accounting for its genetics and to decide between them would require more information than we have. I wondered whether whiteness depended on the presence of a homozygous recessive, the oligo-gene for brownness being dominant and giving rise to brown phenotypes in the heterozygote. This seemed a reasonable interpretation because I assumed that, brownness being almost certainly the 'primitive' plumage of the group and whiteness a derivative (just as brownness is the primitive gull colour shown by practically all juveniles, and white acquired later by the adults), brownness would be dominant. However, it could perfectly well have lost its dominance in the course of evolution. Nor need the various genotypes (and hence colour forms) necessarily possess advantages sufficiently great to maintain their proportions in the population. This rule usually applies in polymorphic populations but it is possible for certain forms to be inevitably and continually thrown up, even if they are then selectively penalised.

This leads to the fascinating but ill-lit topic of the function of white and brown plumage respectively. What does the brownness or whiteness do, in the sense of what advantages do its possessors enjoy? The first possibility, which I suspect should be discounted, is that the colours as such need have no functional significance, merely persisting because the particular genotype which produces them has itself some advantage. Perhaps one of the forms is a heterozygote and persists because of extra vigour so imparted. The colour association with heterozygosity could then be more or less incidental and its effect, whether or not advantageous, merely supplementary. This seems an unlikely state of affairs for the dramatically different colour forms in the red-foot. I am going to assume that the colours are themselves advantageous in different ways and that intermediates are produced by the two forms interbreeding. More or less of either form in a particular area could then be brought about by natural selection acting differentially.

One possibility is that whiteness or brownness could aid the bird in particular activities. An obvious suggestion is that the two colour forms have to do with different hunting methods. Hunting behaviour involves the actual motor skills, but also, and less apparently, the colour of the plumage may exert influence in two important ways. As camouflage, in daylight, white underparts could render the bird less conspicuous to fish – Phillips showed this using an experimental set-up with model birds. Also, as camouflage, brownness may be effective in nocturnal hunting. Red-foots are undoubtedly partly nocturnal, as several people have noticed, and in probable connection with this have larger eyes than any other booby. Brown forms may be more nocturnal than white ones, though unfortunately this is not known. The Tower population, mainly brown form, was certainly nocturnal in much of its behaviour, often returning to feed its young during darkness. Gannets, by contrast, are not nocturnal and will not attempt to enter or leave their colony during darkness. It would be fascinating to know if brown and white forms do differ in their fishing habits, for it seems to me that if the plumage forms have functional significance, a difference in hunting behaviour could be important enough to account for the maintenance of each form in a population. The geographical distribution of each form could perhaps be linked with the differences in proportions of prey species. In the Galapagos we knew from regurgitations that flying fish were an important source of food, and these are just the potential prey (squids are another) that come near enough the surface or actually leave it, and possibly by phosphorescence give nocturnal predators a chance. The swallow-tailed gull, however, is unfortunately a Galapagos species which is both white and a nocturnal hunter, so there is obviously not going to be an absolute correlation between brownness and nocturnal hunting, even in species that all breed in the Galapagos.

---

* Since writing this we have checked the habits of Red-foots on Christmas Island (all of which are white) and found them to be, like the brown forms on Tower, significantly nocturnal.

However difficult it may be to demonstrate the advantages of each red-foot form, the genetics of their situation would be perfectly amenable to observation, the only snag being that boobies breed rather more slowly than lepidoptera or fruit flies. Still, there must be an ecological geneticist who would prefer ten years in the Galapagos to two in a laboratory!

If there is a significant difference in fishing habits, diurnal as against somewhat more nocturnal or crepuscular, might there not be a corresponding advantage in white and brown plumage respectively? White underparts have already been discussed as camouflage against fish, but what about white upperparts? Phillips concluded that, although white sea-birds unarguably attracted others, these were more in the nature of competitors than witting or unwitting collaborators. This induced competition, he thought, was one of the disadvantages of white plumage, but more than cancelled by the advantages. But, of course, it is mainly the upperparts that other birds see from a distance, and it is certainly the upperparts that show most on gannets. When a gannet plunges into the sea after a fish, its dazzling white plumage advertises its dive over a great distance and others stream into the area, literally from miles away; one can see them hastening towards the diving birds. Darwin long ago noted this signalling effect, and suggested that it might 'guide other birds of the same and other species to the prey' (1874). The critical question is: do the birds that first found the shoal gain or lose as a result of having attracted their fellows? If they lose, one might have expected evolution to have produced dark upperparts to help conceal their diving activities, whilst probably retaining white underparts for their beneficial camouflaging effect against fish. But if they gain by attracting others, then the white upperparts, too, would be of functional advantage. It seems likely, though again nothing is known of this particular case, that gannets feeding on a large shoal do not lose by sharing their potential quarry. It is possible that they might gain, by the fish being confused and disorientated as a result of the hailstorm of dives. Thus, it seems most likely to me, one could explain the dazzling gannet plumage. It is unlikely that a species would evolve a characteristic which benefited congeners at the expense of individuals possessing it. The white winter plumage of the ptarmigan and the mountain hare obviously camouflage them against their chief enemy the golden eagle, so there is no problem in understanding the advantage of whiteness in their case. Nor, to take the other side of the fence, can one doubt that Arctic predators like the snowy owl, greenland falcon, arctic fox and polar bear are helped in their hunting by their cloak of invisibility. The gannet, however, is a far different case and so is the white red-footed booby.

Around our camp site on Tower grew a patch of thick, succulent cryptocarpus shrub much favoured by the red-foots which concentrated about 350 nests in 7,000 square yards. This colony, unusually dense for red-foots, was our special concern, thoroughly combed and subjected to the usual indignities of catching, weighing and marking.

From the comfort of our tent veranda we could see who was on duty at certain nests or sally out to catch an individual as soon as he got back. This arm-chair ornithology was a great luxury; the short commuting distance lightened many tasks such as continuous forty eight-hour checks which we carried out in two-hour shifts; after a refreshing swim in the lagoon, the off-duty observer relaxed in the shady tent recovering for the next two hours in the broiling sun. In particular, having boobies in the garden made feasible frequent weighings of chicks over a relatively long period. The information provided a valuable check on the current economic situation, a barometer that helped us to interpret the complex breeding activities.

We marked all nests with numbered pegs, including those of some 250 pairs of great frigate-birds which later nested in the same area. It was a regular slum, thickly studded with the high cones of droppings which accumulate below regular perches, strewn with dead twigs and the musky-smelling skeletons and feathers of starved chicks and clamorous with the harsh calls of booby and frigate rising into the heat haze. By midday in the hottest part of the year the temperature soared to over 110° F. in sheltered spots. The poor booby and frigate chicks were stifled in their own thick down, miserably tied to their excreta-whitened nests in the oven-like heat, whilst we, simply by stepping a few yards to one side, could immerse ourselves in a crystal pool.

When we left the Bass gannets, the spring-and-summer-long noisy activity was finished and the cliffs were empty, rapidly blackening, as the guano washed off in the Scottish damp. Not one of its 18,000 birds remained. The breeding season had come and gone in the same months as last year and, one could safely predict, as next year and many years to come. In late December, when we reached Tower, there would be absolutely no breeding activity on the Bass Rock, at 56° 04′ N., 2° 38′ W.; the day length would be less than eight hours and the weather often abominable. Tower, on the Equator, experiences practically no differences in day length through the year and not much variation in weather. We wanted to know whether the boobies would, nevertheless, tend to breed in a fixed season ro whether they would lay throughout the year, or particularly in certain parts of it. We were not optimistic about our chances of finding out why they followed a particular breeding regime, but we wanted to ask the question. Although gannets on the Bass begin to lay at the end of March and continue till about mid-June, there is a very clearly marked point in the season, actually the four or five days around the end of April, when most eggs are laid; this point remains constant to within a few days from year to year. There is also suggestive evidence to explain why this timing is advantageous, as I will try to show later. The corresponding situation in the red-foot was our present concern.

Such studies may seem trivial, but they are far from it. Classical zoology was for centuries preoccupied with naming and describing animals and later with explaining how various physical features developed and fitted their possessors for their way of life. Description, classification, comparative anatomy and embryology and, after Darwin, Wallace and T. H. Huxley, evolutionary studies were important. It is only comparatively recently that the intricacies of population dynamics have begun to be understood, which is all the more surprising because ecological studies require no complicated apparatus or techniques comparable to those needed in molecular biology, for instance. Although it is directly obvious that a torpedo-shaped body and a paddle-like forelimb aid fast progress through water, it is far from obvious and extremely difficult to demonstrate why a bird breeds at a particular time or what advantages it gains; why it lays two eggs whereas a related species lays one; why some species of colonial birds nest two feet apart and others six feet; why some snails of a species are yellow and others green or brown; why the meadow brown butterfly has more spots on its wings in some parts of its range than in others; why Darwin's finches on one island have an inborn fright reaction to predators whilst on another island they have not, and so on. Yet these aspects are susceptible to evolutionary processes just as much as body shape and may involve a whole series of linked systems greatly complicating the analysis of their adaptive value. It is largely due to the work of such people as Lack, Tinbergen, Cain, Southern and Ford, to mention a group of Oxford zoologists, or the Aberdeen University grouse unit, to take another example with which I happen to be familiar, that some of the intricate problems concerning the ecology, behaviour and genetics of processes which directly concern the animal's survival, are being worked out in the arena where battles are fought – the 'open field' beloved of naturalist-zoologists. Fortunately a few biologists have made field studies scientifically respectable in a way which they certainly were not two or three decades ago, when field ornithology, for instance, was held in low regard by serious zoologists.

To return to the red-foots of Tower Island and their breeding regime, a few figures will set the scene. In late December 1963 there were 235 occupied nests near our camp; about three per cent held eggs, forty per cent held chicks and the rest were empty. Most chicks were between four and six weeks old and therefore had come from eggs laid around the end of September – laid, moreover, in a rather pronounced outburst, rather than gradually working up to a peak. Laying had then tailed off much less abruptly. Less than ten per cent of chicks were older than six weeks, showing that there had been relatively few eggs before the end of September, whereas over twenty per cent were younger than four weeks, showing that quite a few eggs were laid after the main batch. Around the middle of January a new wave of breeding began and eighty-nine eggs were laid between 15 January and the end of February. During this period there was tremendous activity in the colony and many other nests were built even though the owners never produced eggs. Later still, in April, another wave seemed imminent but proved abortive.

These bare facts establish a very interesting difference between red-footed boobies and gannets. Whereas gannets have a single main peak of laying each year, red-foots have two or three peaks separated by periods during which few eggs are laid.

We next wanted to know how different years compared with each other; was there a peak every September and February equivalent

51

to the gannet peak at the end of each April? This was more difficult to discover in our relatively short time, but we made a start. An intriguing question, closely connected with the seasonal one, concerned the factors which were responsible for triggering a wave of laying, particularly since there is little seasonal variation in general weather or in temperature and length of daylight (photoperiodicity) – two factors known to be of prime importance in regulating the onset of breeding behaviour in birds. It eventually turned out from our completed records that some boobies which had reared a chick to the free-flying stage produced another egg almost exactly a year after the previous one, whilst others had not started a new breeding cycle by then, and as we later found, went at least fifteen months between successive layings. Likewise, unsuccessful breeders fell into two categories; many of them laid again thirty-two to forty weeks after laying the previous egg whilst others did not. It seemed that thirty-two weeks was the minimum time required to prepare for another try, excluding immediate replacement of lost eggs which can occur in less than twenty days and really constituted an extension of the one breeding attempt. It also made little difference whether their previous attempt failed in the egg or chick stage; in both cases it was about seven to nine months before they laid again. Those pairs (later unsuccessful) which had laid in February produced their next egg in slightly less time than pairs failing in January. Similarly, pairs laying in March and failing took less time to lay again than did their counterparts in February. However, more than half the pairs that failed in one season, be it January, February or March did not try again within the period mentioned above.

All this answers the first question, for it shows that we need not expect peaks of laying in the same months each year; some successful breeders will try again thirty-two to forty weeks later whilst again others will not. The particular month in which the previous attempts failed will also influence the length of the period before next breeding, so introducing further variability. But what triggers off a wave of laying if it is not weather? Is it some change in environmental conditions or an internally fixed sequence of events in the bird? Probably it is both. It seems clear that many pairs that bred successfully more or less at the same time as each other last season will come again into breeding condition more or less together and so will some of the birds that failed in their last attempt (why some do not do so is a difficult question to answer). This suggests an internal cycle of roughly fixed length for each case. But we also know from many of our records that many such birds can go through all the preliminaries of breeding, including courtship, mating and the building of a nest, and *then* discontinue their activities without ever producing an egg. In these cases it seems as though something has suddenly changed in the environment and over-ridden their obvious readiness to lay.

We came strongly to suspect that the fly in the ointment was fish. If fish were plentiful breeding activity was initiated in a batch of boobies somehow 'ready to go', that is in the appropriate internal state, and these went ahead with their breeding activity and produced an egg. If fish were very scarce, those boobies that would otherwise have begun their breeding cycle were inhibited from doing so. Where birds had started their cycle and, two or three weeks before they were due to lay there came a lean period, the boobies called off the attempt. Birds that were building stopped and pairs beginning regularly to attend their sites became sporadic visitors again. We had evidence for the lean period in the sudden starvation that visited growing chicks just when these other boobies were abandoning their breeding; parents were obviously finding great difficulty in obtaining food for their chicks and presumably the other adults also experienced the shortage. The food squeeze was shown not only by the dramatic evidence of starvation and suddenly diminished attendance of breeding adults but, as later analysis showed, by the rate of growth of young that survived. If one compares the growth rate young red-footed boobies *can* achieve on Tower (shown by the rate they achieved in the better spells) and the growth rate other young of those same ages *did* achieve during January, February, March and April, one finds that just at the time when the breeding activities of pairs that had not yet laid suddenly stopped, the discrepancy between possible and actual growth widened. In other words, irrespective of the chick's age, growth rate suddenly declined and coincided with abandoned breeding by other pairs.

If things had already gone too far and the female had to lay an egg even in a bad period, the egg was often abandoned; as a (presumed) result of the fish scarcity the hunting bird of the pair had to spend so long at sea that the incubating partner left the egg; the tendency to incubate waned before its mate returned. Later when the egg was nearer hatching a bird would sit patiently for seven days waiting to be relieved of incubation.

Of course, even if fish become scarce when the booby is building its nest they need not necessarily be scarce in two or three months' time when the booby is feeding its chick. But it seems that the red-foot's food supply is erratic enough to make it impossible for the bird to predict that far ahead; all it can do is react to the present conditions and hope for the best. It is also possible that it can go through the time- and energy-consuming business of courtship, nest-building and egg-laying only when food is relatively plentiful; otherwise all its energies are bent on catching enough fish to keep alive. This too would produce the link between plentiful food and breeding and scarce food and inhibited breeding.

The situation implied by the above evidence is really the hub of the problem since if the supply of fish on which red-foots mainly feed really does vary in a completely erratic, non-seasonal manner there is simply no way in which the booby could become geared to it so that it had its young at the 'right' time. In such a case it would benefit the population as a whole if groups of boobies came into condition at different times in the season rather than all together, since it would reduce the chances of a general catastrophe. If there was also a connection, even though slight, between the food situation at the time of laying and later in the season it would also pay the boobies to use this as a cue and pursue or abandon their attempt correspondingly. It would be extremely difficult to prove such a correlation, since it would be enough to give survival value even if favourable food at the time of laying and favourable food during the raising of the young were linked only a little more often than by chance alone. In the Galapagos records suggest that red-footed boobies tend to produce their egg peaks more often in the periods September–October and January–February than any other months, implying that there may be a slight tendency towards more plentiful food at these times, or possibly at some fixed period afterwards, when the chicks would benefit. Alternatively there may be other advantages connected with this weak seasonal trend, but yet to be discovered. However, records also show that egg peaks can occur exactly in the middle of the normal 'quiet' season, so we are obviously dealing with a flexible situation in which external factors seem decisive in producing laying. Virtually nothing is known about the abundance and movements of the fish, principally flying-fish, on which boobies feed. The tuna and big-game fishing vessels that frequent Galapagos waters may provide a clue, since flying-fish are one of the prey species of tuna, albacore, marlin, etc. The concrete evidence which could really settle this sort of issue takes years to gather, depending as it does on the observation of a long series of breeding seasons. Still, even a single visit to a breeding area can yield useful information if reasonably full details about the amount and spread of breeding are noted at the time, so it is extremely worthwhile for anybody to use such opportunities.

The preceding paragraphs have at least put the food situation where it belongs – in the centre of the stage – and one could hardly fail to recognise its critical importance for red-foot chicks in the Galapagos. Even in the egg stage of the breeding cycle food exerts an effect. The red-foots on Tower incubated for spells averaging sixty hours and in extreme cases lasting for 144 hours. This is longer than in any other booby and undoubtedly reflects the need for long foraging periods to locate and capture food; red-foots are known to forage well over a hundred miles from their breeding place and may go much further. In British Honduras it has been found that red-foot incubation spells average twenty-four hours (Verner). We found that on Tower twenty-four hours was the minimum time and it seems

*Figure 9* Red-footed booby with nest and egg

possible that the Galapagos situation was appreciably harsher than the Caribbean one. Perhaps twenty-four hours is the incubation regime the species would 'like' but in the Galapagos cannot have. Incubation takes forty-six days and when hatching time approaches incubation spells become shorter. This presumably ensures that the newly-born chick is not caught at the beginning of a long incubation spell. But unfortunately conditions were apparently such that the unlucky young sometimes suffered a long delay between hatching and being fed, and several died. Extremely small chicks cannot survive long periods of starvation – an important point to which we will return.

A newly-hatched chick weighs 30 to 40 gm or as much as a mouse. That is not much, but the average egg weighs only 54 gm when fresh and loses over a tenth of its weight during incubation. The new chick as in all boobies is relatively helpless, blind and very sparsely scattered with down. Its skin has a pinkish suffusion, distinguishing it from the darker young of other boobies. The parents gently prod the scrap of chick into position on top of their webs, from where it occasionally pokes out its wobbly head as the adult rises slightly to feed it. Small amounts of partly digested food are brought up into the parent's mouth, where the chick can get at it. We got the impression that red-foot babies are more vigorous, persistent and orientated in their begging than young gannets. At this stage both parents are very bold, and with raised feathers, flashing eyes and the most fearsome drawn-in screech, dart their beaks at an intruder and violently flail their wings forwards and downwards as though to fly at the enemy. The quality of the red-foot fear/aggression screech is exquisitely harsh and the way in which it is continued throughout the subsequent inspiration of air resembles the struggling howl of an infant that has expelled every atom of air from its lungs in the first almost silent paroxysm. Until it is four to six weeks old the chick is brooded continuously, but after that both parents leave it and go fishing. It is then thickly covered with woolly fluff, impishly sharp-eyed and with a polished black beak. The wretched chick must endure the fierce heat of the tropical sun which at midday turns the airless interior of the island into a furnace, as Darwin remarked with feeling. It hangs its head supinely to conserve energy and raises its stumpy posterior into the air so that heat may radiate from the bare ventral skin. Frequent weighings showed that chicks lost weight most rapidly during the hot part of the day, so any way of minimising this loss would be worthwhile. At night it is chilled and damp, sometimes shivering violently by dawn. Like their cousins the blue-foots on Hood Island, a number fall victim to the fierce Galapagos short-eared owl (Chapter 14) which sometimes kills birds considerably larger than itself. When dealing with large individuals the owl strikes with its talons at the back of the booby's neck and head and the bodies always showed the effects of this savage attack. It seemed surprising that a large booby should be unable to defend itself with that formidable bill but probably it is caught unawares by the first blow as the owl binds to it.

Four unlucky chicks near our camp were killed by adult white boobies, a few pairs of which nested among the colony of red-foots. The way in which the murders took place was distressing – we interfered whenever we could – but most instructive. Males that had failed in breeding or perhaps never tried approached large fluffy chicks, of either their own or another species, and tried to copulate with them. If attacked or even approached by a male white booby, hide your beak – a ritualised posture which often pacifies the attacker. White booby chicks have an innate beak-hiding response and consequently they usually avert severe punishment. Red-foots, however, usually nest well apart from each other and very rarely attempt to molest chicks in this way, so it has possibly been un-necessary for red-foot chicks to evolve beak-hiding behaviour or, more likely, they have gradually lost it. Thus when a white booby molests a red-foot chick, instead of appeasing the chick strikes back. This releases the full attack from the adult, which is naturally more powerful and quickly reduces the chick's head and nape to a raw, bleeding mass, looking gruesome against the white powder-puff of the down. However severely it suffers the red-foot chick dauntlessly carries on the unequal struggle. Consequently it may be killed; in this sort of encounter right is not might, as it often is in territorial rivalry among birds.

Returning to the food theme, no anxious parents ever recorded with more interest (though perhaps with more legitimate pride) the uncertain efforts of their puling offspring to overcome the objective resistance of the weighing-machine. We obtained our information on growth in three ways: weighing each chick every second day of its life gave a rough idea; a fine measure came from a concentrated series of three-hourly weighings for two weeks and a third method, tying in with the others, was a continuous forty-eight-hour watch during which we recorded every arrival of the parents and the number of feeds given to the young.

Young red-foots grow at a snail's pace and in spasms whereas gannets fatten rapidly. At one month red-foots weigh 300 gm, at two months around 700 gm and by three months they reach a maximum weight of 950 to 1,200 gm. The corresponding figures for the young gannet are 1,800 gm, 4,000 gm and 3,500–4,000 gm after dropping from a maximum weight of 4,500 gm. The three-hourly weighings showed how the young red-foots fared between feeds, which came on average just less than once a day, usually in the evening. At each feed, which might involve five or six separate regurgitations or attempted regurgitations by the adult, the chick usually got about half a pound of food. Sometimes both parents came in quick succession and completely stuffed the chick. After a large feed the chick could lose up to fifteen per cent of its after-feed body weight in a night. In the morning there was usually a rise in the rate at which weight was lost. Eventually the rate of loss slowed down so much that it stayed practically the same for many hours.

As the wing and tail feathers grow and the forehead emerges brown from beneath the woolly top-knot, the chick rather loses its charm. In the later stages of feather growth before the last untidy vestiges of down fall away, the red-foot looks a rag-bag, lack-lustre and often sadly pinched, standing with guano-whitened webs on the wreckage of the nest. Soon after it has started regular flights a distinctive change occurs, the feathers become glossy, probably as a result of increased secretions of the waterproofing material from the oil gland. Red-foot chicks took their first flight at about nineteen weeks (sometimes not until considerably later) after long practice on the topmost twigs of a bush or tree where they balance delicately, 'feeling' the breeze with outspread wings and flapping vigorously enough to lift themselves a few inches into the air before grappling for the twigs again. I write 'took' rather than 'take' because it seems that the fledging period is unusually long in the Galapagos, reflecting the slow growth of the young. In British Honduras and the Indian

Ocean Christmas Island, to take two widely separated stations, it is apparently fourteen to fifteen weeks. Sometimes chicks make their first flight whilst still showing traces of down. But these are not home-leaving trips by any means; they return daily to be fed for a further fifteen weeks or more. Before they finally depart they have been fed by their parents for thirty-two to thirty-eight weeks and in one case the chicks' period of dependence or part dependence on the adults lasted no less than forty-six weeks. Compare this with thirteen weeks in the gannet. Throughout this long period they have often been on or below the starvation line. Indeed, one in three starve to death whilst the remainder often suffer severe food shortage and they never know the regular and super-abundant food supply which is the young gannet's favoured lot. It was a depressing business watching them waste away to skin and bone. As I have said, even tiny chicks not infrequently starved, though their food requirements were negligible. Their resistance against starvation is at first slight and if one parent goes away to sea for five days and returns empty the chick has little chance of survival. If the chick is unfortunate enough to emerge during a lean period, the parents are unable to shorten their hunting trips in the normal way and even a newly-born chick may have to wait four or five days. This weakens it considerably even if it manages to survive and reduces its chance of ultimate survival. Older chicks are remarkably resistant to starvation and can fatten up again in times of comparative plenty; in fact their chick life is one long series of fasts and feasts, particularly the former and they are well adapted to the regime. Like all birds, including raptors, that may have to survive hard times they have been rigorously selected for fasting and recovering ability; the strongest survive and perpetuate their quali-ties. I have fairly good evidence that the adult gannet, for example, can survive a fortnight's fruitless hunting in winter; I know that they can survive a fortnight's fast when just sitting on the Bass in the breeding season. During the summer they can find food with the greatest ease, but in winter, out in the North Atlantic or North Sea, they must frequently encounter prolonged bad weather that makes fishing almost impossible, and confers strong survival value on fasting ability.

So perhaps for two or three days the red-foot chick stands on the

F

*Figure 10* Red-footed booby with artificially donated twins; the natural brood is always one

little platform of whitened twigs or on a nearby branch. It may sleep away the heat, tilting forward and using its beak as a prop. Sometimes it plays with a twig or even builds one into the nest, though I never saw one demolish its nest, as they are said to do. Then at last the great moment comes, usually in the evening. One of the parents flies in from the sea. If it is unlucky two or three great frigate-birds, circling effortlessly on their enormous black wings, descend and remorselessly pursue the evasive booby through every twist and turn until in desperation it throws up its bolus of fish, which one of the frigates catches and swallows before returning to its watchful circling. All that work wasted for the booby. Normally, however, it gets through unscathed and with a final descending rush, red feet lowered and spread to aid braking, lands neatly on one of its perches calling loudly. It does not usually land straight on the nest. The hungry chick immediately begins intense food begging, bobbing and feinting with its head, violently and synchronously flailing its spread wings and uttering a subdued but passionate repetitive call. If the parent has food in its crop it quickly flaps and hops onto the nest, bends forwards and opens its beak. Almost too eager to control its movements the chick thrusts its head deep into its parent's throat and with a violent pumping movement that threatens to lacerate the adult, transfers the contents to its own mouth. It keeps the adult's gape at full stretch by distending its own lower mandible sideways as well as opening its beak. Withdrawing its head it gulps down the bolus of fish, usually slimy and already partly digested, but sometimes freshly caught. By frenzied pestering, aiming a flurry of jabs at the parent's bill, striving to insert again, calling, wing flailing and generally behaving as though demented, it usually persuades the adult to open up two or three times more, but does not always receive food.

The harassed and ruffled parent, eyes darting in embarrassment, is now glad to escape to a nearby perch and settle down to a bout of preening and oiling to restore its plumage to good condition. All sulids produce oil from a gland at the base of the tail and waterproof their feathers by rolling the back of their head on the gland and then on other parts of the body. Finally the booby settles down to sleep, burying its louse-infested, flat-fly riddled head into its scapulars. It will be off again at dawn, after a few yawns, a wing-stretch and a good scratch using its comb-like middle claw, which all members of the family possess and which the lice doubtless avoid with contempt. I cannot see what good the pectinated claw is to a sulid, but maybe it helps to re-lock the parted barbs on the feather vane. The booby will then fly steadily out into the Pacific, oaring along with an easy, powerful wing action, alternating with glides, until it reaches some favoured feeding area. Or perhaps it begins random searching when a few miles out from the island. Little is known about the feeding behaviour of sulids, apart from its obvious features. Whatever the method, it will involve endless quartering over the sea, numberless fruitless plunges and then a long haul back to Tower, probably several hundred miles of flying in all. No wonder it looks thoroughly haggard and bedraggled at the end of the long, long season and needs time to recuperate.

What happens, however, on the frequent occasions when a booby comes home empty or with a miserably inadequate offering? Then the chick continues to lose weight, though at a progressively reduced rate until after a long fast it is losing practically nothing, though that bit is serious. During the twelve hours immediately after a large feed, which may almost double the weight of a 500 gm (six to eight week-old) chick, nearly all that extra weight will be lost. If the chick is in good condition it will continue to lose even after it drops to the weight at which it received its last feed. A 1,230 gm chick which has not been fed for twenty-four hours may lose 320 gm in that time, but then declines much less rapidly at about 100 gm the day following, then fifty and eventually just a few grammes per day. Doubtless this is because it has by then metabolised the immediately available fat reserves and is living on its proteins – muscles and liver. Despite its relatively slight weight at the best of times it can continue to lose weight steadily for long periods until it is extremely emaciated and then still recover if a spell of good feeding comes along. One could easily imagine a young gannet, with its enormous fat reserves, surviving long periods, though it very rarely has to, but it is more surprising that the red-foot can do so.

The chick's growth, of course, reflects the availability of food to the adult; young red-foots starving on Tower mean adult red-foots having a hard time finding fish at sea. When, suddenly, all the young in the colony begin to receive regular feeds and put on weight, it means that food is relatively plentiful again. As I have said, it would seem mal-adaptive for all red-foots on Tower to lay their eggs within a few weeks and most within a few days of each other, as gannets do on the Bass Rock. If a scarce period came along just when the chicks were growing quickly and needing most food wholesale mortality would inevitably follow, aggravated by the fact that all the adults on Tower would simultaneously be searching for extra food with at least some of the white boobies.

In the gannets' case, on the other hand, all the evidence suggests that food, particularly herring and the highly nutritious mackerel, is not only predictably present but actually abundant between June and September in every year. So the main crop of eggs is laid at the end of April every year; the young grow up between June and September; none starve and all receive so much food, in the case of the Bass gannets largely mackerel, that they can deposit thick layers of fat even in their short growth period of about twelve weeks. The best solution for the red-foot is to take advantage of the fact that whilst food is often scarce and erratic it is not typically scarcer in one particular part of a year rather than another, so they can draw out the period over which they feed their young (thirty to thirty-eight weeks). Gannets with young in December or January, when days are short, seas rough and some of their favoured prey far offshore, would probably be unable to feed them (though we do not *know* this to be so), but boobies can have young at any time, so they show scattered laying and an absence of any regular peaks from year to year.

A second important point concerns the gannet's strongly seasonal breeding as a result of which most young fledge in the first half of September, mainly before the onset of autumn gales, and so have a much better chance of surviving those first few perilous weeks. The red-foot has no such worries since the weather is much the same all year.

Young gannets are so heavy that once having flown down from their nest on the cliffs (which they do with ease, even covering several miles in their first flight), they cannot lift themselves from the water, thresh as they will, and so cannot return to the nest, if for no other reason than that they are too fat to fly. Nor could the young have evolved the habit of simply sitting on the sea near the breeding colony and being visited and fed there by the parents. Apart from all the other difficulties of such a solution, tides or rough seas would dash them onto the rocks or carry them out to sea. Neither could the parents go with them to sea, since the problem of re-locating a moving youngster at sea, perhaps in mist, after a fishing trip of scores or even a couple of hundred miles, would be too difficult. The net effect is that having fully utilised the temporarily abundant food supply and produced its fat chick the gannet has diverged from the normal procedure within the family, which was presumably also the ancestral way; it is the only member (indeed in the entire order Pelecaniformes) that does not, and under the circumstances could not, continue to feed its chick once this has fledged. One wonders whether, speaking with hindsight, the gannet's method is more effective than producing light young and feeding them after fledging would be, but the question is meaningless. Gannets have followed one evolutionary path and it is impossible to say what would have been the consequences of following an alternative. As we have seen, it is not simply a question of considering such a change in one habit; it impinges on and develops in relation to others, until a substantial part of the bird's total organisation is involved. The gannet's method leads to heavy mortality in its young, since a large proportion, about three-quarters, starve to death before they can acquire the specialised and difficult art of plunge-diving for their food; certainly seventy-five to eighty per cent die whilst still immature. Juvenile boobies avoid this heavy toll but suffer it at an earlier stage in their development; on Tower, in 1964, no fewer than ninety-two per cent of all eggs laid failed to produce fledged young: only nine chicks survived out of 120 eggs – a tremendously heavy mortality.

Another significant point closely connected with the all-important food situation is that the red-footed booby lays only one egg. It is, in fact, the only booby which invariably does so, although in the white booby the same effect is produced by fratricide; the older chick evicts its sibling. Having seen the difficulties which attend chick-rearing in the red-foot, the long period in which they are dependent on their parents even after they can fly and their slow, irregular growth, it may not seem surprising that it lays the smallest possible clutch. If it is hard for one chick to survive lean periods, two would surely die. It is, in fact, a clear case of the limitation of clutch (and brood) size to that which the parents can feed, here the absolute minimum. Food is here acting not only ultimately, in the ethologist's sense, but as the executing or proximate factor. As Ashmole said in connection with another species, they would lay only half an egg if they could. One could scarcely imagine a more complete contrast than that between the ecology of the red-foot and the gannet. Nobody could invent a hypothetical case in which the effects of two different environments on the behaviour and breeding biology of closely related species emerged more clearly.

Having used the gannet for comparison with the red-foot one cannot evade the obvious question: 'Why, if gannets enjoy abundant food, do they not produce more than the invariable single egg?' This is a loose end. It boils down to two things: despite evidence apparently indicating that most of their prey species have decreased this half-century, gannets are showing every sign of enjoying super-abundant food; second, despite this advantage, they are not breeding as fast as they could, and in particular, are keeping their clutch size at one and their age of first breeding at five to six years.

When we experimented by giving twins to several pairs of Bass gannets they easily shouldered the double burden and reared both adequately despite the great demands of these heavy, fast-growing youngsters. The weight of each twinned juvenile was not markedly less than the normal singles and their growth rate was only fractionally slower. It seemed highly unlikely that the adults were stressed by the extra burden. All this is quite unexpected, on the assumption that gannets, like red-foots, are rearing as many young as they can feed. Obviously, at present, they are not. Furthermore, they are failing to take advantage of their reproductive powers in other ways – particularly by almost always deferring the age of first breeding until they are five or even six years old, when we know, from actual examples, that they can breed successfully at four. Personally I believe they could breed successfully at three. Admittedly the gannet population is rising, and rising quite rapidly, but on the evidence it is not rising nearly so fast as it could. Despite the decrease in many fish species known to be eaten by gannets, they are obviously enjoying a favourable food situation. If one assumes that their clutch size of one and system of deferred maturity evolved at a time when their environment was much less favourable, one also implies that, even though it has now changed, the gannet lacks the ability to adapt to the changed situation by stepping up its breeding. This is not impossible to believe, but it is not very attractive either, except perhaps by supposing that such an increase would take a long time to show itself (see p. 66). There is an alternative, namely that breeding is being held down by the species itself, in effect to avoid too large a rise in numbers and subsequent over-fishing of the resources.* It is undeniable that populations of many animals are regulated and it is also clear from Wynne-Edwards's examples that animals often do reduce their own populations. For instance, sixty per cent of young produced by red grouse die before breeding and there is conclusive evidence that nearly all of them die directly or indirectly as a result of exclusion from the better parts of the heather moor by superior males. Here, social behaviour is apparently the mechanism by which a density appropriate to the carrying resources of the moor is achieved and the annual reduction in population is so great that it far exceeds the effect of shooting or not shooting a

* This is the general view, with respect to the animal kingdom as a whole, of Professor V. C. Wynne-Edwards, developed in *Animal Dispersion in Relation to Social Behaviour.*

moor – shooting, in other words, is irrelevant here. However, there seems a vital difference between this example and the gannet. There is no territorial exclusion in the gannet and nothing to stop them rearing more young except the apparent inability to lay larger clutches. Those birds given larger clutches do not reject them for the good of the group, but go ahead and rear them. The discussion can be developed a long way beyond this, but the place is not here.

To say a little more about gannet populations; the British and world population of North Atlantic gannets is rapidly increasing. The early stages of this increase (perhaps up to the beginning of the war) were doubtless partly due to the relaxation of human pressure since young gannets or 'gugas' are no longer culled except on Sula Sgeir and the Faroes; the other British gannetries which once yielded thousands of young and not a few adults now flourish in peace. The present rise, proceeding at a spectacular rate, is more difficult to explain. From fisheries' evidence, the overall food situation seems to have deteriorated during this century, with the temporary exception of the war and immediately post-war years when the stocks around Britain benefited from the drastic reduction in fishing. Certainly there has been no dramatic increase in any fish which could be important to the gannet, nor any big changes in distribution which could have helped it. Yet gannets are thriving and rearing their young with the utmost ease.

So far as their conservative clutch size of one is concerned, it seems that not enough females produce two-egg clutches to allow the habit to spread in the population; if, as we suggested, they have lost the ability at some previous point in their long evolutionary history when, perhaps, food or other conditions were far different from those of today, their tardiness in re-evolving the ability to lay two or more is, we may suspect, due partly to the fact that the gannet is a long-lived bird with a very slow reproductive rate and population turn-over, in which consequently evolutionary changes would be correspondingly slow. Whether or not it would be slow enough to explain this particular phenomenon it is hard to say. And to make the situation a bit more difficult to understand, there are at most gannetries these populations of birds, adult so far as plumage goes, but which do not breed. Very probably they are nearly all young, inexperienced birds, but why are they not cashing in on the good food situation and at least attempting to breed?

So one must leave it that red-footed boobies produce one egg for what appear to be simple and good reasons; gannets produce only one egg and also fail to utilise their reproductive potential in other ways, apparently without simple reasons. It is certainly pleasing to think that what the long-suffering red-foot loses on the swings it gains on the roundabout. Despite the hazards, its population on Tower is larger than any North Atlantic gannetry in the world.

*Figure 11* Red-footed booby perching in relaxed position

Philosophy will clip an angel's wings,
Conquer all the mysteries by rule and line,
Empty the haunted air, and gnomed mine —
Unweave a rainbow —
John Keats, 'Lamia'

This portrait of the red-foot began by describing the impressive size
of the colony on Tower, the largest recorded one in the world. Yet,
unless you sat quietly among the densest group in the cryptocarpus
shrub in the late afternoon or evening when the hunters were
returning from their fishing, you would wonder where all the birds
were. There is nothing remotely comparable to the exhilarating
clamour and motion of a large gannetry; you would hardly know
that you were at a large sea-bird station. Here and there a red-foot
lands with its harsh and rapid calling, higher pitched and more nasal
in the male, gruffer in the larger female, 'rah, rah, rah, *rah, rah,* ra',
the middle syllables louder and higher. But the surface of Tower
remains comparatively unruffled; where are the fights, the threats,
the conspicuous and elaborate displays by males on their sites, the
long and complex meeting ceremonies between pair members and
above all the wing-stirred air as thousands of birds criss-cross the
sky. No wonder the population could be under-estimated thirty-fold.
The contrast between the red-foots of Tower and the Peruvian
boobies of the Guañape Islands is, in retrospect, ludicrous. The
Peruvians seem in constant danger of aerial collision, so dense is the
mass of flying birds, whilst on the cliffs and slopes they form a living
carpet. Even in the densest red-foot groups the nests average more
than six feet apart; in the main they are much sparser, almost out of
contact with their neighbours.

The habit of nesting relatively well-spaced in trees strongly affects

*Figure 12* Red-footed booby: aggressive behaviour between pair members may occur as apparently hostile jabbing

much of the red-foot's behaviour, and not only in the obvious ways connected with perching and nest-building, for it also influences the ritualised displays performed in the context of the pair and between neighbours in the colony. Life in a red-foots' arboreal colony contrasts so markedly with that in a dense, active and highly social cliff gannetry that much may be learnt from the comparison, particularly about the evolution of social behaviour in the family. In this chapter, therefore, we will have a lot to say about gannets, much of which will be relevant, also, to later chapters.

In a close-packed gannetry the nests average about 2.3 per square yard; consequently there is immense activity. Every pair has only the nest drum and the surrounding foot or two as its territory. All around are jealous, extremely hostile neighbours, resentful of the slightest infringement and quick to use their sharp powerful beaks to back up their resentment. Unattended nests are immediately demolished by neighbours, who add the material to their own piles. If a bird tries to pick its way through to the edge of the group to take flight it is pecked and stabbed as it goes; even if it sits quietly it is likely to be menaced or tweaked by a neighbour, as part of the strict and ceaseless pattern of social behaviour keeping each in their place and thus the colony in order. If you are a gannet, in other words, you are part of a highly specialised group, the colony, in which everybody is aggressive to everybody else except mate and chick and to some extent even to them. Above all you are strictly confined to your own small area; withdrawal into a quieter corner of the territory is impossible.

The combination of dense groups and markedly aggressive individuals is clearly unlikely to produce a harmonious colony without strict discipline. The gannet's strict discipline lies in its highly developed and complex system of stereotyped social signals; postures or movements which clearly indicate to other individuals a bird's mood or intentions.

Instinctive or non-learned* behaviour of this kind has several disadvantages when compared with 'intelligent' or reasoning behaviour (much of which is learned, if we accept Thorpe's broad definition of learned behaviour as behaviour affected by past experience) but it is capable of producing the most subtle and beautifully adaptive systems, as the organisation within a gannetry shows. Until the pioneering work of a few ethologists enabled us to recognise the nature of much animal behaviour it was hard to reconcile its apparent purposiveness, suggesting an awareness of the relation between the action being performed and the 'desirable' end result, and its relative inflexibility which can lead to the performance of totally unsuitable behaviour. Now we understand that usually the 'purposiveness' has been achieved by the subtle and all-pervasive action of natural selection in favouring the evolution of the most effective behaviour, down to the last detail, but without the conscious appreciation of the organism concerned.

Repeatedly in the study of bird behaviour one comes across the limitations of instinct; it sometimes misfires; it is often apparently incapable of meeting slight variations in the situation – it runs, as it were, on rails. Yet, despite the lack of reasoning ability or, in relatively primitive species like the gannet, even the slightest pretensions to intelligence, birds react appropriately to thousands of different situations in their lives. They manage to find food, establish a breeding place, attract a mate, co-operate in the business of building a nest, incubating eggs and feeding young; they forage over distances of several hundreds of miles, returning unerringly even in

---

* Nobody has ever reared gannets in complete isolation to find out whether they would still display in the normal manner, but there is every reason to think they would.

dense mist. Imagine doing any of these things without possessing 'insight' into the reason for so doing (try, for instance, working out what, in the absence of any intelligent appreciation of the needs of its young,* could be the *precise* mechanism that decides a hunting gannet to turn and come back to its young instead of staying a bit longer at sea, perhaps fishing a bit more or resting a bit, as it does out of the breeding season). In many instances, too, these things are done without any previous experience. Thus it is possible to gain some idea of the magnitude of the task which non-intelligent behaviour performs apparently so effortlessly.

In reality, of course, these actions are the astonishing result of intricate reactions between systems – physiological and behavioural – each of staggering complexity. At the same time, in the absence of insight or reasoning, it no longer seems so amazing that a black-headed gull will 'unintelligently' incubate a tobacco tin in place of its egg or that a male budgerigar will attack his mate instead of courting her if one paints her cere the male colour, or that a meadow pipit ignores the struggles of its own chicks as they slowly die outside the nest and gives all its attention to the usurping cuckoo. In these and countless other cases, the birds are reacting to stimuli which have the property of releasing specific behaviour patterns. Normally something smooth, hard and cold in the gull's nest will be its own egg, another budgerigar with a blue cere will be a male and hence a rival and the chick within the nest is the one to be attended. Recently I saw a perfect example of automatic and stereotyped behaviour in the gannet. A male of an old pair flew into his nest. Normally he would bite his mate on the head with some violence and then go through a long and complicated meeting ceremony, an ecstatic display confined to members of a pair. Unfortunately, the female had caught her lower mandible in a loop of fish netting that was firmly anchored in the structure of the nest. Every time she tried to raise her head to perform the meeting ceremony with her mate she merely succeeded in opening her upper mandible whilst the lower remained fixed in the netting. So she apparently threatened the male with widely gaping beak and he immediately responded by attacking her. With each

* If the reader doubts this, remember that a gannet will allow its chick to starve rather than go to feed it a short distance from the nest; it shows no 'appreciation' of its chick's needs in that case, and indeed seems entirely oblivious of it.

71

attack she lowered and turned away her bill (the way in which a female gannet appeases an aggressive male). At once the male stopped biting her and she again turned to greet him but simply repeated the beak-opening and drew another attack. And so it went on despite the fact that these two birds had been mated for years and that the netting, the cause of all the trouble, was clearly visible. The male was reacting automatically to the signal behaviour which the female was inadvertently supplying. This sort of thing makes one cautious about accepting anecdotal accounts of lower-order birds and mammals behaving with apparent insight, and the 'lower-order' should perhaps be stressed, since some birds and mammals, corvids, seals and, of course, primates among them, seem extraordinarily intelligent. If I heard that a male gannet, under the circumstances described above, had purposefully disentangled the netting and released the female, I could not believe it. A friend described how he had seen a gannet help its fallen youngster to regain its place on the nest, but this is so unlike gannet behaviour that I suspected, rightly as further details confirmed, that the adult was in fact attacking it by pulling at its wing, so seeming to haul it on to the nest. The anthropomorphic interpretation comes so naturally that the temptation is to apply it too often; where valid it is of great interest, but such cases are relatively rare, though in the higher primates they are apparently genuine and even common. It has been remarked that there are three categories of behaviour – human, chimpanzee and all other animals.

Again, if a strayed gannet chick tries to return to its nest its parent may attack it furiously 'because' to an adult gannet a chick on the nest is right but a chick approaching is an intruder and usually treated accordingly. Since chicks hardly ever wander and at least one parent is constantly on guard throughout the entire nesting period, this works well and averts the possibility of two or more chicks getting on to one nest leaving another empty, so overworking some adults whilst others remain idle. Of course gannets are capable of recognising their own chick; they can certainly recognise their mate, and chicks their parents, both by sight and sound, but despite this they react 'automatically' to a given stimulus situation, even if it means attacking their own chick. Perhaps some people would refuse the implications of this and say that the parents were punishing the 'chick to teach it a lesson, but such interpretations are vulnerable and unsatisfactory.

It is an astonishing fact that, as I have mentioned, a male gannet bites his mate every time they meet at the nest. It makes no difference whether they have been partners for ten minutes or ten years, he will still bite her and bite her hard. Towards the end of the breeding season his attacks become even more violent than they were in the middle and may look so hostile that it is hard to believe the two birds really are partners. Coloured rings, however, leave no room for doubt about identity. This aggression is partly because late in the season his gonads again produce more sex hormones, one of whose effects is to increase aggression (or possibly the androgen level stays more or less constant but the inhibitory effect of other hormones is reduced). So, even in old pairs, the male may severely attack his mate with whom he has just reared a chick for perhaps the fourth or fifth time. The point is that he is responding to the female in the manner partly dictated by his internal condition, which powerfully influences the way he reacts to an external stimulus such as the ones described. Yet if you saw them nibbling each other's head feathers, eyes half closed in enjoyment, a picture of accord, you could indulgently imagine that such a pair had developed affection. Perhaps they have, but if you then saw the male stabbing and biting the female and attempting to push her from the nest you would certainly think again. Such common and conflicting observations are almost impossible to explain from an anthropomorphic viewpoint, but are quite consistent with the ethological interpretation.

Before becoming involved in the later events of the red-foot breeding cycle one important point remains. Aggression in the gannet has loomed large in this account but nothing has been said about its role. Wife-beating may be a side effect but it is not the *raison d'etre* of the aggression. Fighting, in fact, is an important part of the gannet's life; fighting and fishing are two things it does expertly, which is perhaps to be expected since they are not independent of each other. Male gannets fight over, or compete for, nest sites and females fight over males. Why males fight so much is a question on several levels and one which I again mention but to defer. They fight with tremendous vigour and at great length. I have watched truly homeric struggles between rival gannets, in which for almost two hours the opponents have exerted all their strength in a grim battle, massive beaks interlocked except when stabbing and worrying each other about the head and face. Imagine two immaculate white males locked in combat; the heavy rains of early spring may have turned the colony into a stinking quagmire between the nests, many inches deep in sulphurous mud, rotting sea-weed and excreta. In the intensity of the struggle the rivals thresh around, spattering their pristine neighbours but reducing their own splendid wings and tails to muddy tatters, so glued with ooze that flight may be impossible when at last one breaks away. I have seen such a male spiral crazily down to the sea, two hundred and fifty feet below, to land in a tangle of wings, leaving a muddy trail in the water. Tattered plumage and broken flight feathers are not the only damage; there may be a bleeding face and head, pock-marked with stab wounds from angry neighbours. If they are really unlucky one eye may be a gory mess, perhaps permanently blinded, though even badly damaged eyes usually recover.

These fights are not exceptional; they can be seen several times on every spring day at a gannetry. For whatever reason, it is a matter of real importance for a gannet to get a nesting site which has certain qualities, among which closeness to others is obviously one, for it is noticeable that they will fight for a particular foot of earth within touching distance of a neighbour when there may be yards of gannet-free terrain adjacent to it.

What about red-foots? Do they fight bitterly for a tree or a place close to another red-foot in a bush? The short answer is no. They do not need to nest densely or, in other words, there is obviously not sufficient advantage to be gained from so doing. I do not intend to sneak away from this interesting but rather difficult topic without further comment, but our present concern is behaviour and the red-foot's lack of territorial aggression when compared with the gannet. With its lack of this trait and of dense nesting, the whole background of the red-foot's social behaviour is very different from that of the gannet. Although the red-foot rarely fights for its territory, it shows impressive aggression when its territorial rights are severely infringed. It utters fearsome screeches and, plumage bristling, lunges repeatedly at the intruder with wild but synchronous strokes of its wings. This is high-intensity threat behaviour and it is

TOWER ISLAND
1  A tidal creek at the head of Darwin Bay. Juvenile frigates (white heads), adult male frigate and adult white booby in foreground

2  Our Darwin Bay camp. This low coral beach is occasionally breached by extra high tides

3  Red-footed boobies soon found our tent

4  The mocking birds, alert and thieving, were a constant delight or irritation

5 A young sea-lion looks amazed at the sight of a native on Hood Island

6 Our tame Darwin's finch—a large-billed *magnirostris* male from Tower

7 June with red-footed booby in the crow's nest

8 Carl Angermeyer makes a good barber on *Beagle II*. Here he practises on the author

VISITORS
9 *Beagle II*, the vessel of the Charles Darwin Research Station

10 H.R.H. The Duke of Edinburgh with the author on Hood Island

GALAPAGOS HERONS
11 Adult yellow-crowned night heron

12 Small Galapagos blue heron stalking prey

13 Great grey heron, much like our own

RED-FOOTED BOOBY
14 Brown and white forms of the red-foot

15 White form. Teamwork in defence by mother and chick

RED-FOOTED BOOBY

16 Male, left, 'advertises' (a sexual display) to female. Notice this species'
short legs

17 Reciprocal aggression between members of a pair. Bird on right showing
synchronous wing-flailing and evoking threat from mate

the reception which a female red-foot will accord a human intruder when her chick is tiny and her maternal feelings are strongest.

It was soon obvious that red-footed boobies in their large tree territories have many fewer pair and social contacts, fewer opportunities for 'misunderstandings' and less severe penalties to pay than gannets in their dense colonies. This might suggest that red-foots do not require such well-developed social signal behaviour as gannets.

When I first saw a male red-foot fly in and join his mate I was struck by the different pattern of events as compared with gannets. He came rushing in much more swiftly than the less agile gannet and, calling rapidly and gutturally, landed near the nest instead of on it. Then, with wings wrapped closely to his spare brown body, he hopped onto it calling loudly, neck fully stretched forwards and head swinging from side to side, almost down to the twigs which he gripped and shook. This 'forward head waving' is the red-foot's aggressive display used against territorial rivals and signifying ownership of the nest site; it is probably derived from 'attack' directed to a harmless 'opponent' (the nest or twigs) rather than to a neighbour – hence the twig-biting. Meanwhile the female often showed slight signs of fear by ruffing her neck and head feathers and trembling – reactions which she shows when alarmed by human 'intruders'. She seemed anxious to avoid pointing her bill towards the male and kept turning her head aside in a flinching gesture. Suddenly the male aimed a savage jab at her and she jabbed back from a withdrawn position. The male then bent and gripped the twigs again, shaking them slightly with a side to side movement of his head. Often when they meet at the nest they do not even come into contact; during incubation the bird being relieved simply rises, moves off the nest and takes flight without even touching its partner.

What a difference between that primitive, hostile-looking jab – or in many cases a lack of any meeting behaviour whatever – and the gannet's ecstatic meeting ceremony which may continue for five minutes at full pitch, the partners standing breast to breast, wings outspread and fencing with their bills. Why can the red-foot manage with such a poorly developed meeting ceremony, or putting it the other way round, why does the gannet need such a complicated one? All sulids are aggressive as they fly in to their sites, but the arrival

G

of the male red-foot is mild compared with that of the gannet, who lands like a thunderbolt and fiercely grips his mate's head, turned away from him in a pronounced gesture as she simultaneously pushes up to him. This pushing behaviour is understandable, because, other things being equal, a female gannet close to a male is less likely to draw aggression than if she were slightly off the nest. The male then releases her and they begin their clamorous and excited meeting ceremony. Whereas the female booby, in her large territory, can easily hop onto a nearby perch and so avoid her mate, the female gannet, hemmed in by neighbours, cannot move for fear of trespassing. So the gannet needs some display to appease or reassure the partners after the initial show of aggression by the male. Red-foots, in fact, usually do keep well apart in their territory except when, for obvious reasons such as mating, they have to come together. Then they appear to overcome their initial antagonism by performing a display whose other function, perhaps its main one, is rather different (it is in fact the display called sky-pointing by which a male attracts a female to his territory in the early stages of pair formation) but which red-foots use also in this secondary context, apparently because they have no other.

The greeting ceremony in the gannet (like its equivalent in other species) obviously fills a very important role. Because those males most successful in competition for breeding sites have left most offspring, and the aggression which led to their success is to a large extent heritable (this has recently been shown to be true even in hens), a situation has gradually developed in which aggressive males are favoured by evolution. The stimulus releasing a gannet's aggression is another gannet on its breeding site, but it would be disastrous if this hostile response, which first enabled it to compete successfully for a site, were now to succeed in driving away its mate. One may ask, 'But why need a male attack his mate, if he can recognise her?' Partly because, as I have said, birds react to the broad conspicuous features of a stimulus situation as well as to the details, and the one response often overrides the other. Who believes that a male robin cannot see any difference between a bunch of red feathers and another robin when his sharp eyes can spot a crumb from twenty yards and an intruder robin from ten times that distance? Yet in a very simple experiment, Lack (1946) showed that he will attack such a bunch of feathers placed in his territory, in preference to attacking an entire robin lacking the red breast feathers. In the same way, to a male gannet the sight of another gannet in his territory (the bunch of red feathers) evokes some hostile feelings even though he can, in terms of visual ability, distinguish the details which show her to be a particular gannet – in fact his mate. So the stimulus situation 'another gannet on my site', to which willy-nilly he to some extent responds, elicits a nervous response which is translated into muscle action. This is the necessary situation on which natural selection has had to work. The male *must*, of course, continue to react aggressively to the general stimulus of another gannet on his site if he is to retain it against intruders; natural selection cannot produce a non-aggressive gannet just to do away with intra-pair hostility.

So we can see that a female gannet approaching the male 'excites' his aggressive feelings. The question now is, what can he do to express this aggression (in the sense of getting rid of it) without damaging the pair relationship? There is, of course, no question of purposive behaviour, of the gannet knowingly doing the best thing – as we might deliberately let off steam by vigorous exercise or even smashing something – and, in effect, directing its own evolution along certain channels to achieve the best results. It cannot 'see' that it is better for the species that male gannets should find some alternative way of expressing aggression to the female, as we can understand that it is better to let off steam in some relatively harmless way rather than by attacking the person who arouses our hostility. Nor is it helpful to imagine some supernatural agent thus directing it along the right lines. Instead, by numerous subtle interactions too complicated to imagine and largely impossible to demonstrate, gannets (and boobies) have had to evolve suitable behaviour in every situation, working always by trial and error. Their raw material has been and is the variability in behaviour within the species, itself dependent on genetical variability. Some individuals no doubt were too aggressive and, though successful in competition for a site, left no, or fewer progeny because females literally could not stand them, or even, perhaps, because they had too strong a tendency to attack their own young. The particular genotype conferring that tendency would die out. Others readily accepted females, but were too easily displaced by rivals; the same fate would befall their genotype. We cannot know by what small steps successive genotypes managed to produce male gannets that had just the right aggression to displace rivals, to bite their female without actually wounding or driving her away and then to express their hostility by mutual fencing with her in a 'friendly' way, though we can reconstruct some of the probable steps. In this case, for example, it seems that mutual fencing developed from the gannet's aggressive territorial display, itself derived from a simple nest-biting movement which the birds perform after landing, just as the red-foot bites a twig – essentially an aggressive act directed at the nest instead of at the mate or a neighbour. And this process of derivation makes sense, for one would expect, on the basis of what was written above, an aggressive reaction from male to female, yet one that would not drive her away. A modified form of the ownership display would be better suited to this purpose than would an outright attack. It developed as a response to intruders (which the female is) but is capable of alterations in form which can transform its meaning. Somehow the gannet has managed, in evolutionary terms, to translate its response into this modified expression of aggression when it is reacting to the arrival of its mate at the site. Now it can, as it were, continue to 'feel' aggressive (for we must infer this, although sexual motivation may also have become involved) but express it without endangering its pair relationship. Indeed, mutual fencing now helps the pair relationship by 'reassuring' the partner and probably strengthening the pair bond, though this effect is difficult to prove. Nevertheless, Lorenz has recently written that the comparable triumph ceremony in grey-lag geese is in his opinion the most powerful factor in keeping the pair together, even more important than sexual attraction. In 1958 Huxley wrote: 'When I studied bird behaviour forty-five years ago all I had to go on was the Darwinian assumption that all displays were epigamic. I introduced the idea of mutual selection and paved the way for the concept of the pair bond by suggesting that the mutual display served as an emotional bond between members of a mated pair in species where both sexes played similar roles in caring for eggs and young.'

As a final point underlining the incredible complexity of the whole process, remember also that the size and strength of the beak, so important in fighting and sure to be subject to natural selection in that capacity,* is also very much concerned with feeding. Changes in bill length or jaw muscles for one function inevitably affect the other, so the two must evolve in balance if one or other activity is not to be disadvantageously affected. No wonder Huxley called animals a bundle of adaptations. The power of natural selection in producing organisms so finely adapted to their environment and mode of life is indeed impressive.

This lengthy digression has a great deal to do with red-footed boobies because it helps one to understand why their behaviour differs from that of the gannet. When the female red-foot hops three or four feet away from her mate and spends, as she does, most of her time out of reach she is at once solving, simply, the problem which the gannet has solved by the evolution of its elaborate meeting ceremony, and so she makes such a complex ceremony unnecessary. If this ceremony, or its equivalent, sublimates aggression and the red-foots lack it, we may suspect that they will also tend to avoid the situations in which such aggression could be aroused. Keeping apart is one way; another is avoiding behaviour which requires them to point their bills at each other, since that is the position from which aggression begins. So it is interesting to discover that red-foots entirely lack the habit of preening each other by simultaneously nibbling each other's head feathers, though males sometimes preen females and vice versa. Then, however, the bird being preened keeps its head averted. Gannets 'mutual preen' very frequently but they do not mind pointing bills at each other; they have mutual fencing to absorb aggression if necessary. If all this makes them seem rather like feathered automatons, remember that they often strike the observer in just that way. But again, the sum is clearly more than the parts, or is it that the automatons are so formidably complicated that comparison with the finest machine is coarse and inadequate?

Controlling the aggression apparently so necessary to the gannet's breeding success has clearly required the development of complex social behaviour. We have instanced the meeting ceremony; we could have chosen other examples. The red-foot has not evolved such nice controls, not because it has no aggression, but at least

---

* In fact gannets are the only members of the family in which males have larger bills than females and this may be an adaptation for fighting.

partly because it has 'simpler' means of dealing with it; simpler means which are feasible in a species nesting so much less densely than the gannet. Since the red-foot seems relatively so poorly equipped with the means for handling the aggression that exists between mates, it might be expected that certain situations would be less finely controlled than in the gannet. It was indeed noticeable that after intrusion by another red-foot, or any serious disturbance such as the twig-stealing swoop of marauding frigates, the male vented his aggression on the female, or to use a more objective phrase, redirected his aggression onto her. A male gannet under comparable circumstances would initiate a bout of the greeting ceremony. A pair (number 14) bred successfully in 1963–4 and had one of the oldest chicks in the colony when we arrived. It first flew on 7 February and finally left to fend for itself on 5 May. The adults, which bore our colour rings, still came to their territory to rest and sleep, but it was the end of their breeding season and probably the male was showing a slight revival of sexual and territorial activity. It seemed that his sexual interest in the female was not sufficient to inhibit his aggression (a system which is known to operate in some animals) and on 6 June, to my astonishment, he attacked his mate and started a battle that lasted several minutes – in fact it was the best red-foot fight I ever saw. This just could not have happened with an old pair of gannets because with the male's first aggressive act his mate would have shown appropriate appeasement behaviour, and initiated the mutual fencing display. The female red-foot, by jabbing the male in retaliation, encouraged a real fight.

The ways in which birds find a mate are fascinating, but difficult to observe; partners are usually already together when we notice their courtship activities and one rarely knows whether they are seeing each other for the first time. In the red-footed booby and its relatives, pair formation involves a conspicuous display by the male, which is nicely called 'advertising', although since it occurs only when a female is within sight it ought strictly to be called by its more objective and descriptive name of 'sky-pointing'; real advertising occurs in the absence of the object solicited. Males do not sky-point until they have first found and established themselves on a site; on Tower that presents no difficulties. The sudden urge to establish a site is the result of internal changes, probably in the main maturation changes in the gonads of the male. Between leaving the nest as a juvenile and setting up as a site-owning adult, a red-footed booby lands somewhere in or around the colony hundreds of times. Yet, until an inner condition or 'feeling' compels it to set up a territory (and it is entirely unknown exactly how the sum of gland secretions produces a qualitatively new set of reactions to essentially the same old combination of external stimuli, though it must involve bio-chemical changes in the nervous system), it does not react to the bushes as territories or nest sites; it does not show the typical aggressive calling and head-waving after landing. But immediately *after* establishing a territory, it shows the appropriate changes in behaviour; the same motions of flying in, the same bushes, the identical external environment which formerly failed to elicit any-thing but ordinary landing behaviour now automatically elicits quite different behaviour. It is as though the bird sees through different eyes, which, I suppose, in a sense, it does.

The male booby who now flies in to his site and performs his distinctive site-owning behaviour is thus different. Now, though he did not before, he reacts to the sight of a nearby female by sky-pointing. Whether the internal changes that made him take up his site are now making him react to the female or whether the site as a new sort of stimulus has also contributed to his state, is not clear. However, sky-point he does. Before sky-pointing a male peers or stares at the female as though willing her to look at him, then stretches his neck, points his bill skywards, lifts his tail and wing tips and utters a grating call. Then he relaxes and again fixes his steady gaze on the female. He makes slight reaching movements towards her as though he would bite her and often he is overcome by his aggressive feelings and suddenly attacks. Here again we see the flashes of aggression which the female, as an intruder, elicits from the male even when he is sufficiently stimulated sexually to advertise to her, which is saying, in effect, 'come here'. When the female responds to his conspicuous posture by approaching he often jabs her fiercely, even if until then he has not done so. Meanwhile the female looks thoroughly discomfited, trembling visibly and flinching away from the male. Her head feathers stand on end, as they do when she is afraid, for instance of a human intruder. Eventually she begins to sky-point in return and the pair stand near each other and posture

A Reciprocal aggression between mates, female on left

B The hostile-looking mutual jabbing, which sometimes occurs after the pair meet

E The pelican posture: after a hop, the bird arches its neck and tucks its bill into upper breast. This position may be held briefly after wings are closed

F Aggressive male reaches towards female, who faces away. The 'reach' is aggressive and may be followed by an actual jab. The 'facing away' is largely fear-induced and probably an appeasement posture

*Figure 13* Red-footed booby

repeatedly with the utmost solemnity, now alternately and then in unison. This may continue for an hour or more and a funny pair they look as they stretch and groan, stretch and groan. Every few minutes the male looks restless, flicks his wings rapidly open and shut (indicating that he is about to fly), perhaps gives them a brisk

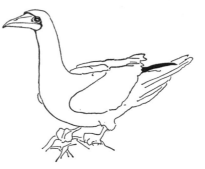

C A territorial encounter: the male on the left is in the forward head-waving position and the male on the right is showing aggressive wing-flailing

D Forward head-waving; in this aggressive display the head swings down from side to side, whilst the bird calls rapidly. It signifies ownership of a site

G The male, on left, sky-points (the sexual display by which he advertises for a female) whilst the female looks interested

H Sunning. This is not a display, but a posture adopted to help the sun to penetrate the plumage – wings are spread and feathers loosened. It may act against feather parasites, but this is not known

shake and then hops onto a take-off point. Immediately after a hop he arches his neck and presses his bill tip against his upper breast – a posture found in all boobies and associated with movement on foot – then he springs into the air and circles the area a few times, coming in as though to land with each circuit and eventually sweeps in with his rapid landing call and performs his head-waving display. Then they fall to sky-pointing again. As I pointed out earlier, my interpretation is that this prolonged ceremony of mutual sky-pointing, which occurs almost entirely in the early stage of pair formation before the egg is laid, takes the place of the gannet's elaborate meeting ceremony in establishing and strengthening the bond between pair members. By mutual sky-pointing red-foots can at least temporarily establish good enough pair relations to permit the necessary copulations; after egg-laying they need not see much of each other and, as already described, make little actual contact. They can also stimulate each other so that the degree of precise co-operation involved in copulation is achieved. That, in fact, is what most courtship display in animals is about; a male courts a female so that when he is sufficiently sexually stimulated to mate, she is sufficiently stimulated to co-operate. A sexually excited male that approached a stone-cold female would have little chance of successful mating.

Before the female produces an egg the pair attend the site and build the nest for three or four weeks. In the territory there are always one or two favourite perches with pyramids of excreta beneath. Often, when all trace of the nest has disappeared, these mounds betray a nesting area. Red-footed boobies construct the nest of dry twigs and sprays of green material which the male brings in bouts of furious activity. If the handiwork of previous years survives the structure may become a genuinely imposing pile, even three or four feet high and containing several barrow-loads of twigs. Whilst the female builds each new piece into place the male springs into the air and flies swiftly away to some gathering area where he breaks off twigs by violent but straightforward tugging; he cannot swing upside down on a twig to break it off as a rook will. It is a curious peculiarity of nest-building sea-birds that they are very poor judges of what they can take and carry, and what is worth the trouble. On the Bass, shags queue for hours to tug desperately at a fixed three-inch-thick rope, or try to take off with a mallow stalk two feet long and two inches thick, whilst standing on part of it. Gannets solemnly circle the Bass two or three times carrying a single feather in their formidable bill, before coming in to deliver their useless offering to their mate as though it were a major triumph, and as such it is accepted. The male red-foot hurries back with his twigs, trying to avoid the piratical frigates that are always on the look-out for twigs to steal for their own nest. Others have seen red-foots steal from neighbours but we were struck by the red-foot's reluctance to do so or for that matter to pluck nest material from the area immediately around the nest. Very occasionally we saw them take a twig from a long-forsaken pile, but they certainly preferred to fly some distance, even two miles, to gather material from an area more or less devoid of nesting boobies. If the near presence of nests inhibited them from gathering nest material, it could be an interesting adaptation preventing them from denuding the area around their own nest and so eventually depriving their young of cover, which could be important to its survival, as shade or shelter, At all events the red-foot's relative reluctance in this respect formed a strange contrast to the inveterate pilfering habits of gannets, who will demolish a huge nest pile in a matter of moments. The suggested function of this special restriction is similar to Tinbergen's interpretation (1962) of the black-headed gull's tendency, experimentally demonstrated, to leave green-coloured, even though artificial, objects placed near its nest but to remove the same objects when differently coloured. Removal of green vegetation could increase the chick's exposure to predators – hence leave green alone.

Until the egg is laid red-foots frequently copulate between trips for nest material. The male hops onto the female's back with a long-drawn, grating call but does not grip her head as the gannet grips his mate. Red-foots are the only boobies with a mating call. They often copulate at night, even in pitch blackness and are generally far more nocturnal than the gannet, which quietens down so much that a gannetry at night can be silent.

Even though the red-foot's egg, with an average fresh weight of 54 gm, weighs only about half that of the gannet, in proportion to the size of the female it is larger, weighing five per cent of the female's weight against three per cent for the gannet. Furthermore, despite its much smaller size in absolute terms it actually takes two days longer to hatch than the gannet's egg. Even very young red-foots may suffer from lack of food, and in a sense particularly so, since they cannot endure long periods of starvation when very tiny. Perhaps the larger egg and longer incubation period permit greater development of the chick before hatching and increase its chance of survival if it is unfortunate enough to hatch when food is scarce.

Like all other members of its family, the red-foot lacks a brood patch and incubates its egg by wrapping its webbed feet around it. The principle is the same as the brood patch and there is no reason why heat should not be transmitted to the egg that way. The only biologists who have measured the relevant temperatures (Howell and Bartholomew) say that the web's is not higher than the egg's and they conclude that heat is not being passed from web to egg. It would be very strange if the red-foot should prove different from the gannet, even though incubating in exactly the same way, for there can be no doubt that a gannet's feet are the fire at which the chick embryo warms its cells during the bitter days of April, when it is forming within the shell. I still believe in feet. Why else would even the red-foot wrap its webs round the egg during the cool nights, but stand clear of it during the heat of the day?

During the forty-six days' incubation period the adult's stints are extremely long, in fact the longest of any member of the family. Sometimes a bird sits without a moment's respite for over six days, though the average duty spell was sixty hours. Males take slightly longer spells than females and a bird that has incubated for five days takes about that long to feed and recuperate so its mate gets a fair share of the onerous and gruelling incubation duties. Adult red-foots reach their lowest body weights, not when feeding their demanding young but during incubation.

If food becomes scarce during incubation wholesale desertion of eggs occurs. Of 109 eggs laid in early 1964 seventy per cent were deserted or lost before hatching. This state of affairs is absolutely unheard of in gannets. Wherever we turn we find the red-foot dominated by its scarce or erratic food supply; all its breeding activities are geared to make the best of this factor. Even the long foraging journeys and consequently the length of incubation stints and the number of young it can feed, eventually relate back to the nature of the food supply.

Despite the harsh penalties which it frequently endures, the red-foot is a successful species. Perhaps the way in which it scores most heavily over the gannet is in its gentle and painless fledging process and then in continuing to feed its free-flying young until they have fully mastered the difficult and specialised art of plunge-diving. This extra period of feeding is a valuable subsidy for the young at a critical time. The juveniles play around in the bay, practise fishing and come home every night to be fed by their parents. This comfortable launching into independence must save a large number of juvenile lives.

The gannet juveniles which leave the nest once and for all at thirteen weeks face a much harsher trial and most of them die. The majority of those fine fat youngsters never complete their first year of life. They must learn to fish before their fat reserves give out, otherwise they starve. Having been fed until the last moment they are extremely fat and can probably survive without food for at least three weeks. Their two or three pounds of fat weigh them down so solidly that although they can fly miles at the very first attempt, they cannot rise from the sea once having alighted, though they thresh violently in the attempt. Instead they immediately swim away from the rock and begin the long paddle south (though sometimes they go north first). I have watched many scores of young gannets take their maiden flight, and known even as they made their somewhat bewildered jump from the security of the nest into the unknown, that only about twenty per cent would survive to breed. Some, of course, die through accident; they may be entangled in a fisherman's net as they dive excitedly into the struggling mass of silver herrings being drawn to the surface; they may be shot or break a wing. But many of the black youngsters setting off so sturdily will die of starvation.

When one considers the skill required to dive from a height into the sea and catch a slippery, swiftly moving fish, it is obvious that a great deal of practice will be needed. Imagine the eager but inept attempts of the juvenile. When swimming along he often puts his head under water for a second; indeed it is one of the first things he does after getting down to the sea. Immediately a membrane slides across his eye and gives him clear underwater vision. One such time, perhaps many days after the juvenile's harsh baptism, a fish swims into view. It will not bear much resemblance to the slimy bolus which his parents regurgitated for him, but he has probably seen enough recognisable fish, perhaps accidentally spilled by his parents or protruding from their mouths during partial regurgitation, to establish the necessary link between fish and food. Or perhaps he is born with a built-in response to a fish shape – some species have such a mechanism. Either way he recognises this fish and eagerly snatches at it, but it is too deep. He is buoyant and cannot force himself underwater by thrusting with his feet, so he misses it. But now he will frequently thrust his head under water and look for fish. Eventually he sees others and by jumping forwards and a little upwards, perhaps aided by wing beats, he manages to make a sort of dive. One can well imagine how many times he must miss before he is lucky enough to catch a fish. By now he will have metabolised nearly all his fat and as a result will be able to lift himself from the surface and fly, so he will probably see many more fish and dive after them, no doubt clumsily. The rest depends on practice and weather. The weather could spoil everything; a few days of rough seas and high winds just when the juvenile is physically at a low ebb could easily mean disaster. Probably gannets have evolved a breeding season which produces the vast majority of fully grown young mainly before the end of September partly because these have a better chance of avoiding such gales in the deteriorating weather conditions of the North Sea and North Atlantic, with the familiar series of depressions coming from the Iceland low.

The situation for the red-foot juvenile is utterly different; this testing period of achieving full independence does not worry him. For one thing he isn't fat and heavy, quite the reverse. By the time he ventures out over the sea he has already made many practice flights around the breeding area and is agile on the wing. For another, he is most unlikely to run into bad weather. But far more importantly, he can come home every day with a good chance of getting the odd flying-fish or squid from a parent. Like all subsidised bodies, as nationalised industries, he can afford to take things easier. Compared with gannets many fewer, proportionately, die at this stage. The gannet loses hardly a chick during their period in the nest, but many die soon after leaving, whilst the red-foots starve in their thousands in the nest but once on the wing most of them survive.

Apparently, then, the best way the gannet can utilise a seasonally restricted but abundant food supply is to pack it into the young whilst it is there. This makes them fat and heavy and the rest follows, since they cannot get back to the nest once they leave, and have to fend entirely for themselves. It takes a gannet thirteen weeks to grow and a red-foot nearer thirty-three. For the gannet food may not be available that long. It would be futile to have a long and slow growth period and then have to go and learn to fish minus both parental subsidy and fat endowment, and for good measure in the period of worsening weather. Far better for the gannet to make hay whilst the sun shines and risk the rest. In the end it boils down to the same thing; both gannets and red-foots satisfactorily maintain their population levels. The interest lies in the nice way each is adapted to its particular environment.

*Figure 14* A male red-foot, momentarily aggressive to the female, elicits slight withdrawal (fear) from her

The web of experience is largely of your own weaving
when you live on a small and remote island where
there are no other human inhabitants. The little world
of rock and herbage is beneath your feet and you share
it with many other forms of life in which you may be
interested. But only you can think reflectively, and it
depends on you and your companion, if there is one,
whether the island becomes a prison or a satisfying,
private world for the time being.
Frank Darling, *A Naturalist on Rona*

It is first light; all is quiet. Suddenly there is a violent clattering
outside the tent, as though somebody has kicked over a pile of pots
and pans; somebody has. The mocking birds are cleaning up the
remains of yesterday's supper. June stirs on her worn and patched
old safari bed; it gives a tired creak and, if it is that kind of a day,
collapses. The scraping and pecking noises continue, mingling with
the loud chirps of an inferior bird being persecuted. There is a
scratching on the canvas and a small black finch with an enormous
beak like a hawfinch squeezes in through any hole he can find and
hops up boldly on to my face. Inches behind the tent, among the
coral shingle, a swallow-tailed gull makes the funny combination
of choking and squeaking by which the male precedes his courtship
feeding of the female, probably on the squid he caught last night in
the darkened sea. A loud, harsh 'arrk-ar', full of despair, tells us that
another red-footed booby is being victimised by frigate birds.
Nostalgic Galapagos sounds.

    I open my eyes and peer suspiciously around, looking for giant
centipedes which come into the tent at night. They are particularly
unpleasant arthropods; some are at least ten inches long, broad to

match, flattened, shiny brown and equipped with two strong biting mandibles and an apparently infinite number of powerful legs (actually twenty pairs). Of course, by now, they are all back in their hiding-places under boulders, behind bark or beneath our ground-sheet. An inquisitive watcher would see the tent flap move and a shaggy head peer out. Each morning I looked to see if the dinghy had been washed away or beached and whether we were still alone on our desert island or a yacht had crept into the bay. The swallow-tails drew themselves up thinly and screeched their alarm whenever we first emerged; they never got used to it.

*Figure 15* A yellow warbler catching a small fiddler crab

Our personal appearance, apart from the vagaries of nature, depended on several variables, chiefly the weather and the state of the wash. We were not fussy about our looks. If we ran out of shorts and shirts we went without, a natural state to which even inhibited north Britons quickly become accustomed. I drew the sartorial line at wearing just boots; nothing or shoes and at least shorts was my firm principle. June lacked such fine feelings and often did one of our routine checks in a straw hat, sunglasses, tennis shoes and a neck scarf. The scarf was not for elegance, merely to stop sunburn on the collar-bone.

The first chore was to milk the cow. 'Solly' our cow was the solar still, which produced drip by tardy drip half to three-quarters of a gallon daily. It was rather primitive but perhaps worth describing

H

since there are few published details and people planning to live on a desert island (there must be thousands) may find them useful. We were rather proud of our still; it actually worked and could have supported us indefinitely on a waterless island. Many islands have been considered impracticable for field work simply because they lack sweet water. Besides this, there was the spendthrift pleasure of manufacturing real, potable water from the Pacific Ocean. The basic plan came from existing literature on solar stills.* The base was a rectangular pit in the sand (where there is no sand a tarred wooden box will do) 3' × 8' and six inches deep, lined with black polythene as a heat-absorbent material and filled with sea-water. The polythene eventually began to leak from innumerable pin-holes caused by small crabs or amphipods from beneath, so a spare supply proved a wise precaution. Over the pit we placed a ridge-type greenhouse roof of transparent Mylar† stretched over a framework made from driftwood; the bottom edges of the Mylar bent under to form a trough. The sun's heat, absorbed by the black polythene lining, produced water vapour which condensed on the under-surface of the roof and ran down into the troughs. The whole structure sloped slightly to persuade the water to run along the troughs into collecting cans sunk in the ground. The practical snags were to get the whole apparatus water-vapour tight, to make a satisfactory trough and to persuade the water to run down the roof instead of collecting in droplets and falling back into the pit. Fine striations on the underside of the Mylar or perhaps a smear of detergent to lower the surface tension of the water droplets and cause them to run, would probably have helped.

A feasible yield from this kind of still under intensive sun is about 0·09 gallons per square foot of base per day. Our best day's yield was a gallon – *very* satisfactory, but we couldn't keep it up. A lot depends on the weather and the performance deteriorated for a number of reasons, chiefly leakage in the floor of the pit which meant frequent topping up and so cooling of the system. Inefficient drainage of the distilled water, which often fell back into the pit or leaked from the trough before reaching the collecting can, was

* Kindly lent, with additional information, by C. C. Noakes, Institute of Tropical Products.

† A trade name for a Du Pont product.

another fault. The distilled water we did make, however, was untainted and if necessary we could have survived on it. There seems no reason why two or three such stills, better constructed than ours, should not provide, indefinitely, enough water for a small party on a waterless island. The necessary materials are compact, easily transported, cheap and unbreakable. Naturally, before relying on a home-made still under potentially dangerous conditions it would be sensible to try it out beforehand. As an illustration of the potentialities of the system, a large still of several acres, in Mexico, produced 5,000 gallons per day for about forty years. Farrington Daniels, an expert on solar stills, who visited the islands with the Galapagos International Scientific Project, made a much more permanent affair than ours on Santa Cruz, but it was not in use when we left. The islanders collect rain water for drinking and tap the unlimited supplies of brackish water for general purposes.

The next job was the naturalists' early morning walk. Off we went lurching over the lava and threading through the scrub, with attendance sheets, canvas weighing bag, spring balances, dividers, ruler, notebooks, camera, binoculars and a certain lack of enthusiasm. In Meiklejohn's immortal verse:

> The ornithologist at work
> presents a sight to fright a Turk,
> with gumboots, telescope and glasses,
> protective hat festooned with grasses,
> little boxes filled with ants,
> patent, imperishable pants,
> notebooks, aluminium rings,
> traps, cameras, elastic slings.
> With many other things as well,
> contrived to make birds' lives a hell.

We tried to do the most tiring work, such as detailed checks of two hundred red-footed booby nests, involving the weighing of chicks, before ten a.m. or after four p.m., when it was cooler. Pushing through dense scrub, cumbered with paraphernalia, with a million small flies tickling and scrambling into eyes, ears and nose, was trying enough without frying in the midday sun.

Research may sound impressive, but it involves sheer drudgery.

However interesting and wide-ranging the conclusions may be (but rarely are) the work that supports them is almost always highly repetitive and the massing of relevant information often boring or even irksome. Observations on animal behaviour are less tedious, since there is always great pleasure simply in watching a bird or higher animal. Even then, it is essential to make detailed notes, constantly to question one's accuracy in observing, one's understanding of what the animal is doing and why, and to keep alert to the effects of its behaviour on its mate, chick or neighbours (or even on oneself). Postures used in bird displays seem tremendously obvious when crystallised in a drawing or photograph, but they are often fleeting and when performed at a low intensity, difficult to recognise. Except at first, when one is getting the 'feel' of the animal, there often is not time simply to enjoy watching its behaviour. Further, one astonishingly quickly gets into a rut and acquires a block against new ideas. It seems necessary to prick oneself awake to make even trivial advances in interpretation and to keep the boundary between mere ideas and facts in good repair. Many and insidious are the biases which can be introduced by careless methods of gathering information, much more subtle than the apparent tendency for frogs to spawn and birds to migrate at weekends. The inductive process is perfectly valid, as a method, but there are special dangers in arguing from the particular to the general and behaviourists perhaps meet them in exceptionally alluring form. My own approach to gathering information on behaviour is laborious, but fairly safe, since I do not usually begin with a hunch and select the range of my enquiry accordingly. This is often a rewarding way when the initial hunch is correct and the method of gathering the selected items of information stringently guarded against bias, but it calls for a high degree of intuitive understanding of animals and great clarity in the initial formulation of the problem. As an alternative one may, as I do, try to look at the total range of behaviour in a certain situation, say the breeding colony, and by gathering quantitative information acquire the pieces with which the jig-saw can ultimately be more or less assembled. This is particularly rewarding when one is trying to relate behaviour and ecology in a whole group of species; one really needs the details to make a coherent story (see Chapter 17). It is surprising how many apparently irrelevant minutiae become vital clues, and perhaps the main requirement in this process is to visualise the potential usefulness of these details. Nothing is more annoying than to miss a valuable clue through mental idleness.

After the checks came the pleasantest meal of the day, breakfast under the tent veranda, often in warm sunshine. We took half a hundredweight of milk powder and plenty of oats; tinned bacon was strictly rationed but bread was not. Bread-making became a ritual; the deities invoked in animistic rituals are basically hostile and unpredictable and so was our bread god. I don't think the bread turned out twice alike. The paraffin oven performed badly, partly owing to the dirty paraffin and when the flour became extra weevily the bread emerged even more dejectedly. Flour weevils are known to secret a substance which lowers reproductive rate in other weevils and so limits the population in the flour bag; no one knows what its effect is on man!

As an undergraduate I once did summer work in a large modern bakery. I remember the relentless ascent of rows of tines bearing empty bread tins, and the right to left moving conveyor belt bearing lumps of dough. As the belt moved along the operator simply took a lump of dough ready cut to size from his left, twisted it into a certain shape and plonked it into the left-hand tin on the ascending row. Seizing the next lump, by then in front of him, he plonked it into the tin second from the left and so on till the row was filled. Things were so timed that he just managed to fill the right-hand tin before it rose out of reach. Grab, twist, plonk; grab, twist, plonk. The work was so monotonous until suddenly you had to move a little further to the left for the next bit of dough, then further still. Soon you were dashing down the conveyor belt, chasing the dough before it fell off at the end, rushing back and with a frantic leap filling the inexorably rising tin. You couldn't win once it had you on the hop. Somehow, though, you always thought you would overtake the system. The pile of dough on the floor and the rows of tins coming out of the oven destitute of golden loaf showed otherwise. I never criticised our small, sunken loaves coming from the battered oven.

Around low tide we often tried for langusta. When European settlers first came to the Galapagos these lovely crayfish were so common that on Santa Cruz one could pick up any number at low tide simply by paddling. Now they are usually further offshore, but still numerous, at least on Tower. There are also many langustas in the much colder water off the coast of Hood Island. They lurk in small caverns or cracks and the best way to find them is to peer closely in, looking for the tell-tale long orange antennae. Apart from a few gaudy blue and orange parrot fishes, which rather disgusted us by scavenging for faeces in our sea-washed latrine, crayfish were the only natural food we could get on Tower. Outside the bay, forsworn territory to us because of the dangerous currents, there were fish in abundance. Inside, the swarms of voracious *Lutianus* species, small fish with horizontal stripes, cleaned our crab-baited hooks in seconds. Not for us, unfortunately, fish from the streams, wild fowl from the jungle, sweet potatoes from the earth and fruit from the trees. Unless one ate crabs, iguanas and sea-birds and obtained water from the cacti, it would be impossible even to survive on the natural resources of Tower Island.

A small colony of fur seals flourished in one corner on the east side of Darwin Bay and a magnificent colony of Galapagos storm petrels inhabited the eastern horn. Both these rarities attracted us, and with our rowing-boat, the *Plus Ultra*, were just a pleasantly long row away instead of an exhausting grind over difficult terrain. Near the fur seals on the east side we chanced across a negotiable crack in the cliffs leading to a flat, ashy area, strewn with whitened blocks of lava and dotted with shrubs. White boobies are scattered about and a few frigate-birds and red-footed boobies look down from their superior nests in the bushes. The remnants of wooden huts set up by the last American oceanographical survey lie about. Just around the corner one suddenly emerges from shirt-tearing scrub into an astonishing plain of scoriae and lava, absolutely bare of any vegetation and almost perfectly flat. It looks like the efforts of some town council in a mining area to make a huge car park out of ashes and slag. The deep reddish brown surface is seamed and fissured, there are lava bubbles everywhere and in places one crashes through the thin surface crust into cavities up to two feet deep.

Nothing could look more dreary, yet there is a teeming city beneath the arid surface. And I am not cheatingly referring to microbes, spores, protozoa or other devices of the micro-biologist trying to make his diminutive world sound interesting. There is here a huge colony of petrels at least 5,000 strong. Beneath the lava crust they must inhabit a maze of cavities and tunnels, for one hears a constant muted churring and calling and occasionally a petrel squeezes out of a crack and flies off. Overhead they flit about like a cloud of midges, twisting, turning, fluttering and sweeping out to the cliff edge and back again. What are these thousands of birds doing in this mazy flight? Train your glasses on one and follow it around. It hawks about, now apparently following the bird in front, but then turning aside. This is obviously not a pair formation display flight; they are just so many individuals, sometimes colliding with an audible bump because the air is so full of their flitting forms, but not interacting in any consistent way. Now our bird swoops down onto the lava and patters lightly along, wings fluttering, just as it does when feeding over the surface of the sea. It even runs its beak over the lava and moves its mandibles as though feeding, then rises and rejoins the throng. Round it comes again and down to exactly the same spot as before. The next time it suddenly pops into a crevice and joins the throng underground. It seems that he at least was house-hunting. But that can't be true for the majority; they continue their communal flighting from dawn till dusk every day for months on end. If we suggested that successive waves of newcomers, all looking for nesting places, accounted for the activity throughout the extensive period of this communal flighting we should end up with astronomical figures for the total population. In any case their behaviour has, most of the time, nothing to do with house-hunting. Birds fly round for long periods without ever landing. Until we know whether or not the same individuals are involved for several successive weeks it is idle to speculate on the meaning of this interesting behaviour which, one should add, renders the petrels very vulnerable to predation from the partly diurnal Galapagos short-eared owl. Scattered over the lava in shady recesses there are many sinister owls' 'parlours' containing the skulls, bones and feathers of scores of petrels, which probably form the main diet of several pairs of owls preying constantly on the colony. We saw more owls in that area than anywhere else and estimated that if each owl ate one per day at least 3,000 petrels a year would fall prey to them. (Fig. 16).

*Figure 16* Galapagos short-eared owl pursuing petrel

The petrels nest in chambers beneath the lava, which usually forms only a thin layer between them and the tropical sun. During the day they must endure terrific temperatures under stifling conditions. There is a maze of subterranean passages through which the birds travel considerable distances, since they enter with difficulty through narrow, deep vertical slits which could not afford them exit. Safely entombed, they churr and cackle in an astonishingly ventriloquial manner and are almost impossible to track down by ear, even though the sounds seem to come from beneath your feet and all around. We found a large number of fresh, broken eggs at the openings of nesting cavities and it seems as though they must have been ejected by the petrels; although mocking birds are egg thieves, they could hardly be expected to go pot-holing for their booty, which would in any case be protected by the incubating petrel. Measurements of a number of disembodied wings showed that there were two species present at the breeding colony (the Galapagos storm petrel *Oceanodroma tethys* and the Madeiran storm petrel *Oceanodroma castro*)\* and it may well be that some of the egg loss was due to hostilities between them. The whole situation bristles with interesting problems. On the face of it this flighting seems an example of a population interacting *en masse*, with all the attendant excitement and stress, so gaining some sort of information about its own numbers. The phenomenon whereby animals provide some kind of quantitative sensory cue, whether of smell, noise, the visual impact of flock size, the thickness of a beaten track, or a trail of filaments produced by caterpillars, which *could* indicate that species' local numbers and density, occurs widely throughout the animal kingdom. However, the ways and means by which they use or even could use this information about their population is a thorny subject, especially if it is held that they use it to regulate their own reproductive efforts (Wynne-Edwards). So far as the petrels are concerned, even if one accepted the flighting in these terms, there are several snags, among them the fact that whereas in many species such displays of numbers take place at dawn or dusk and for a limited season, all members reacting to the same external changes and acting in concert, the petrels performed *their* flighting many hours each day and for months on end.

On this particular day, my thoughts were brusquely dispelled when we returned to the crack. It was getting late and ahead of us was a long row back to camp. But there was no boat. From the cliff-top we could just see its outline beneath the surface. It had dragged the anchoring boulder, grounded on a submerged rock and then filled with the tide. It was far too late to return to camp overland; the deep fissures and jagged lava would have been suicidally dangerous in the dark. A night out on the lava with no food or drink and very little clothing also seemed unattractive, so we leapt into the sea and by furious hand-baling managed to raise the boat. The oars had floated away, but one was visible just out in the bay. A boat seat furnished a rough paddle and hastening out we retrieved both oars and thankfully set off back across the darkening bay.

Evening on Tower was always peaceful, except when a Galapagos owl sat on the tent ridge and laughed its weird, cackling old man's

\* Nelson, 'Flighting behaviour of Galapagos Storm Petrels'.

laugh. To us, of course, the owls looked quite appealing with their large, blinking, golden eyes and knock-kneed stance, but no wonder the swallow-tailed gull chicks crouched motionless in cracks or between boulders. The owl's strong talons found every single one around our camp. But even peaceful evenings can be rather dreary. There were always plans to be chewed over in minute detail – most of which had to be ditched when it came to the point – diaries to write and, if one felt energetic enough, field notebooks to pore over and get into some sort of order prior to the long job of turning into a reasoned account. But these things don't make much of a change. Conversation became threadbare, reading ran out and the age of meditation dawned, but I, for one, tend to belong not to those who sit and think, but to those who just sit. During full moons we ate our spaghetti and sardines out in the warm night air, watching the late incoming red-foots etching the sky. On dark nights the evening flight of insects made it impossible to take a lamp outside. Beetles, flies, mosquitoes, dragonflies and moths swarmed round the lamp, not only immolating themselves but in so doing wrecking another of our fast-dwindling stock of mantles. Some of these insects are now in the British Museum, where at least one has the honour of forming a 'first ever' for this monumental institution. Our most beautiful visitor was a huge brown saturnid moth, measuring precisely seven and a quarter inches across, with a double-banded eye spot on each hind wing; at first I thought it was a bat. I know the measurement is correct because the pencil lines which marked the extremities of its wings as it rested are still visible on the veranda roof. During April and May several more came to us, but none so large as the first.

I could not have lived and worked on Tower for seven months in complete isolation without severe depression, though there are doubtless many who could, and in less restricted, desolate and frustrating terrain it would be fairly easy. We often discussed whether we would have liked somebody else there. It might have been pleasant to have had another couple on the other side of the island – far enough for elbow space but near enough to see and talk with every other month. In particular I would have enjoyed talking to a Beebe or a Tinbergen about our work. Since continuous and fairly long-term field work of this sort is so hard to organise and carry out it is a great pity to miss useful evidence simply through lack of foresight; discussion helps here. But the wrong people would have been disastrous and we could well imagine why the advertised attempt of an American party under the leadership of Harsh, to colonise a Galapagos island, was a dismal flop. Imagine living with the answer to an advertisement. Some of them never even landed on the islands – one look was enough.

It was time to turn in before we had done much after supper. Out for some sea water for teeth-cleaning and a lick with sea water soap, then the rigmarole of putting up the beds and battening down the hatches against centipedes – a sock to stuff up this hole and a shoe to wedge that flap. Routine was both helpful and extremely irksome. The very knowledge that certain chores were inescapable every day irritated when superimposed on the larger restrictions of a very basic camp life, where activity is limited and diversions more so. Romantics who have never experienced genuine and prolonged isolation may find this hard to believe, hearing only the lazy murmur of the surf and the wind-rustled palms. In small, primitive and self-contained communities the practical man is both more valuable and probably, despite his grumbles, usually more at home than the intellectual idealist. Yet it is probably the latter who dreams of desert islands but fortunately rarely gets there. A blend of practical ability and matter-of-fact outlook with artistic sensitivity would be ideal, but failing that Beebe's *Noma* set-up of contrast had much to commend it: 'We gathered at last, all telling of the new and unexpected things seen and collected, all sensible of the spirit of weird isolation of this land. At dusk we climbed the companion-way to our home of orderliness and electricity, a land of linen and cut glass, of delicious food and drink, easy chairs, music and absorbing books. Each made the other so much more worthwhile.' We, for our part, stepped from the beach outside to the beach inside the tent – much the same except for the litter of well-used cooking and camping gear – a land of tin platters and bottles, delicious dehydrated potatoes, camp chairs, the hiss of the paraffin lamp and all too few books.

Broadcasts from British Honduras (Belise) came through fairly well on our transistor and despite the one-way traffic created an illusion of contact. We found their homely announcements particularly endearing: 'The Orangewalk Veterans Basketball reserve team will meet for practice in Riverside Hall on Sunday morning'; 'Will Mrs Florence Usher of 1 Monkey Walk please collect baby as Grandmother is leaving today.' If we wanted John Bull to guard the tent we could listen to loyal Radio Belise playing the British national anthem before closing down; it was encouraging to find that the British are not quite universally reviled. With the darkness came silence, the prelude to stealthy scrapings and scratchings on the canvas as the land crabs began their foraging. They were quite welcome to the freedom of the tent, but not so the giant centipedes, whose powerful claws and hard chitinous plating scraped particularly loudly and menacingly in the total blackness. Many a nocturnal hunt reduced the tent to a shambles as the speedy centipede flashed into a succession of hiding places before capture. And so finally to canvas, with the dishes stacked ready for the dawn reveille by the mockers.

*Figure 17* Galapagos blue heron

# *The White Booby*

Many ethologists are by tradition field observers, and
they are thus in a good position to see the animal in
its continuous struggle with the very complex
environment that has molded them. I believe that the
type of work I have been discussing might well lead
to a better knowledge of the powers of natural
selection in general, and to a higher regard for these
powers with respect to all functions and structures as
we find them in present-day animals.
N. Tinbergen

There are many shades of white. A gannet is whiter than a gull, or
at least to my eyes it always stands out at sea with greater brilliance,
but the white booby is the whitest bird imaginable; it positively
dazzles. Black wing feathers and tail set off its snowy plumage against
which the stout orange-yellow beak shines assertively. In some parts
of its range, as on Ascension Island, the beak is pinker. A striking
black face mask, actually the soft skin around the base of the beak,
and piercing orange irises bring you face to face with the white,
masked or blue-faced booby, an aristocrat alongside the brown-
plumaged red-foot.

Although it is the largest booby, with a five-and-a-half-foot wing
spread, it weighs only two-thirds as much as the gannet, which is of
comparable size. As in all other boobies, the female is slightly larger
and heavier than the male, with an even more formidable bill. She
is not only bigger, but has a raucous, trumpeting voice which she
uses freely, whilst once the male has outgrown his juvenile plumage
he also outgrows his lusty voice, which degenerates into a pathetic
piping whistle. It takes some time to accept this ludicrous sound as
normal but then it even acquires evocative qualities; one of my most

nostalgic memories is the dawn awakening to a chorus of white booby whistles.

Many barren, oceanic islands harbour the white booby but despite its considerable range in tropical waters, it never nests in great concentrations comparable to those of the Peruvian booby or gannet; its colonies are rarely more than five thousand strong and the vast majority are much more modest. This may be, at least partly, because they are so-called 'blue-water' boobies, feeding in warm tropical seas where food tends to be scarcer on the whole than in cold water regions. Great concentrations of boobies in a small area would be at a disadvantage in finding fish. The gannet and Peruvian booby inhabit colder waters, richer in food, and their colonies sometimes reach spectacular size, particularly those of the Cape gannet. Nor do white boobies nest in dense colonies, as do the gannet and Peruvian boobies. It would be a mistake, incidentally, to jump to the obvious conclusion that dense nesting in these two latter species is because they both concentrate in an area of rich food to such an extent that all the available nesting places are crowded. This is true for the Peruvian booby, which has to share a limited string of islands off the Peruvian coast with millions of other sea-birds, but it is

*Figure 18* White booby – alert posture

certainly too facile to draw the same conclusion for the northern gannet (see Chapter 17). The relatively wide spacing of nests in white booby colonies is an important point because it has affected the extent to which they have had to evolve social behaviour to maintain the orderly and efficient functioning of the group, the idea being that dense nesting, especially in an aggressive species, puts a premium on clear, unmistakable signal behaviour so that a bird's intentions are quickly and accurately understood by its mate and neighbours. The gannet is the prime example of this.

Our experience of white boobies was confined to Tower, Hood and Daphne, though they nest in more than a dozen Galapagos localities if one includes small islets. The Tower colonies are widely spread over the island, but mainly concentrated on the two horns of Darwin Bay. White boobies are versatile and can use different kinds of nesting habitats, including cliffs, hillsides, flat sandy ground without cover, and small clearings amidst dense shrubs and trees. On Hood, the Punta Suarez colony is among jumbled boulders and on Daphne white boobies nest all around the rim of a volcanic crater, whilst inside the crater, on the flat bottom, the large colony of blue-footed boobies has not a single white booby. In general, white boobies clearly prefer bare terrain, especially with a steep slope. On Tower, red-footed boobies are neighbours to the white boobies; both red- and blue-foots are smaller, but stoutly defend themselves in border clashes against the larger species. I have already described how, on Tower, white boobies, particularly the males of pairs that had lost their egg or chick, made a nuisance of themselves by attacking chicks of their own species and of the red-footed boobies. Often the attack developed from sexual advances made by adult males to chicks, but whereas white booby chicks hid their beaks and switched off the adult's attack, red-foot chicks lacked the infantile submissive beak-hiding behaviour and were in consequence savagely treated or even killed. The lack of the 'right' behaviour here had fatal results. Even simple behaviour patterns like beak-hiding, which one might (wrongly) imagine to be an obvious precautionary measure, rather than a specially developed, ritualised behaviour pattern, may nevertheless be confined to some species and absent in close relatives.

In the Galapagos, white boobies have a fairly well defined breeding season lasting from September/October to June/July, although there are a few weeks' difference in the start of the breeding season on different islands and between different years on the same island. It is not nearly so well defined as the gannet's breeding season, but rather more so than that of the red-foot. Even when they inhabit the same geographical area the different species of booby have different breeding seasons, and differences in area introduce further complications. The important point is that only the gannet has evolved a breeding season which, every year, produces young which mainly hatch in June and fledge in September. The reasons for this are probably that the gannet's breeding period has become finely geared to seasonal fish movements and abundance, particularly herring and mackerel, and also to the time of year at which the newly-fledged young can best make the perilous transition to independence. So the production of young in the gannet has become tied to these important and seasonally consistent factors, both of which greatly influence breeding success and are therefore susceptible to natural selection. These points do not apply nearly so forcefully to the white booby.

When we arrived on Hood, it was distinctly 'back-endish'. There were hardly any adults present and dead, fully feathered young were scattered around, lying where they had starved. Just as thousands of juvenile gannets die on the dispassionate waters of the North Sea and north Atlantic, growing feebler as their fat reserves are used and yet prevented, perhaps by weather, from acquiring that vital but elusive ability to catch fish, so many a white booby juvenile sits stoically through the hot days until it quietly starves, waiting for the feeds that never come. Its parents, their ties to the colony and their chick now loosened, are fishing the seas for themselves and no longer for their young. Juvenile gannet and booby had been so near to success, but the last hurdle was too severe for the former and luck, or whatever made its parents lay late, weighed against the booby. Although the end result is the same, chick and juvenile mortality seemed to be flaunted more in the Galapagos than in our islands; dried corpses and heaps of bones lay everywhere. This was partly due to the dry heat mummifying and preserving corpses which on the Bass would be buried in slime, covered with seaweed dropped by nesting birds and quickly obliterated.

For three months, the white booby colony was dead. The adults were nearly all away, probably leading oceanic lives. A few occasionally returned, but they simply sat around sleeping or preening and waterproofing or 'oiling' their plumage. They had absolutely no interest in territorial or sexual display; they were 'switched off'. Then, on 25 September, my diary says: 'New breeding season began today.' A male advertised to a female and signalled the new season as clearly as the first cuckoo says 'spring'. Soon the attendance of males at the colony rose. Now they were less addicted to sleep and more to posting themselves conspicuously on boulders in their territories and performing a special aggressive display to other males. Frequently they gave their still folded wings a brisk shake as though to loosen them, and then, after hesitating several times with half-spread wings, they crouched, sprang into the air and made a wide circuit of the area before flying in whistling loudly and landing on their territory, with wings held upwards in a steep V and tremoring gently (fig. 19). After landing, they swiftly touched the ground with

*Figure 19* White booby 'V flighting'

their bills and then went through an odd-looking, highly stylised procedure in which the head slowly swung in a wide arc from side to side whilst simultaneously nodding rapidly up and down. This was the display they had been aiming at rival males whilst standing on a

I

vantage point in their territory and it signified an aggressive site-owner ready to defend his territory; its function was to keep other males at a distance. In this kind of case, circumstantial evidence, such as the reaction of other birds to a particular display, can provide a quite acceptable picture of its function. The nest- or ground-touching movement in the white boobies' territorial display is equivalent to the nest- or twig-biting of the red-foot and the nest-biting of the gannet. This basic behaviour pattern is shown in one form or another by all boobies after landing on their territory and gannets often bite the ground or their nest fiercely. In the gannet, nest-biting after landing has given rise to an elaborate display which occurs solely on the nest site and advertises ownership of it. The original rather simple and wild-looking biting has been transformed into a very polished, ritualised display, 'bowing', though the biting also persists and occurs under special circumstances – particularly when the bird is feeling highly aggressive. No booby has gone quite as far as this and they all make the ordinary after-landing behaviour do duty, also, as their site-ownership display; one cannot detect any difference between the display performed in these contexts. This is a typical difference between gannets and boobies; the gannet has often gone further in the process of elaborating signal behaviour. As I have said, this is probably connected with its special need for certain kinds of communication behaviour, particularly those to do with ritualised defence of territory.

After landing, the male white booby might potter around in his territory with a rather exaggerated step, whistling softly and picking up and dropping small pebbles, apparently aimlessly. They spend a great deal of time in this symbolic nest-building activity, 'symbolic' because it has nothing to do with producing a real nest of use in holding the egg or young, but important, nonetheless, in other ways.

When a male gannet brings sea-weed and the female takes it from him and builds it into the structure, the formation of a substantial nest drum is only one of the important results; another is the formation of a strong pair bond. Every time the pair meet and go through behaviour involving their intimate co-operation, they share an experience which becomes part of their behavioural 'background' and to some extent changes them. However it works, experience affects the central nervous system of birds as it does man, and their subsequent behaviour is different from what it was before. A fully co-operative relationship between pair members cannot be built up in a day; every meeting, greeting ceremony, mating, session of mutual preening and joint nest-building activity helps to form it. In the white booby, this emotive or bond-strengthening function of pair interaction is enhanced by the habit of symbolic nest-building. The booby does not have to fly off and gather sea-weed or grass as the gannet does; it need only take a few steps from the nest site, pick up a ridiculous fragment and return to the female. In a concentrated bout of activity, it may bring over two hundred individual offerings and some nests contained at least two thousand pieces; two thousand journeys and returns; two thousand opportunities for the female to take material from his beak or share in the placing of it. The red-footed booby cannot compete for sheer number of items, but it gets more value from each piece; a springy twig gives plenty of opportunities for mutual building.

But the male must first acquire his female before he can interest her in the mysteries of symbolic nest-building. Like the red-footed booby, he does so by advertising. If a female lands anywhere near his territory he becomes alert, lengthens his neck, points his bill vertically upwards, lifts his wings slightly and whistles. This is one of the happy performances that immediately 'clicks' with us. He looks as though he is whistling to a female and he is. The next event depends on how well the pair know each other. She may be a young female responding to a newly-established male or she may be the male's mate of several year's standing, returning to him for a new season. New pairs are often rather aggressive to each other; the female is afraid, she looks ruffled and apprehensive and often shouts loudly and abruptly, particularly when near the male. As they meet, they tensely appose bills and, with parted mandibles, fling their heads at each other, clashing their beaks, though not actually biting. Then they turn away and pointedly stand parallel, as though to avoid looking at each other. If one makes a slight movement the other immediately jabs at it and triggers off another 'sparring' bout. This may continue for many hours, though the mutual jabbing bouts become shorter. All the time the female shouts and quacks in short, quick bursts, rising to a harsh yell whenever they jab at each other – the sound carries for miles.

If one of them turns to leave the site, it is likely to suffer a spirited jab to speed it along. This is not the treachery it seems, but is probably because the aggression which is obviously an element of their relationship is somehow released when one turns its back and moves away. One could partly explain this in terms of the aggression being inhibited by sex interest when the partners are together at the nest, but disinhibited when the sexual stimulus is weakened or removed. Precisely the same thing often happens in the gannet, where even the female may attack a male under certain circumstances, when he (or she) is off the site, but not when he is actually on it, so one can get the apparently crazy situation in which a female attacks the male until she can join him on the site, when her attack is then switched off.

To signal impending movement away from the site, the departing white booby often assumes a very odd-looking posture in which the bill is pointed upwards, backwards and tilted sideways all at the same time (this has been called bill-up-face-away: Dorward). Significantly, white boobies do this when moving *off* rather than *onto* the site and it seems to be behaviour which by exaggerating the intention movements of turning away, communicates this intention and at the same time leaves the performer in a position to respond if the partner jabs. If, in these ways, it reduces the chances of a leaving bird being attacked, it is properly called appeasement behaviour.

Under similar circumstances, a gannet leaving its site uses a different display, easily recognisable, in fact, as a very close relative of the advertising display which boobies use to attract a female; the two displays look almost identical. It seems that this display for which a very apt descriptive name is sky-pointing, was originally, in the birds ancestral to both gannets and boobies, a signal of impending movement as it still is today in the gannet. It was probably derived from the neck lengthening which precedes flight in birds. But in all the boobies, it has become the sexual advertising display, thus completely changing its signal value. How this happened cannot now be known  but it shows clearly how a ritualised display can become entirely freed from its original context and assume a new meaning. This happening meant that boobies had to evolve another posture to replace sky-pointing in the pre-movement situation and their answer seems to be the bill/upwards/backwards/ and/sideways (better, bill-up-face-away), a posture which the gannet simply does not possess. It is impossible to lay too much emphasis on the rigidity with which each species sticks to its own signal behaviour patterns; they are just as diagnostic as anatomical characters. A gannet would no more use its sky-pointing to attract a female, or adopt the bill-up-face-away posture under any circumstances than a gull would grow webs between all four toes instead of the usual three. Interestingly enough, the bill-up-face-away, like sky-pointing, has also been derived from the intention movements of flight. Thus two highly ritualised and entirely distinct postures have evolved from the same roots, one to replace the other which has been emancipated. (Composite fig. 20.)

Every time a white booby moves around in its territory, it fleetingly and repeatedly presses its bill tip to its breast. All the boobies show this 'pelican posture' when moving around. The red-foot arches its neck strongly and 'pelican postures' as it hops from twig to twig and the blue-foot presses its bill tip to its chest as it parades around its territory. Since gannets have only a very small territory, they cannot parade around, and even where they can, as for instance on the outer fringes of a group, they do not perform the pelican posture, except in certain well defined circumstances. The situation in which they use it has changed and now it occurs in a variety of contexts, usually when the bird is experiencing strong and conflicting drives, of which one is aggression. It has been incorporated, for instance, into the gannet's aggressive site-ownership display and also occurs time and again during intense threat encounters between rivals. The movement is very like a fleeting version of the chick's beak-hiding, from which it probably stems. Whilst chick beak-hiding is obviously appeasing, it is more difficult to interpret the function of the pelican posture in the adult, but because the bill is hidden, it may well be appeasing behaviour there, too.

If you now visited a white booby colony, you would understand most of their behaviour; it would make sense and you could test your understanding by predicting what would happen in given circumstances. When one first meets a new species in the full spate of display, it all seems despairingly complex and meaningless; things fit together only gradually. When they do, there is a real satisfaction in having decoded some of the signals and, of course, an enormously heightened pleasure in watching the animal. Perhaps, however, you

*Figure 20* Comparison of the sky-pointing display within the family. All boobies use it as a sexual advertising display, but its function in the gannet is to communicate the intention of movement

find this kind of behaviour detail rather boring and much prefer humorous or exciting anecdotes of animal behaviour and may well ask why ethologists bother with it. Unpredictable behaviour is by definition behaviour that we do not fully understand. If we really understand a system, we can predict. Because most of us take a long time to register what we see, behaviour that an animal repeats over and over again in a stereotyped fashion is often the easiest for us to understand. Displays like the ones described here are stylised and repetitive enough to let us see and recognise them and their circumstances time and again, and yet obscure enough to challenge understanding; their function and motivation are not as obvious as eating, drinking, fighting or mating. If we want to understand an animal's behaviour, particularly social behaviour, a good account of such displays forms a sounder basis than anecdotes about unusual and, in most cases, unverifiable incidents, fascinating though these may be. This is obvious, but the difference is not always given due weight and a critic of behaviour studies would rightly disparage theories erected on the flimsy evidence of a few uncritical observations. The unusual anecdote is entertaining and often provides some insight into the creature's behaviour, but normally it cannot be pressed very far. If it is claimed that a white booby male advertises for a female by sky-pointing, and the posture is accurately described and illustrated, anybody can subsequently recognise it when he sees it and can check the interpretation of its function. If the same thing is done for all the boobies, and for a variety of displays, some interesting and sound conclusions about, for instance, the evolution of behaviour, may emerge. If, on the other hand, I describe but do not illustrate an encounter between a female and two male Galapagos pintails on a crater lake, and 'explain' that the female was trying to entice one male to demonstrate his affection for her by fighting the other, I may entertain but nobody could verify the interpretation, which may indeed even puzzle the reader by its semi-mystical nature.*

The bare nest scrape of the white booby, often with every tiniest fragment of material 'gardened' into a perfect semicircle around the bored, incubating bird, eventually holds one or two chalky white

---

* This actually refers, though in less than objective terms, to a complex ritualised interaction found in many ducks.

A Intense territorial display: rival males interspersing jabbing and wing-flailing with a high intensity form of 'yes/no head-shaking' (see text)

B Typical form of the territorial display yes/no head-shaking – the head is nodded up and down and simultaneously turned from side to side

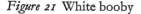

E Mutual jabbing between pair members: a rather 'simple' meeting ceremony

F 'Parallel standing': pair members avoid pointing bills at each other

*Figure 21* White booby

eggs; in about two-thirds of the nests on Tower, the clutch was two, laid five to seven days apart. Three months later, nearly all the nests hold but a single youngster, though a brief search usually discloses a small, dry carcase trampled into the dirt. It has been well-known for over fifty years that white boobies rarely, if ever, rear two young, despite laying two eggs. Recently, Dorward, working on Ascension Island, followed earlier authors in suggesting that the larger chick

C Male sky-pointing: sexual display to attract female

D Pair about to touch bills

G One partner turns away in a special posture, bill-up-face-away, indicating his intention of movement. Here the bill has not quite reached the full upward position

H During movement white boobies 'pelican posture'

usually caused the death of its brother by taking all the food or even by active persecution. I saw this antagonism on many occasions, and managed to photograph a stage in the process of eviction, which occurs at a surprisingly early age. Even a chick a few days old will attack its brother and drive it from the nest, though it can hardly yet control its own wobbly head. Still, it lunges and worries away, missing as often as hitting its equally helpless target. Like the baby cuckoo working blindly to throw out the eggs or young of its foster-parents, the white booby chick perseveres in its efforts to drive its nest mate, in this case its blood brother, from the sheltering adult out into the killing sun or the damp night air. In one experiment, we gave a pair of white boobies two evenly matched chicks and whenever one gained the upper hand, we removed it and let the other get all the food until they were even again. The mutual antagonism persisted, however, and one was eventually kicked out and died during the night, presumably unable to cope with the cold. The total and unreserved nature of this sibling murder deserves emphasis, since Lack (1954) has suggested that under favourable circumstances the parents might rear both youngsters; the way in which brood reduction occurred so early in life, when food was not scarce, seems to refute this. There is nothing new about this way of ensuring that one or two members of a brood are adequately fed even if it means the death of the runt or weakling. So far as the species is concerned, this is much better than that both are in-adequately fed and remain stunted or leave the nest weaker than they should be, perhaps both to die before they succeed in breeding. It is well known in eagles and other birds of prey, as Oliver Pike stoutly maintained, against considerable opposition, more than fifty years ago. But the white booby goes a step further than most, including its own cousin the blue-footed booby, for it often makes the reduc-tion in brood size well *before* the pinch can possibly be felt by the youngsters and whether or not food happens to be plentiful at the time. In the blue-foot, two or even three chicks commonly grow up together and only in times of severe shortage does the largest drive his brother away from the adults when they return with food. Obviously, the food situation for the white booby now so rarely allows it to rear two young that it is most economical to reduce brood size as early as possible, rather than waste food on a second youngster that will certainly die before it reaches independence. As to why they lay two eggs in the first place, in my opinion, the probable answer is that they are gradually losing the habit, but in evolutionary terms 'gradually' takes a long time! Rearing two young was presumably at one time, or in some places, a practical proposition but no longer is so. The red-footed booby, which, at least in the Galapagos, suffers perhaps most of all the boobies from scarce and erratic food supply, has reduced its clutch size to the minimum

*Figure 22* White booby feeding chick

though it produces a slightly larger egg in proportion to its body size.

A few pairs of white boobies were unlucky enough to nest near our camp and bear the full brunt of our activities. The birds were not agile enough to take off from difficult positions, and so we cut off their escape to windward and easily ran them down. Soon every bird had been caught, examined and weighed and carried its coloured rings. Those spirals of cheap plastic, intended for the sturdy galli-form limbs of the battery hen, the ultimate in captivity, now quarter the sparkling waves of the Pacific and fade in the intense sunlight of the islands. The chicks were even more unlucky; they had to put up with daily weighings which they bitterly resented, swearing and stabbing, first in fear as we approached and then in anger when it was all over again. During our period in the Galapagos, we carried out 3,216 weighings of young and adult sea-birds; layers of guano and albatross oil gradually thickened our weighing bag. Fortunately, because there were so few, we could catch the juveniles without disturbing anybody else and so could follow their progress even after they were free-flying, to us, a most interesting and informative period of their lives. It is impossible to catch and weigh fully grown young in a gannetry without causing havoc.

White boobies hatch at about 56 gm and females, which are

heavier than males, reach a maximum of around 2,800 gm before they fly at about sixteen weeks old, though most of them never reach this weight. Somewhat retarded chicks may reach an age of nineteen weeks before they try their first real flight, by which I mean remaining airborne for at least a hundred yards! As down-covered youngsters, they are nothing like so attractive as red-foots. Their down is thinner and the patches of bare pinkish skin around the face, together with the flatly receding forehead unimproved by much cotton wool, give them a brutish, unintelligent appearance. More than fourteen weeks go by before they fully grow their true feathers and then they look totally different from the adult. A juvenile white booby is white only beneath and then not entirely; the brown on the sides of the neck encroaches onto the throat and the sides of the upper breast. The head, neck and back are a dark, glossy brown, with pale edgings to wing-covert feathers. The beak is yellowish-horn, shading to blue at the base, and the feet and legs are dark grey. The iris is brown, and a bluish orbital ring surrounds the eye. Immature boobies are confusing things to identify at sea, but the drawings on pp. 292–3 show some of the differences.

The first flight of the juvenile white booby is an extremely modest enterprise; they gradually wander further afield, trying easy flights from place to place before venturing over the sea. Young gannets, by comparison, must make one great effort, perhaps to struggle and dodge through hostile adults to the edge of a high cliff, and then leap into the air on untried wings to cope immediately with half a gale or the turbulent air that usually plays around cliffs. White boobies, like all other boobies, regularly return to the nest site and the parents continue to feed them there for about fifty to sixty days. During this time they keep up a fairly good weight, due in no small part to parental subsidy. The male parent in particular, however, becomes progressively more disenchanted with his offspring. As his tendency to care for and feed the youngster wanes, and his late season recrudescence of aggression builds up, he begins to alternate between feeding and attacking his own offspring. Of course, the two actions have much in common, and as the juvenile's frantic begging is similar to hostile jabbing, it is not surprising that the male may be stimulated to retaliate. Sometimes he attacks the importunate juvenile furiously, only to react to its next supplication by feeding it, then reverting to attack. No doubt this encourages the juvenile to leave home for good.

As soon as the juvenile begins its daily explorations on the wing, it also starts showing full adult-type aggressive behaviour. It was always something of a surprise to see the drab brown juvenile, until so lately a helpless, downy begger of food and appeaser of adults, soar into its parents' territory, shouting loudly in the typical aggressive in-coming manner, and follow it up with a perfect performance of the site-ownership display. Nor does it now hesitate to attack an intruding adult, which it can easily put to flight. Alas, however, it is still tied firmly to the parental apron strings and when one or other arrives it reverts to its infantile behaviour and madly supplicates for its daily ration.

After its fifty or so days of exploratory flights and, as we saw in a few cases, fishing expeditions fairly near the island, returning to the territory each day, the juvenile white booby suddenly disappears for good. There is no gradual decline in his attendance; one day he is there as usual and the next day gone. Probably the juveniles disperse into the surrounding waters and lead a nomadic life for the first year or two, before coming back to breed. Most will return to their island of birth, though there is a record of a white booby breeding on an island twenty miles from its birthplace.

For a short time, the parents show renewed sexual and territorial activity and revert to their courtship habits of preening each other and symbolic nest-building, sometimes every bit as keenly as in the early days. Soon they begin to spend less time on the site and the close season is upon them. For nine months they have displayed, incubated, and laboured early and late, flying in with first light or, on moonlight nights, up to midnight, to feed the insatiable young. Now they moult and recuperate. Many birds moult some flight feathers whilst rearing their young, but the main moult usually occurs outside the breeding season. The effort of feeding young is probably enough of an energy drain without the additional strain of growing new feathers, though it is interesting to note that gannets moult body feathers just before the eggs hatch and follow this by continuing the suspended moult of flight feathers actually *whilst* feeding their young. This is yet another hint that they enjoy a super-abundant food supply at that time; they can stand both feeding young and moulting simultaneously.

We never saw adult white boobies diving for fish around their nesting islands, as gannets and blue-footed and Peruvian boobies do. They are mainly far-out feeders, staying away from the nest for lengthy periods, exceptionally for four or five days. Red-footed boobies do the same and this habit has important consequences. Necessarily, it sometimes means long periods without any food for the young, putting a premium on their ability to withstand starvation, and a feed divided between two or three mouths is less fortification for an enforced fast than if they each got the two or three shares. The only way to achieve this (if the adults are already fishing as hard as they can) is to cut down the brood size. As I have described, this is exactly what white and red-footed boobies (but not the other species) have done. The two species we have yet to meet – the blue-footed and Peruvian boobies – provide further insight into this interesting topic. The white booby labouring to supply its hungry offspring, with the body of the dead brother lying alongside, reminds us that the Lord does not feed the ravens (or the boobies) as individuals, but as a species. 'So careful of the type he seems, so careless of the single life.'

*Figure 23* White booby sunning itself

# Intruders 8

Only those who have known can appreciate the
emotions of loneliness; the lonely and the lost, who
have once stared into unknown skies at the earth's end.
And have marvelled at their own ignorance, wondered
at the labours of their little fates and seen again . . .
the deathless, ever-present spectre of no-return, the
ghost of no-go-home.
Alan Thompson, *Only the Sun Remembers*

We really felt the measure of our isolation-to-be when a friend gave
us a bit of medical advice; if in pain from suspected appendicitis
try fasting, antibiotics and God, in that order; if the abdomen still
becomes inflamed and painful stick a knife as far as it will go into
the tenderest spot.* We could, of course, have had our appendices
removed beforehand, as, I understand, Hans Haas suggests for
members of his expeditions, but the English are ever the amateurs;
we also hung onto our teeth. Friedrich Ritter, the ill-fated Berlin
dentist who settled and died in the Galapagos, had all his teeth
extracted and replaced by a steel plate.

But living on desert islands is a serious matter; accidents usually
involve other people in the end, and there is no excuse for irresponsible behaviour or lack of proper planning. We took reasonable care
and were luckily accident-free, but it might have been otherwise.
Two young German biologists, Curio and Kramer, could well have
lost their lives in the Galapagos just before we arrived. They were
camping on Wenman Island which, like Tower, is waterless and
extremely inhospitable; a peculiarly oppressive and dead-looking
island. One night heavy rain started a landslide which swept away
their precarious camp, burying food, equipment and notebooks in

* Dr Scheine's *Advice to Young Recluses*, Chapter 3, 'Morto-surgery'.

rocks and mud. They managed to save their drinking water and a few oddments of food and equipment, though conditions in the black of night were difficult in the extreme. They transferred the remains to a sheltered ledge, almost a cave, which sea-lions used as a resting place; it was heavily fouled with excreta and pools of urine. Then they had to face a wait of over two weeks before Miguel Castro came to collect them. Their food situation was grim. They caught lobsters and, with great difficulty, a few fish, but the heavy seas frequently dashed them against sharp rocks. To make matters worse an exceptionally heavy sea swamped their ledge, washing more things away. Curio had to cling to the rocks to avoid a similar fate. If they had been forced to survive three months before rescue instead of two or three weeks their position would have been desperate. Our first job was to plan an escape route and a place to store our movables in the event of a sea swamping our precariously low beach.

Even the remotest uninhabited Galapagos Island rarely passes a year unvisited and about three months was our longest spell without glimpse of a vessel of any sort. Our visitors, of which this Chapter is an honest record, though welcome indeed once the ice was broken, initially induced the oddest mixture of excitement, apprehension and a real desire to flee. On the few occasions when a strange boat appeared in the mouth of the bay we almost willed it to pass across and out of sight. When the dot indeed became steadily larger our hearts began to beat uncomfortably hard and the nature of the arrival was discussed in feigned calm. The final manœuvres before the boat anchored and somebody came ashore were hard to bear. Ought we to carry on as normal, which might mean leaving an empty camp and giving the impression of unfriendliness? Yet to hang around often wasted hours, while no doubt the visitors dubiously considered this unexpected phenomenon, a camp on an island charted as uninhabited.

Only nine days after we had set up camp a rakish black yacht sailed into Darwin Bay. The crew buzzed ashore in an outboard powered dinghy, their swarthy, bearded faces obviously Spanish, Italian, Turkish or perhaps Greek. I waited in the surf mentally rehearsing 'Hello, who are you, I am etc. . . .' in Spanish, a difficult job since I was only at lesson three in my pocket grammar, but from an orifice somewhere amidst the visitor's hairs an unmistakably cockney voice hailed us. The yacht was under the charter of Francis Maziere and his Tahitian wife, on their way to look at the archaeology of Easter Island, with a three-man crew held together by the inevitable Englishman.

The yacht tried to buy fish from the *San Marco*, a small fishing-boat from San Cristobal which happened to be in the area, but the fishermen seemed to have no sense of proportion and asked a ludicrously high price, or failing that, a few pints of rum which was certainly an optimistic request. Eventually they exchanged twenty large fish, about a hundredweight, for an old jacket, which the captain wore with great elegance.

The *San Marco* caught an astonishing quantity of fish. Each morning in the grey light before dawn, when the lava looked its most desolate, they worked the shallow waters at the edge of the bay, netting small fish for line bait. Soon after dawn they started up the engine and chugged out to the open sea off the south-west coast of the island where they fished steadily till noon. Occasionally, when working on that side, we saw their tiny boat tossing up and down against the lonely waste of sea and sky. Then they returned to the bay and ignoring the swell anchored hardly a spit from the cliffs and beach, to gut and salt their catch before spreading the fish on the beach to dry. Finally, they trekked at least two miles over toilsome lava to collect driftwood; back they stumbled with the awkward, heavy loads for the brazier which burned on a cradle at the stern of the boat and cooked their food – poor fare too. Just before dark they finished their twelve to fourteen hour working day. Seven men lived for three weeks on that boat, hardly twenty feet long. One developed sunstroke, another became infected with boils and a third fell and deeply gashed both legs on the razor-edged lava. It seemed a gruelling existence under harsh conditions for little reward and inspired us with great respect for the strength and endurance of the islanders. They may be indolent, but they are tough.

Every day black sharks swarmed around the boat and soon began to wait for its arrival, their dorsal fins restlessly cutting the green water. The smaller white-tips seemed not to compete with them, though there were plenty around. As each fish head was thrown overboard the sharks went mad in a maelstrom of swirling water. Occasionally, for fun, the fishermen hooked one and attached the

K

line to a glass buoy against which the fish struggled savagely. Eventually they beached it and it lay motionless, its streamlined blue-black body gleaming with a dull metallic sheen, its head menacing – a weapon. Every line of a shark is powerful and graceful; the blunt, smooth slope of the forehead inclines upwards to the torpedo-shaped body equipped with small wings, the forward-set pectoral fins, and a powerfully propulsive, unequally fluked tail. From the cliff top we could often see their distorted outlines wavering in the glassy water as they contoured the sea bed in the shallows, gliding slowly and gracefully, but to see their true power one had to watch them feeding, chasing their prey in spurts of unbelievable speed, beaching themselves with the savagery of their rushes. The fishermen delivered the *coup de grâce* by severing the shark's head, releasing rivers of blood that stained the sea for many yards around. Sometimes they cut off the dorsal fin to sole their shoes and removed the jaw-bone as a trophy. The heavy body moved sluggishly for weeks afterwards as the fringe of each high tide washed the rotting form that had once moved so irresistibly.

I watched the death struggles of the shark during the casual and pointless kill and not for the first time it struck me that even kindly people easily become inured to seeing animals suffer, and to killing them if they do it often enough. Probably this is a useful psychological defence mechanism and seems not necessarily to imply the danger of equivalent callousness in other spheres, though there may be some risk. Extreme cases of divided approach are schizophrenics, like Charles St John, the Scottish naturalist who slaughtered birds of prey in the last century. Quite sincerely, it seems, he lamented the shooting of eagles, whilst in the same breath describing with the greatest gusto and detail just how he lured one down, shot it and then shot its mate which was returning again and again to its stricken partner, calling it to rise. Then he went on to shoot the last ospreys, even as they sat on the nest. Yet, of course, there is no gainsaying that quite 'normal' sportsmen are often keen naturalists and deeply and sincerely concerned with protection and conservation of wildlife; they are simply good at compartmentalising their activities, which everybody does to some extent. Some animal-lovers seem incapable of seeing that one can shoot and yet have a genuine interest in and concern for wildlife. An unduly one sided and sentimental approach antagonises many who have much the same interests at heart. An instance from Beebe shows how irrational and emotional we can be towards animals. 'Desiring a specimen [of hawk] but not wishing to injure the skin, I backed away and at a considerable distance fired at it with fine shot in the third barrel of my gun. The bird turned a complete somersault, landed on the ground on its feet, lowered its head and ran full speed towards me and brought up exactly between my legs. I picked it up without resistance, placed it in a large basket and took it off to the yacht where it readily took fish, preened itself and made no attempt to escape. Today, seven months later, it is living in good health at the New York Zoological Park.' Beebe fired at the hawk to kill it, yet when it actually delivered itself into his hands, he protected it. Had it run *away*, I suspect he would have chased it and finished off the job.

After three weeks the fishermen loaded the *San Marco* with fifteen boatloads of fish, dried on the coral beach in the fierce sun with flies swarming over them and at night the centipedes gnawing them. Tying up a bit of ragged canvas which served as sail on board and awning ashore, they set out on the hundred-mile trip home. I believe they used no navigational instruments, despite the dangerously strong and variable currents. By report, this same captain of the *San Marco* once broke down on the way to another island with a boatload of women and children. After drifting for part of a day and a night they were incredibly lucky to be picked up by a liner heading for New Zealand; the ship's crew even repaired his engine and took him to his destination. Ships are rare in these waters; he could easily have drifted for weeks and they had no provisions, water, oars or sail. Under such circumstances they can be curiously fatalistic. We heard at first hand an account of another breakdown to which the islanders on board reacted solely by making matchstick crosses and tossing them overboard, whilst the Europeans got on with the job of rowing and trying, successfully in the end, to repair the engine.

In January we were invaded by twelve American marine biologists who zig-zagged into Darwin Bay draped all over the Ecuadorian patrol boat P.O.5 – the steering gear was damaged. They were some of the sixty scientists who arrived on Santa Cruz for the Galapagos International Scientific Project, to mark the official opening of the Charles Darwin Research Station by carrying out a short but varied investigation of Galapagos fauna and flora. An hour later a motley assortment of tarpaulins and bivouacs sprang up alongside our tent; new and elaborate camping equipment lay everywhere and our peace was cheerfully shattered. Three busy days later they pulled out with their collection of marine life and our outgoing mail, leaving us a crate of out-dated tinned emergency water, some dried egg, half a tin of cooking oil and three 'sea rations'. Their medical doctor, Martin, had lived in Samoa investigating a species of anemone which is apparently used as a narcotic. When eaten it first anaesthetises and then if enough is taken kills painlessly; most natural poisons, such as snake venom, are harmless when swallowed and need to get directly into the blood stream to take effect. No doubt the Samoans were practising anaesthesia and maybe even euthanasia whilst we were still in the dark ages.

The *Floreana* and the *Vilamil*, lobster boats from Guayaquil six hundred miles away, often stay in the Galapagos a month or more, moving around the islands. The thorny and exquisitely beautiful Galapagos lobsters are really large marine crayfish and lack the large claws typical of our lobsters. They are very reluctant to enter traps or creels and are simply caught by hand; the Ecuadorians dive and extract them from their crevices and holes on the rocky bottom. Over thirty men live on board the lobster boats, diving in small groups which each receive a tiny commission on their catch. They buzz around the coasts and reefs in small dinghies powered by outboard motors and whilst one man cruises in small circles his two friends dive repeatedly, often coming up with a lobster in each gloved hand. Although they use face masks and flippers, it must be exhausting work diving for hours each day. The langustas are stored in a refrigerator on board and eventually taken to the mainland hotels and shops. Some find their way to North America, where the poor Galapagos crayfish, like Scottish grouse, endure the final ignominy of nourishing overfed businessmen in an overfed land. I am sure the lobsters preferred to end up in an old bucket over a driftwood fire on the beach. An American in the Galapagos recently had the bizarre and certainly unbiological idea of breeding a strain of lobsters that could regenerate their entire abdomen, which he would sell whilst his obliging crustaceans got on with the job of growing another: an extreme case of the red crab and Galapagos purple heron relationship in which, according to Beebe, the heron snaps off and eats a leg or two but the crab scrambles away to grow new ones. The unco-operative lobsters quickly died because, as Edgar Pots suggested, they didn't know whether he was cutting off their heads or their tails.

A trio from the *Vilamil* spotted our tent and came to investigate. Some dubious characters from Guayaquil serve as casuals with these boats but we were charmed by the courtesy of our visitors as they drank coffee and politely ate the vile, vanilla-flavoured *galletas* which Elias Mayorga, supplier to Her Majesty's Navy when in port, had dredged up from the recesses of his crammed store. Conversation was limited but, as usual with our Ecuadorian visitors, worked round to a topic which, judging from their covert glances, evidently bothered them. 'Yes,' we were married; 'how long?'; 'four years'; 'any children?'; 'no'. They always persevered. 'Why no children?' It was too involved for our Spanish, so June answered, perhaps a trifle ambiguously and certainly to the further mystification of these prolific people, 'because it is too difficult'.

It soon became fully automatic to glance frequently towards the mouth of the bay, so we always spotted and scrutinised our visitors through binoculars long before they reached the head. How many people on board; men or women; did they look English (bearded, ragged and dressed in bits of canvas no longer good enough for the boat).

Yachtsmen who call in at places like Tower are sure to be interesting characters. The twenty-foot yacht *Popeyduck* (the old Cornish name for a puffin) sailed into Darwin Bay on 17 March with its English owner and builder, Bill Procter. At the age of fifty-five he was sailing single-handed round the world after a severe illness and premature retirement from a Civil Service desk job which could hardly have been worse training for the physical hardship of such a voyage. People who think that after forty life can hold nothing new should ask Bill Procter. He built his yacht in two years in the garage at home, to blueprints drawn by Laurent Giles and Partners. It looked beautiful; light and graceful, yet strong. The interior was planned to use every inch of space and there was an automatic rudder so that one could leave it on course and go to sleep. That must be the eeriest thing on a solitary voyage, to lie in the pitch darkness alone, listening to the gurgle and swish of the water as your little boat cuts along, and trusting that no unsuspected hazard is looming nearer and nearer. Imagine the panic when (as Procter did) you suddenly become aware of the roar of breaking water; in the blackness how can you tell where it comes from; I suppose it is easy in theory to time one's landfall for daylight, but after a long ocean voyage, difficult in practice. *

Whitehall spent three days with us and helped to catch and ring white boobies. He showed the keenest curiosity about wildlife and panted, as he pursued the fleeing boobies in the fierce heat and caught them with his bare hands regardless of snapping beaks, that this sort of thing was exactly what he had dreamed of doing when he first conceived the idea of emulating Joshua Slocum and circumnavigating the globe. We swopped a few trifles of food, passed on one or two paperbacks and off he went, a tiny figure dwindling to a speck as his little boat sailed out of Darwin Bay. Ten months later he wrote from Fiji, full of praise for the charming South Sea Islands. His creed was: 'If you *really* want to go before you die, you will.'

The American yacht *Kismet* brought two American couples† who were roaming the world on the combined abstinences of eight years. The women lavished infinite care on their boat, almost beyond reason. Pat remarked, perhaps unoriginally, that there was something about the womblike interior of the boat (with, no doubt, the slopping of the sea for amniotic fluid) that aroused strong maternal feelings. The day after arriving in Darwin Bay they spent on hands and knees filling in minute holes in the deck, or up the mast renewing stays and retrieving the remnants of their pennant which frigates, attracted by its fluttering, had ripped to shreds. Boobies, frigates and bosun birds could come and go; there was work to be done. The saloon stove gleamed brightly and every piece of equipment had its once-over. I must admit I rather liked the free and easy *Lucent*, where any locker might yield a few marine specimens among the debris and you had to open a can to know what was inside, or the *Beagle* with its cat, marmoset and Richard's crabs.

The *Lucent* had left us on Tower in December, due to return in

* Bill Procter died in 1966, in the shipwreck of *Popeyduck* in the South Pacific, circumstances unknown.

† Jim and Pat Wales and Ken and Bebe Wunderlich.

March or April with more paraffin and water. The weeks flew so quickly that it seemed no time before she slipped back into Darwin Bay. Edgar Pots, the ebullient manager of the Charles Darwin Station, came ashore with a basket of fruit, vegetables and eggs from the Angermeyer and Potts households; typical of the kindness one receives from these hospitable people. Edgar and his kind can do anything from mending a watch to building a house. These days they are the true inheritors of the earth; wherever they go they can animate sullen machines and have an unerring mastery of three-dimensional objects and topology; they know what goes where and how. Their comments are always practical and heavily jocular. 'How many fish have you caught; not many?' And he pointed out that the hooks needed sharpening, that the angle of the barb was wrong, we had probably used the wrong bait and fished in the wrong spots. 'Let me demonstrate,' said he. During that morning, whilst parties of graceful tropic birds flew round the *Lucent* screaming in their courtship display, frigates soared above and inquisitive, deeply interested lava gulls watched from the rails, Edgar fished, and caught one pathetically small blowfish or puffer. It puffed itself out on the deck and lay there, totally inedible. One can make an unusual and effective lamp from a blown-up puffer with a bulb inside, but we had no electricity. Back at the camp under the veranda we cheerfully didn't have fish for lunch whilst the *Lucent*'s crew helped dispose of the six bottles of pilsner which they had kindly brought for me. We floated a fifty-gallon drum of paraffin ashore and then they left and we tasted for a second time that peculiarly forsaken feeling as the last link with people slowly parts; what may not happen before another boat sails into the bay?

At midday on 21 May 1964 a tall-masted ketch under full sail swept into the bay, probably the first to do so for over half a century. She was *Beagle II*, the 'new' research vessel of the Charles Darwin Station, on her first visit to an outlying island and we were the first visiting workers to have the privilege of welcoming her. She was manned by most of the crew that had sailed her from England – Roger Jamieson, Richard Foster and Julian Fitter – with the prospective skipper, Carl Angermeyer on board and David Snow trying out his Station's new acquisition on her maiden scientific trip. Jamieson had been commissioned by the Station to find, fit out and deliver a vessel suitable for visiting scientists to work and live on, in addition to carrying out conservation patrols between the islands; the Gulbenkian Foundation was to donate most of the cost. He found the *Beagle*'s hull rotting at Falmouth after a harbour accident and with the help of strong and willing natives from the south of England (including Richard and Julian), who hammered, sawed, caulked and painted for the price of several pints, eventually transformed her into *Beagle II* and sailed her from England to the Galapagos. To me she was a romantic boat, beautifully shaped and with her high poop deck, giant bowsprit and great spar-rigged masts magically appropriate to the wonderful Galapagos landscape, the wild bays and coasts by which she anchored. The red-footed boobies approved, for she was full of comfortable perches and they flocked in droves, winnowing above, striving to find footholds and quarrelling over the best perches (fig. 24). Before she anchored in Darwin Bay she was festooned with the descendants of boobies that doubtless perched on Darwin's *Beagle I* in 1835.

She was a marvellous recall of the seventeenth century when the Galapagos Islands were a favourite careening haunt of buccaneers. The *Bachelor's Delight*, a pirate ship, had trouble locating the 'Galipoloes' in 1684 for precisely the reason that gave the islands the centuries-old name 'Las Islas Encantadas'; namely that the currents constantly threw vessels off course and made the islands appear to be floating about on the surface of the ocean. Later an Admiral Porter interpreted the origin of the name Enchanted Islands slightly differently, supposing that it stemmed from the great difficulty in getting away from them, due to delaying calms and variable currents. James Bay, Santiago, was a favourite buccaneer and whaler resort with drinking water available and the *Bachelor's Delight* put ashore, among other things, eight tons of quince marmalade captured from Spanish merchant vessels. More valuable treasure is supposed to have been looted from the viceroy of Peru and buried in the Galapagos. The Incas are reputed to have removed vast quantities of gold and jewels and taken them to the Galapagos before they fell to the conquering and avaricious hands of the Spaniard Pizarro. If so, they are yet hiding their glitter beneath the dull lava.

The introduction of goats, now such a pest on most islands in the archipelago, dates from the privateering period. The demise of the giant land tortoises began with the whalers, who exploited the islands following the publication of Colnett's map of the Galapagos in 1798. Tagus Cove on the west coast of Isabella was a favourite haunt and the famous Post Office Bay on Floreana came into use. Letters 'posted' there travelled long and adventurously before reaching their destination and the bay became a regular port of call for mail. Whalers used to stow a hundred tons or more of live tortoises in their holds to ensure a supply of fresh (and delicious) meat for many weeks, since these reptiles, to their own downfall, can endure long periods without food and water. Darwin (1890) quotes 700 tons as the amount one whaler might take away. Nobody knows how many thousands met their end this way and they have since been further exploited by visitors and colonists, perhaps particularly, too, by the introduced pigs and dogs. Goats and donkeys add their bit by destroying cover and exposing the young. Less than ten years ago tortoises were openly for sale in the Galapagos. One of the most important jobs of the Charles Darwin Station is the conservation of all forms of wildlife, including plants endemic to the Galapagos. But, in particular, the rare or vanishing animals of which the giant tortoise is perhaps the most spectacular and important must be urgently conserved.

We had several trips in the good old *Beagle* and remember her with great affection. We had wonderful turtle soup and less exotic concoctions in her saloon and often slipped ashore in the blackness of a tropical night after an evening on board with the ever-hospitable Carl. On a blinding hot day in July she took us off Tower after seven months. How we sweated, tugging the heavy boxes down and loading them into the awkwardly lifting long boat, and how odd it seemed sailing right out of the mouth of the bay at which we had gazed so often for nearly two hundred days, until our camping beach was first a tiny white spot (had we really lived on that for so long?) and then hidden by the curve of the bay. We had been restlessly looking forward to that moment for the last few weeks, but no sooner had our beach really disappeared than we already felt sad and wondered if we would ever return.

Later the *Beagle* took us to Hood, and off Hood, and back to Tower, and to Daphne and finally put us ashore at Seymour, so it is no wonder she occupies a favoured niche in our affection; taking us to these wild places, turning up always on time and with the same joking, good-natured crew to help us load our gear and then sailing us back to Santa Cruz. She never failed to make a rendezvous or to time her voyages perfectly. The memorable occasion on which we left Tower at five one evening and found ourselves within twenty-five miles and heading her way at dawn the next morning shall be as decently shrouded as Carl's comments when he found the wheel lashed and the errant helmsman asleep at his post.

We have been sick in the *Beagle*, and the loo stank a bit, and she creaked and groaned as I imagine any old and well-weathered ship does, but these were trifles. The bunks were good, the food was ample and the crew were grand. The bronzed, bearded faces in the lamplight, smoking vile mixtures, grouped round the table, looked fine and friendly to us after months alone and there was always Carl, strumming his guitar and singing German songs to the sea-lions (more appreciative than we) or trying to call Edgar Pots over the ship's radio. I don't know how we would have fared with a radio transmitter, but despite new high-powered sets, with aerials specially designed for rough work, the *Beagle* rarely managed to establish two-way communication with the base on Santa Cruz – at least from Tower, seventy miles away, though a little more success-fully from Hood. Perhaps it was especially difficult because of interference from the higher islands. Whatever the reason, Carl's nightly call became an amusing ritual.

'Dis is de *Beagle* calling Charlie D, Charlie D, Charlie D; *Beagle* calling Charlie D – do you hear me Edgar, over.' Pause. '*Beagle* calling Charlie D, you faint Edgar, you faint away. I near nuthin Edgar, nuthin; you are dead man, dead, dead, dead; try again – over.' 'Dis is de *Beagle* calling Charlie D, Charlie D, Charlie D, no good Edgar, I tell you no good. Will try again in de morning, try again in de morning – so good night from de *Beagle*, over and out.' Click. Carl turns towards us, grins and shows his fine gold fillings (everybody has gold fillings in the Galapagos). 'Don't know what de hell's wrong with dat set. Edgar must be on de wrong channel.' Back on Santa Cruz, Edgar is mopping a perspiring brow (he always perspires) and sticking pins in a wax model of Carl's big end.

In the latter weeks of our exile two marvellous feasts came our way. They would have been good by any standards; by ours at that time, after nearly a year on vitamin pills and sardines with the odd goat as a treat, they were exotic.

We sat reverently before the first at eight p.m. on 31 October in the dining-room of the *Puritan*, a tuna boat under the command of an American (whose hobby, at which he was unerringly successful in every port, was collecting gold coins). The menu: fish soup, prime rib of beef, potato salad, green salad, celery, kidney beans, rice, tomatoes and fruit salad and ice cream.

Tuna are fished either by nets or line. This was a 1,000-ton net boat, whose eighteen tanks would hold 950 tons of fish. I suppose line fishing would be more exciting, standing in the scuppers, sometimes awash, with the rod resting in a leather socket attached to a belt around your middle, heaving a hundred pounds of tuna over your shoulder as fast as you can clear your hook. However, netting has its compensations; for one thing you catch more at a time. This skipper once landed well over a hundred tons in a single haul, which almost broke his lifting gear. During catching operations the *Puritan* and her nets were towed by a huge, flat-bottomed barge with enormous diesel engines. Once lifted on to the clearing deck the fish were fed, without gutting, straight into the refrigeration tanks cooled by liquid ammonia. On a really good trip a skipper may empty some of his fresh-water tanks to make room for more fish. Not that this means any hardship, for tuna fishers live extremely well. The Captain and Chief Engineer had lovely cabins with fitted carpets, television and private bathroom. The crew eat well, too (it's their only pleasure) and the cost of keeping such a boat at sea can run at over $1,000 a day; fruitless voyages are costly for the two 950 h.p. engines gulp fuel at a prodigious rate. Since the Ecuadorian government levy a fishing fee commensurate with the capacity of the boat (in this case the permit would have cost almost $10,000) it clearly behoves a tuna boat to catch tuna. In fact they almost always do; they make sure of that by staying out until they encounter the fish. They are paid on the basis of their catch and if they catch nothing they get no wage, although they have had their keep. The skippers bears the main responsibility, for he decides where to go and, with powerful binoculars, does most of the scanning for tell-tale signs such as the jumping of fish on which tuna or sea-birds are preying. Many boats, particularly Japanese, evade the permit fee and run for it if challenged. The Ecuadorian navy have too few patrol boats really to enforce their law, although they occasionally capture an errant tuna boat and impose a heavy fine. The Commandante from San Cristobal proudly brought such a one into Santa Cruz on Christmas Day 1963.

Our visitor had a tough-looking mixed Portuguese, Puerto-Rican seventeen-man crew, with American officers. The youngest member had a sullen expression and a head swathed in wrappings; both due to the enthusiasm with which his messmates had observed the ritual of crossing the line – Neptune had removed all his glossy black hair. They came ashore on Hood riding easily in the flat-bottomed barge. A stocky Puerto-Rican stood on the bows guiding them in over the rocks, which in the clear water looked deceptively near the surface. I stood on the beach indicating the main rock-free channel but he evidently thought the water was getting too shallow and jumped overboard, expecting to go up to his knees; he went in over his head. At midnight when we came ashore in pitch blackness the two Portuguese handling the boat swung so far out to avoid a reef that they almost avoided the island too; it took us twenty minutes under power and much anxious gabbling to cover a straight distance of four hundred yards.

If tuna boats eat well there are those who eat better. Our second marvellous meal of 1964 was on the Royal Yacht *Britannia*. H.R.H. the Duke of Edinburgh called at Hood Island on 4 November during a three-day visit to the Galapagos. A less strict regard for the truth might allow me to describe how, early one morning, a trim motor vessel slid snugly round the tip of Punta Suarez. A smartly lowered dinghy manned by immaculate sailors surged ashore. Hastily donning clothes, we went to meet it, when who should step ashore but Prince Philip. It came within an ace of happening in exactly that way, but Roger Perry, then the brand-new Director of the Station, had visited Hood some five weeks earlier and given us the news.

The *Beagle* had been rendezvousing with the *Britannia* at various points in the archipelago, with Carl Angermeyer as guide. At exactly eight a.m., as arranged, the *Britannia* slid round Punta Suarez and the little *Beagle*, with Fritz at the helm, hastened in from the north after a rough journey from the other side of the Equator (Hood and

Tower lie in separate hemispheres). With the *Britannia* still under way a rubber dinghy took to the water and circled the yacht. This was an unofficial visit to see and photograph the wildlife of the Galapagos, which was perhaps why we were included in the itinerary though I suspect that the albatrosses and blue-footed boobies had the edge on us. This was a momentous visit, the first time a member of the British Royal family had set foot in the Galapagos, whose English names commemorate the Stuart line. We removed the inhospitable sea-lion barricade and tried to make ourselves present-able, for we were by then in a tattered state. It didn't matter in the slightest that I looked like a half-starved castaway – I pretty nearly *was* one. Thorns, lava and sea-water had ripped my shorts to shreds but it hardly seemed right to don the lounge suit which for some obscure reason mouldered in the bottom of a chest. Shorts, a beard and bare feet seemed not inappropriate. June, by some magic, surfaced with smart green ski-pants, an entire black sweater and *real* footwear. No doubt the visitors would have tolerated a far more basic appearance, befitting the environment; they had arrived unexpectedly they would certainly have found one. The Duke of Edinburgh is justly admired for his realistic attitudes and genuine charm, and quickly dispelled any awkwardness we may have felt about our dishevelled looks.

Major Aubrey Buxton, well-known naturalist, director of Anglia Television and man of many parts, was with the group, which also included Mr Corley-Smith, the British Ambassador to Ecuador. Both are keen bird-watchers and with Prince Philip as interested as anyone we spent four hours watching albatrosses, boobies and tropic birds and taking photographs under a grilling sun. The albatrosses even came out from the shade and performed their courtship dance as a Royal Command Performance. Normally they are sunk in lethargy at that time of day and loath to start even the tiniest ecstatic ritual. Corley-Smith nearly fell over the cliff trying to photograph tropic birds and Aubrey Buxton stuck cigar stumps on the bushes at intervals to provide a back-trail. Whilst we were exploring, a giant centipede trailed its ugly, red, chitin-clad length in front of us. It was the first time I had ever seen one abroad in daylight, though Curio tells me that on some islands they are habitually diurnal. He suspects that the difference in habit may be connected with the habits of mocking birds, which on some islands apparently search out and kill centipedes; on such islands, therefore, these arthropods do not venture out. On Hood, the mocking birds present on this occasion circled the centipede warily but would not approach. However, they may have been young birds, which tend to show fear of unusual objects. Whether or not the Hood mockers were habitually scared of centipedes we could never find out, since the latter normally stayed under cover during the day, as indeed they did on Tower. The connection between mockers and centipedes must be regarded as unproven, though an interesting possibility. The Galapagos short-eared owl preys on centipedes and is common on Tower, where we never saw a centipede by day. However, the owl also occurs, though less commonly, on Hood.

The invitation to lunch on the *Britannia* was as irresistible as it was unexpected, whatever our misgivings about our appearance; I surely presented the footman with the most ragged posterior he ever guided to a *Britannia* chair. Of course we looked incongruous, but nobody batted an eyelid.

After his very first day ashore on Indefatigable, Beebe was thrilled by the contrast between the forbidding desolation of the Galapagos scene and the well-ordered luxury of his boat, the *Noma*. Imagine then the contrast between almost a year's Galapagos camping, inured to washing in sea water, eating weevily spaghetti and beetle-infested flour, using a sea-washed gully for latrine, and all the many tiny but somewhat sordid necessities of such a prolonged camp in those surroundings, and the magnificence of the *Britannia*'s suites and dining-room. Many appreciative guests have been entertained on the Royal Yacht, but none could have done that lunch fuller justice than we did.

And that was far from the total of our debt. Needles to repair ravaged clothes, razors to restore hirsute jowls to elegant smoothness and sandals to enclose lava-leathered feet, must be added and had it not been for our unbelievable perverseness in having planned to leave Hood the next day, food would have been ours too. Above all, the *Britannia* kindly brought some of my notebooks and film safely back to England and the air-conditioning of Buckingham Palace. On an expedition such as ours one always fears the loss of scientific material on the journey home, which in our case involved several transferences from boat to boat, with disaster conceivable at some points. The Duke's visit was a fine and unexpected climax to our Galapagos venture. Whatever happens to the memories of a year's boobies and monotonous food, the fresh cream of the *Britannia* will aye endure.

*Figure 24* Royal Yacht *Britannia* rendezvousing with *Beagle II*

# The Waved Albatross of Hood Island

Albatrosses (family *Diomedeidae*, thirteen species) together with the petrels, shearwaters and fulmars comprise the order Procellariformes or tubenoses. All albatrosses have a hooked upper mandible covered with discrete horny plates, with the nostrils opening from short tubes, one on each side of the middle plate. Tarsi relatively long and feet webbed between three toes instead of between all four as in sulids. A special gland, the proventriculus (part of stomach), secretes the oil on which the young are fed.

Nine of the thirteen species are found in southern latitudes, mainly between 30° and 60° S., ranging down to Antarctic ice. Three species occur in north Pacific, breeding on small atolls, and the remaining species, the waved albatross, is endemic to Hood Island in the Galapagos.

Albatrosses are notably oceanic, ranging vast distances, especially out of the breeding season. Black-browed albatrosses have been known to penetrate further north than they have reached south in their native hemisphere.

Albatrosses are both clownish and magnificent, goony birds and royal. In their element, wind-swept oceans, they are peerless. On their breeding grounds they dance and display with incredibly droll antics, their regal dignity shattered in one bout of bill-clappering, head-swaying, donkey-braying ritual.

Albatrosses are associated mainly with stormy Antarctic seas; the black-browed and wandering albatrosses breed in the rigorous fastnesses of South Georgia and the royal, sooty, grey-headed, Buller's and others range the cold southern oceans. But the black-footed and Laysan albatrosses, the 'goony' birds, nest on the tropical Pacific atolls of Midway and Laysan and the waved albatross breeds nowhere in the world except that speck of time-smoothed Galapagos lava, Hood Island.

There are probably not more than 3,000 pairs of waved albatrosses

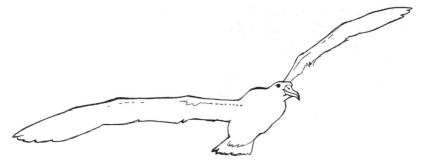

*Figure 25* Waved albatross in flight

in existence. Whilst this is far from a large number and would be perilously near to extinction for some species, the waved albatross is in no danger and is apparently maintaining its numbers. There have probably never been very many more than at present. Fortunately it has never had the commercial value of the flamingo, or its fate might well have been sealed.

Waved albatrosses are a bit larger than a farmyard goose, with imposing chests covered in fine wavy lines. Their eight pounds are gracefully borne on a majestic eight-foot wing spread. They walk easily on long, rather thin legs, placing their large, pale grey feet with rolling dignity, rather, one imagines, as Dr Johnson rolled his majestic frame. Their huge bills, about six inches long and very deep, with a respectable hook on the end, are a shiny yellow, grossly artificial like that of a bath-tub duck. The deep brown eyes, with prominent eye ridges and a rather flattened forehead, give them a peculiar facial expression, at once stupid and severe. But no bird with large brown eyes is devoid of dignity; indeed, one illogically tends to expect more intelligence from brown-eyed birds. Hens, with their pale yellow eyes, look as silly as they are, whilst the limpid brown eyes of the tawny owl contrast with the mad yellow light in the irises of the short-eared owl; it is the tawny that symbolises wisdom. The clean white head and neck of the waved albatross is variably suffused with yellow. I have often wondered why the heads of gannets, the white form of the red-footed booby and the waved albatrosses are stained yellow. Perhaps they all acquire the colour fortuitously as ingested pigment from crustacea, but if so why does it affect the head only. There are also objections

L

to assuming that it comes from the oil gland. From the lower throat right back beneath the tail, the underparts are covered with close-set wavy grey lines which fade gradually into the paleness of the throat. The upper tail coverts are also finely barred and the back and wings a fairly uniform brownish black, in which the pale straw-coloured shafts of the outer primaries stand out conspicuously. The legs and feet are pale, smooth grey.

The south-east Pacific is theirs to roam. We first saw them between the Guayas Gulf and the Galapagos, some two hundred miles east of the islands, but they range vast distances from Hood. Albatrosses probably range further during the breeding season than any other bird and waved albatrosses have been seen in Japanese waters, though they may have been non-breeders. They have the long, narrow wings of the far, fast flier and glider as in our own fulmar. They revel in wind and are helpless without it. In ocean areas covered by dependable wind systems, vast crossings are no energy problem to an albatross. In flight their feet project slightly beyond their tail and doubtless add a few welcome inches of surface area with which to combat unruly currents. Similarly, the long, flexible tails of bosun and frigate-birds may be valuable stabilisers when these birds are feeding close to the surface in changeable air currents.

After a few days at sea I became slightly obsessed with the thought of the awful monotony of an albatross existence, forever gliding and flapping over the endless, featureless sea. It looks marvellous at first gliding along so effortlessly; the play of light on the backcloth of sea is delightful and there seems infinite variation in the waves, but after watching it for a few hours the mind reels at the thought of a lifetime of such wandering. A condor soaring over the peaks and valleys of the Andes, familiar with each crag and knowing a refuge in every gale, seems enviable but thirty or forty years of exchanging one square mile of sea for another goes beyond the imagination. But then albatrosses do not have a mind comparable to ours and are, to a large extent, automatons. Glorious automatons it is true, but fully 'satisfied' by the processing of such environmental information as enters their nervous system through the senses – mainly eyes and ears – and not troubled by the complex demands of a well-developed cerebellum. I imagine their consciousness as a blank screen, quiveringly sensitive to the impinging of the thousand and one stimuli to which it must respond, but until such stimuli come along, blissfully blank. How else could birds remain 'sane' during a fifteen-day incubation spell, gazing at the same boulder?

To find Hood across thousands of miles of ocean requires fixed point rather than simple unidirectional navigation. This implies the built-in knowledge of where Hood is from any point on the earth's surface. Whilst bico-ordinate navigation can be tolerably well explained in terms of sun navigation and an internal clock which allows the bird to mark the passing of time and hence navigate by reference to a moving sun, the ability to find a fixed spot from any other point is still a mysterious performance. Before landing on the island, the albatrosses often gather in large rafts half a mile or more offshore, a habit common to several, though by no means all, oceanic birds that nest in colonies. Kittiwakes and shearwaters, for instance, gather in dense rafts at the beginning of the breeding season, before they first come in to their cliff-ledges or burrows. It seems likely that after a winter at sea they are too wary and frightened of land to come in immediately. In many species, including gannets, spontaneous 'dreads' or 'panics' occur at frequent intervals for the first few weeks, the birds suddenly taking fright for no apparent reason and dashing out from the cliffs in clouds. Later they never do this.

Landing and taking off is difficult for an albatross on Hood. Natural runways, used literally as such, are thickly strewn with boulders, large and small, and stubbled with scrubby, spiny bushes. Albatrosses cannot brake very effectively because they have the high stalling speed that goes with long, narrow, high aspect-ratio wings and they hit the ground quite fast instead of floating gently down like a gull. Perhaps because of the boulders they try to stop suddenly instead of landing at a run and often fall flat on their faces. Leg and foot injuries are common results of bad landings and we found two birds that had killed themselves, obviously when landing. Accidents of this kind are probably one of the main hazards in these long-lived birds; large predatory fish may be another. They are capable of recovering from extensive bone injuries, and skeletons (of another species) have been found that had repaired massive damage to the sternum. They were not the only ones to come croppers; when chasing them we fell too and were far from confident of our ability to repair broken breast bones. When taking off along their runways they run fast, with wings outspread and feet pattering lightly and loosely over the ground, gradually working up speed until airborne. Or they may collide violently with a boulder, coming to a jarring halt before limping off with their ludicrous nautical roll. At other times they plod dourly to the cliff edge – a wearisome business calling for frequent rests. One would expect them to nest as near to the cliff edge as possible, but not a bit of it. Sometimes they nest many hundreds of yards inland, penetrating dense scrub and giving themselves enormous trouble with every journey. They rise from a sitting position in two stages, first onto the tarsi, which rest flat against the ground, and then on to their large flat feet.

Like most long-lived sea-birds, albatrosses do not breed until they are several years old; if the other members of the family are anything to go by, waved albatrosses will probably be at least five before they lay their first egg. But they probably return to the breeding colony before then. All albatrosses have an extremely complicated courtship ritual which they practise long before they breed. This 'dance' of the albatross intrigued us and we spent many hectic hours watching and recording it. We devised a shorthand sign for each of the many postures and movements involved and I then dictated the sequence of events, scoring them against time (in seconds) with a stop watch whilst June scribbled frantically. It would have been far more sensible to have taken a tape recorder. We used three columns, one each for male, female and pair so that we recorded the exact time relationship between both birds' actions. Anybody overhearing us might well have wondered at the monologue: fifty seconds, male ha-ha-ha; female clappers; male sky-point and moo; fifty-two seconds, pair bill circling, and so on. It was easy to find displaying birds; they gathered in groups in clearings amongst the scrub and their courtship could be heard easily half a mile away with its prolonged howls, derisive 'ha-ha-ha's and loud bill-clappering like a football rattle.

When we arrived on Hood in July the egg-laying for that season was over and there were already some month-old chicks, hiding under the dry scrub whilst their parents were away at sea. But there was spirited display among birds without egg or chick, particularly in the early morning and late afternoon; during the day they mainly rested quietly beneath the bushes. By marking them with coloured rings we discovered that these foot-loose males returned to the same area each time they came to the island, but wandered quite extensively and danced with several different females, although they stuck mainly to one partner for the duration of a 'shore leave'.

Some of these dancing birds, all of which were obviously without egg or chick, were young adults three years old. We knew this because they were ringed and we managed to catch four and, later, look up their history in the records of the Charles Darwin Station. They were ringed in 1961, on Punta Suarez – in other words, they had returned to the precise area in which they were born, as do most sea-birds.

The remaining twenty-eight ringed albatrosses, some of which were dancing on Punta Suarez in July–September 1964, had been ringed as adults, twenty-four in 1961 and four in 1962. Taking, first, the birds ringed in 1961, eighteen of the twenty-four had been designated as 'breeding adults' at the time of capture and in 1964 six of these definitely had an egg or chick; the remaining twelve had nothing. Most of these twelve birds returned fairly infrequently but sometimes for long spells (a week or so) during which intense dancing might occur, though in most cases they displayed half-heartedly or were not seen to dance at all. Two of them were a mated pair that had been ringed as such in 1961 and were quietly resting together when caught in 1964. In one or two cases more, specific pairs usually danced together but the records could not show that they had been ringed as pairs in 1961.

These recoveries give a tolerably clear-cut answer about how frequently albatrosses breed. Twelve or two-thirds of these fitted nicely into an alternate-year regime, breeding 1961 and 1963 (presumed) and not breeding 1962 (presumed) or 1964 (known). The accuracy of this conclusion depends, of course, on a correct interpretation of their status in 1964. If we were wrong about their status, that is, if they were in reality breeding birds that had left their chicks and gathered in small groups, displaying occasionally, then our argument would be useless. However, judging from what we knew of the behaviour of birds that definitely did have chicks, our interpretation was almost surely right. But what about the six birds that were designated as breeders in 1961 and again had chicks in

1964? They were obviously out of step with an alternate-year regime. In one case a bird (male) was ringed as breeding adult in 1961, recaught as breeding adult with downy chick in 1963 and again had a chick in 1964. In this and the other five cases one could assume that where breeding or attempted breeding occurred in two successive years, the first of these had been unsuccessful. Thus, if these six birds had been unsuccessful in either 1961 *or* 1963, they could have been out of step and bred again in 1964. This assumption requires only a very reasonable level of egg and chick loss (less than fifteen per cent), particularly since there is some question whether, in fact, all the 1961 birds were correctly classed. Some were queried breeders at the time since they were not actually on nests.

None of the four birds ringed as adults in 1962 were classed as breeding, so they cannot shed any more light on the question, but in fact two of them had eggs or chicks in 1964, which slightly reverses the trend of the 1961 birds and so still agrees with an alternate-year hypothesis. However, Lévêque recorded eleven birds breeding (with eggs) when ringed in June 1960 and again with eggs in June 1961, and unless all these were failed breeders in 1960, trying again in 1961, it seems that breeding in successive years is possible. Still, it seems fair to conclude that annual breeding is not usual among waved albatrosses, which probably breed (in the absence of complications) every second year.

Lévêque also recorded a bird which bred on Punta Suarez in 1961 and was caught dancing on Punta Cevallos (at the other end of the island) in January 1962. Perhaps it was temporarily attracted by the presence of other dancing birds before carrying on to its 'proper' breeding ground.

The dance, or 'ecstatic ritual' as it has been called, is one of the most extraordinary displays imaginable. It is highly entertaining, but also a complex piece of ritualised behaviour in which the dancing partners co-operate with great precision. Dancing albatrosses face each other so that when they lean forward their bills come into contact from about half way down to the tip. The basic movement is then a bill-circling in which they rapidly and irregularly slide their bill over the top of the other's, not in a full circling movement but rather a half circle and back again. The bills are mainly in contact throughout the display, but often jump apart, then meet again

*Figure 26* Waved albatross display

making a wooden, clattering noise. Dancing 'excites' the birds and a slight secretion of oil seeps from the tubular nostrils and lubricates the bills which become glossy and slippery. Time and again, whatever other movements intervene, the partners return to this rapid bill-circling. Frequently one bird, usually the male, breaks off and snaps bolt upright, staring fixedly ahead with the peculiar expression imparted by the flattened head and conspicuous 'eyebrows'. The other may follow suit or else keep on bill-circling in mid-air, too slow to react to the withdrawal of its partner's bill. With a swift forward and downward bow which takes it slightly below the level at which the pair bill-circle, each bird then returns to the circling with sustained vigour. Then, suddenly, one arches its neck and, holding its head motionless, fixedly touches a spot on its flank (there is something special about this spot as I will describe later). Even as its head sweeps down to touch its flank, the partner, still in the forward, low, bill-circling position, clappers its mandibles together so rapidly that they are just a blur, whereupon the side-touching bird stretches its neck, throws its bill vertically upwards and utters a loud, prolonged and high-pitched 'whoo-ooo'. Then a swift bow, and both birds fall to enthusiastic bill-circling again. In another part of this esoteric and athletic display one or both birds suddenly click into an upright position, necks fully stretched, and silently open their bills in the widest possible gape, as though advertising Bird's custard powder. Then they snap the bill closed with a loud resonant 'clunk' which owes its quality partly to the sounding chamber formed by the mouth (one cannot produce the noise with a dead beak and skull) and return to the circling. After some time one bird turns away and with the most ridiculous walk imaginable, a grotesque caricature of a movement in which, with the bill tucked into the chest, the head sways right over and down at each step, leads the other, also walking in the same exaggerated fashion, to some particular spot. This ludicrous 'sway-walk' is a highly exaggerated version of normal locomotion; by increasing the extent of the head and foot movements a conspicuous ritualised walk has evolved. After several minutes, perhaps even half an hour, the display ends for the time being with one bird assuming a squatting position, head down, neck retracted and bill pointing between its feet, and bobbing jerkily up and down, meantime uttering a repeated low note. This 'forward bobbing' is actually a special display indicating ownership of a site and it is unfailingly performed, for instance, when a bird settles down after returning to its egg or small chick. It also plays an important part in the chick's life as we shall see.

When things become really hectic the various display movements and postures follow each other in rapid succession with never a moment's pause. When several pairs display simultaneously the air is full of weird noises – whoops, grunts, rattles and clunks and mad laughter. Rival males stretch to their full height and with beaks gaping widely, as in the display described above, run at each other uttering a 'ha-ha-ha' call and occasionally biting at each other, although things never develop into a real fight. In dancing displays it is the male that performs this aggressive beak-gaping most often; considerably more than females. Again, therefore, we find an aggressive action incorporated into a display between pair members and demanding greater expression in the more aggressive sex, here the male. In fact, when dancing with a 'new' female the male sometimes runs at her as though she were an intruding male. The male is also mainly responsible for switching from one part of the dance to another; in a sense he directs the dance and the female reacts to her cues. Whilst there is a highly stereotyped pattern to these dances, a certain amount of variation in the order of the component parts is permissible. However, this must not go too far, and the displays of different species of albatross, though in some cases very similar, are acceptable only to their own kind. This, of course, is not surprising since it is well established that the development of species-specific behaviour patterns is one way in which closely related species breeding alongside each other may avoid hybridisation. Nevertheless the similarity in display may tempt members of two species to dance with each other, as in the case of the Laysan and black-footed albatrosses, both of which nest on Midway Island. Two American ornithologists (Rice and Kenyon) saw them dancing together but apparently the 'mistakes' which each made in terms of the other's formal procedure always led to confusion and ultimately to frustration and outright aggression.

As in many complicated displays in which both male and female participate, the action of one is partly a response to the partner's previous posture or movement. When the female clappers she usually does so because the male has just arched his neck and touched his flank, not because she has reached that line in her recital anyway and it just happened to coincide with the male's flank-touching. If he had not touched his flank she would not have clappered. In other words there is a clear link between these actions. Yet, the flank-touching and sky-pointing and 'whoo-ooo' are linked together independently of what the other bird may do. Once a bird has touched its flank in that particular way (though not in ordinary preening) it will then immediately perform the sky-pointing and 'whoo-ooo'. Thus there are two different processes working together to produce the complicated display and it is the co-operative one, the dependence on what the partner has just done, that improves with practice. A well-practised pair perform together very smartly, whereas birds new to each other seem indecisive and do not synchronise correctly. As we have just seen the Laysan and black-footed albatrosses sometimes pair up for display but it always ends in frustration because they do not know the right lines for each other.

Different species of albatross vary in their so-called 'scapular action', in which, as they touch their side with their bill, they also raise one or both wings, though still keeping them closed. The waved albatross does not really raise either wing, but I was intrigued by the precision with which they invariably touched a particular region on their side and never anywhere else. There was no bright patch of feathers there, comparable to the vivid wing speculae which some ducks touch during display, nor any conspicuous structure to which the movement could direct attention. Whilst weighing and

A  Partners face each other                    B  Bill-circling

 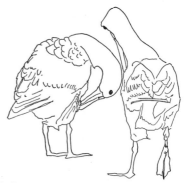

E  One bird begins to sway walk whilst the      F  One partner moves off in sway walk,
other sky-points                                whilst other side touches

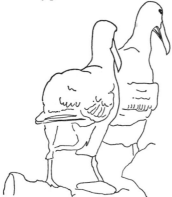 

I  Partners move off to nest site: they may     J  After a bout of display they often
display some yards from it                      wing-flap and then produce a sighing,
                                                groaning expiration, as the bird on the left
*Figure 27* Dance of the albatross             is doing

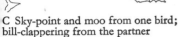

C Sky-point and moo from one bird; bill-clappering from the partner

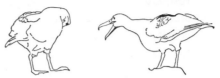

D Side-touching from one bird and clappering from the partner. Many albatrosses accompany side-touching by 'scapular action', in which one or both wings are raised, but the waved albatross does not typically do this

G Display starts up again, with the male performing a ritualised threat gape

H An aggressive encounter between two males, using threat

K A bout of display ends with forward bobbing from a sitting or crouching position

L Normal gait in a waved albatross

measuring adult albatrosses I looked closely at this spot and found that beneath the thick, quilt-like contour feathers there was a large discrete patch of dense filoplumes – feathers with loose, downy structure. I could not decide whether this patch is particularly sensitive to touch and reinforces the display movement by association with a pleasurable tactile stimulus, or has some other connection with the movement, but it seems a specialised area worth closer study. This albatross habit of allying a display movement to a morphological feature invisible both to the displaying bird and its dancing partner seems a rather unusual phenomenon, worth adding to the well-known range of movements directing attention to local colour or external structures. Why or how the specialised patch of feathers evolved is another question.

The fact that pairs gradually perfect their co-operation suggests one of the functions of this dance; a biological reason for its existence. When asking the question 'why' about behaviour it is deceptively easy to move from one level to another and from causation to function. To many biologists the 'why' which aks what *causes*\* a particular phenomenon seems both more interesting and often capable of more stringent proof than the 'why' of function or the 'how' of adaptation. Perhaps it is thought that the latter 'why' involves suspect teleological reasoning. The 'why' we are discussing here, concerning the albatross dance, is 'why does it do it' in the sense 'what effect does it have'. Of course, female albatrosses display *because* they are mature or maturing, and *because* it is the right season and *because* their gonads are secreting sex hormones and *because* their partner has just leaned forward and begun bill-circling. All these are causation 'whys', though on different levels. But why has natural selection produced albatrosses that go through this bizarre performance? What effect does the display have on their reproduction? Co-operation is, I think, a keyword. Display helps to synchronise the internal conditions of the partners so that the complicated and lengthy breeding routine is carried out smoothly. Admittedly they do not display all through the breeding cycle, but by it they start off precisely in step.

Internal factors are of some importance in determining a bird's actions and there is no reason to believe that a pair of albatrosses

\* In terms of the mechanism(s) involved.

could return to the breeding grounds, mate and go smoothly into incubation behaviour and nest reliefs, all without any display. In the first place, display helps ensure fertilisation by leading to coition. Even in lower animals, for example amphibia, males may perform complicated displays so that the females are stimulated to carry out their part of the reproductive behaviour. In the breeding season the male crested newt does not simply approach the female and then produce his sperm packet (spermatophore). If he did it would be wasted, for the female would ignore it. In any case he cannot produce it until sufficiently stimulated. He displays ardently to the female for an hour or more, throbbing his conspicuous tail and frequently lashing the female with it. Then when he is sexually stimulated, he crawls away from the female and deposits his spermatophore. She is by now hypnotised by the male's throbbing tail and follows it as he creeps away. So she passes over the spermatophore, which is sticky and adheres to her cloaca, into which it is quickly drawn by reflex muscle action. Once there it fertilises the eggs before they are laid. In this chain of co-operative reactions, the display has played an indispensable part; without it, the male could not lay his spermatophore nor entice the female to follow him and so pick it up (fig. 28).

Display also strengthens the bond between pair members and ensures their compatibility perhaps by encouraging the disruption of pairs that do not function well together. Compatibility between pair members of extremely long-lived birds like albatrosses can be of decisive importance in breeding. Many sea-birds have prolonged greeting ceremonies and it has recently been shown that if a kittiwake loses its mate its subsequent breeding success will be adversely affected for at least two years, even should it be lucky enough to acquire another mate as experienced as the first. Albatrosses may expect to live at least twenty years, probably very much more, and it will be well worthwhile acquiring a compatible mate and sticking to it; most sea-birds, as I have already mentioned, keep the same partner for several years or for life.

The single large egg of the waved albatross, weighing nearly half a pound, is laid on the bare ground, mainly in April and May. There is not even a pretence at nest building, either real or symbolic. Sometimes, indeed, the female lays the egg in a crack between

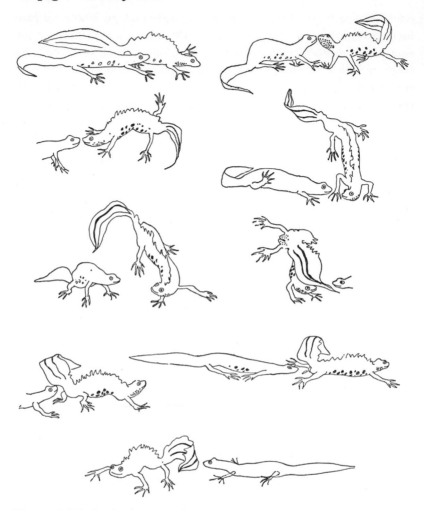

*Figure 28* Display in the crested newt

boulders and then cannot incubate it and is apparently too dull to roll it out with her beak. The egg is incubated against a single large brood patch, into which it fits snugly. Because of this albatrosses cannot incubate a donated extra egg, unlike boobies, which incubate their eggs underfoot and can manage to stretch their webs a bit further to deal with an extra egg. Albatrosses settle on their egg by lowering their breast and then giving a gigantic hitch upwards and

152

forwards. They make the same awkward movement when hoisting their bulk on to a tiny chick, much to its discomfort.

Albatross chicks are most delightful objects, thickly covered with chocolate brown, beige or even a beautiful silvery grey down and with their eyes open when they hatch, so they look attractive from the start. They cheep musically and constantly and each time the parent lowers itself to brood it calls softly in a disyllable; each call covers a considerable range in tone, giving room for variation between individuals. Poor albatross chicks; they have a long, boring, uncomfortable and undignified time ahead before they take to their wonderful wings and become ocean wanderers; they have first to become little more than gigantic bags of oil. The parents brood their chick for the first two weeks or so and then leave it unguarded, returning only to feed it, though for a short period they brood it after each feed. Soon the chick hobbles and wobbles away from its nest and finds a hiding place under the bushes. It often favours one resting place for weeks, excavating a snug hollow into which the convex curve of its bulging stomach fits comfortably. Soil and small stones are scuffed out with backward scraping movements of the feet. Albatrosses nest in scattered groups, so there is often a handful of chicks dotted about a patch of scrub, into and under which they burrow, probably to find shade.

I quickly began to wonder how the parents located their chick; obviously not by wandering around peering under every bush and calling their offspring by name. Luckily I saw what happened. An albatross swept in from the sea, landed a hundred yards away from me and began walking towards a chick nursery a good many yards away. I immediately dashed to the area by a roundabout route and hid behind a bush. The adult came along, stopping every few yards and in the forward bobbing position uttering the repeated low note which I have already described. This note electrified one of the chicks hidden in the bushes; it stumbled to its feet and moved towards the adult. When still out of sight of its parent it gave the plaintive chick version of the call. Just as the baby sea-lion homes onto its mother by calling, so the albatross chick and its parent found each other by moving towards the right voice and the two made contact about five feet from the site. This immediately suggested one good reason why adult and chick call so frequently in the first hours after hatching; this is when they learn each other's voice. It also explained why that particular call was used; it was capable of considerable individual variation. Even I could detect individual differences in the two-syllable combination and there would be little chance of the chick mistaking its parent's voice.

Lying hidden beneath the scrub I could also watch the entire feeding operation from extremely close quarters. Tubenoses mainly feed their young on an oily secretion manufactured by the proventriculus – actually a part of the stomach. A great advantage of this system is that the adult can continue feeding for days at sea until it has manufactured large quantities of oil and then fly vast distances back to the colony, perhaps still manufacturing as it goes. By contrast, a booby or frigate has to hasten back before the fish in its stomach or crop are digested and assimilated. Far from making food for their young from it they can give them only the raw material and cannot even significantly hold up digestive processes, so their fishing range is limited by this factor quite apart from anything else. If they take too long there will be nothing left. Albatross oil is mixed with more recent stomach contents such as fish, pieces of squid and crustaceans, in this case rather like prawns, and the whole lot is poured from the opening of the oesophagus at the back of the adult's mouth.

When the adult first returns from sea it is usually willing to feed the chick unasked but the chick helps matters along by nibbling gently near the base of the parent's mandibles, a way of begging very different from the frenzied lunging of the hungry young booby. If the adult is ready to regurgitate, the nibbling of the chick is highly stimulating and it lowers its head and foreparts, without actually

*Figure 29* Albatross feeding chick

squatting, and opens its bill. The chick usually inserts its beak from the side, the adult depressing the lower mandible extensively and also lowering the tongue to reveal the pink, slightly swollen tissue surrounding the top of the food pipe. In the case I saw most clearly the chick placed its bill so that the upper mandible was above the adult's swollen epiglottis and stroked the swollen tissue by moving its lower mandible up and down. In effect the chick was continuing the nibbling movements which had been directed to the adult's bill but now laying its beak sideways against the inside of the parent's throat. It had gained entry and was working the adult up to the point of regurgitation. A thin stream of stomach contents squirted from the aperture, passing into the chick's mouth from the side of its parent's beak. Much to the disappointment of the attendant mocking birds there was very little spilt. During this process I could clearly see how closely the side of the chick's lower mandible was applied to the sponge-like tissue of the adult. Sometimes chicks take liquid from the trough of the adult's lower mandible. At intervals the adult closed its bill and swallowed convulsively, clunking its great mandibles together. A chick may wheedle as many as twelve feeds in quick succession though the last ones involve much effort by the parent, which makes a deep snuffling, almost a grunting, and pumps violently as it forces the food up from deep down. Its supply exhausted, the adult moves away and rests, champing noisily and head shaking so vigorously that the mandibles rattle like false teeth in a tumbler.

The chick swells visibly as the oil hoses into its stomach. In one bout of feeding, lasting a few minutes only, an albatross chick can take about 2,000 gm of oil; over four pounds of concentrated food at a sitting. For the first four months of its life the chick is hardly more than a great, oil-filled skin, covered in matted brown down. It is grotesque, with the fascination of the truly ugly. After hitting the oil hard, its bulging stomach protrudes in a majestic curve and it waddles slowly and heavily, with its tarsi flat against the ground; it is far too heavy and unbalanced to stand on its feet. Its head and neck feathers become oily and stick together in spikes, revealing large patches of corpse-like bluish skin and the rather ugly external opening of the ear. But its eyes redeem it; full, liquid, dark brown eyes into which one can easily project an air of patient suffering of

M

this obese, obtruding belly and these prolonged indignities. Oil dribbles from its bill and it constantly gapes and swallows as though exhausted by its gargantuan feast. Even the mocking birds that run round scraping up the spillings were heavily oil-stained. We called them the mechanics and could always recognise the oily mockers from the albatross area when they came scavenging around our camp.

In bare facts and figures, albatross chicks weigh about 200 gm at birth and rise pretty steadily to a maximum 5,300 gm at five months, 2,000 gm more than the parent. They fledge at a weight much less than their maximum; feather-growing makes considerable metabolic demands and it is also possible that the youngsters are fed less frequently towards the end of their wearingly long period of dependence on their parents. Between feeds they just sit in the shade, but nevertheless lose weight very rapidly. In the twenty-four hours after a feed a young albatross may lose as much as 1,100 gm, though the longer it goes without food the more slowly it loses weight. The chick may be fed on several successive days (seven was our highest figure) but it may, on the other hand, go just as long unfed. On average it gets a feed about once every two or three days. This regime gives the parents the opportunity, on occasions, to remain at sea for between one and two weeks or alternatively, if food is available near at hand, to return daily. There was nothing to suggest that the parents encountered the bad patches common to the frigates and some of the boobies. No albatross chicks starved whilst we were there. The period between hatching and flying is certainly at least twenty-four to thirty weeks. The juveniles probably practise flying over short stretches of the island some time before they go to sea; other species certainly practise flight. If they do, it is very likely that their weight on leaving the island will be no more than average adult weight and probably less, since heavy fat deposits would certainly hinder flight. Since in other albatrosses for which information is available, the juveniles do not return to be fed by their parents, it is safe to assume that the same applies to the waved albatross. This unaided transition to independence probably means that a large proportion will fall by the wayside, as we know happens in some comparable cases – an interpretation strengthened by the fact that, apparently rather few chicks die between hatching and fledging and the adult death rate is also very low. The axe must fall somewhere and the most vulnerable stage would seem to be that immediately after fledging, when the young albatross, magically transformed from the ugly duckling, launches out into the Pacific.

One of my field notebooks is heavily stained with yellow oil, its dirty, smelly pages are limp and the pencilled figures look impressively ancient. It holds the albatross weight records for those unfortunate young which regularly suffered our intrusion, and the oil signifies their detestation of this interference. I don't know who disliked the job most. As soon as we appeared they rose from their dusty scrapes among the boulders, in which they had been squatting impassively, and stumbled and lurched off to the bushes, falling over their stomach and feet. The unfed ones were light and could even sprint; the others were easy prey. When we put out a hand towards them they adopted the submissive beak-hiding posture which they show to an attacking adult. The idea was to snatch their bill and keep it firmly closed, not only because we wanted their true weight but because their oil stank like rotten turnips. Poor birds, but at least they were not harmed; it is a miserable attitude that regards higher animals simply as so many specimens for collecting or for scientific investigation, regardless of the suffering caused them – an arrogance which is all too easily assumed.

It was difficult to understand why the Hood albatrosses nested where they did. They generally avoided the cliff edge even though it was easy to land and take off there, because the young were so clumsy that they often fell and would have toppled over the cliff at the slightest excuse (I saw one do it). Their total lack of elementary caution was astounding; they also seemed unable to distinguish between spatially dangerous and spatially practicable manœuvres. Ignoring their girth they hurried themselves down inclines with the dignity of a runaway barrel or jammed their portly bulk between boulders with equal disregard for consequences. I was in no doubt whatsoever that waved albatrosses were basically adapted for flat ground nesting and it was of great interest to find that the young when in the nest scrape or in a nesting place, even showed the backward kicking movements by which the black-footed albatross chick, for example, prevents itself from being buried alive in blown sand. Nowadays the waved albatross no longer needs such behaviour but it has apparently survived as a relic from its ancestry and no doubt is still slightly functional in preparing a more comfortable scrape than would otherwise be possible.

But why did the waved albatross nest many hundreds of yards from the cliff edge, among dense spiny shrub that meant picking a tortuous, obstacle-strewn route to their nest, when there were lovely open spaces, fringed with the necessary scrub for shelter and yet empty of albatrosses? I never knew. Indeed, the factors responsible for the precise choice of habitat in birds are far less understood than might be expected.

I would also like to know why the albatross population stays so small. There was plenty more space and with their feeding range and small numbers, surely plenty of food. There are not even other species of albatross in the general area to act as possible competitors. There were no natural predators, although man has done some killing. There seems no reason why they should not be far more numerous. Although the problems of sea-bird populations and the factors limiting them are varied, difficult and of great interest, a long digression here would be inappropriate. It may be said that apparently not every species is inherently capable of substantially

*Figure 30* Albatrosses 'sway walk'

increasing its numbers. Some do so because a hitherto restrictive feature is suddenly removed – but it seems possible that others may have reached a point of balance with unknown factors responsible for limiting their numbers and now simply maintain the status quo. Sometimes it even seems that internal factors are limiting, for there are species, such as perhaps, the Galapagos hawk, in which discrete island populations remain far below the level at which external factors such as food or nest sites or predators, could maintain them. We then ask, but why this or that particular state of balance – why not 30,000 waved albatrosses instead of 3,000? The answer may lie partly in the price the waved albatross must pay for its specialisation. Its reproductive rate is so slow that even without limiting factors such as food or enemies, it can only replace losses caused by accidental death. If it is to feed as it does, perfect its complex dance as it does and do all the other things it does, presumably it must also and inevitably reproduce as it does – that is, late in life, less than once a year and one chick at a time; in other words slowly. This still leaves the question of how and why it arrived at its present population of three to six thousand.

Sea-lions are eared-seals. They belong to the family *Otaridae* of the sub-order Pinnepedia, which includes the walruses and in turn belongs with the Fissipedia (cats, dogs, bears, otters, stoats, etc.) in the great order of the Carnivores. The Californian sea-lion, *Zelophus californianus*, has three distinct forms of which the Galapagos sea-lion is one; another occurs in the Sea of Japan and the third on the west coast of North America. They are thus tropical to temperate in range, or because of the anomalous Galapagos climate, perhaps sub-tropical to temperate. Galapagos sea-lions are quite distinct from South American sea-lions, *Otaria byronia* which occur in much colder waters from Peru southwards. The highly intelligent circus sea-lions belong to the Californian species. This chapter refers solely to the Galapagos form.

. . . a pup rushed from behind its parent and dived into
the water. Almost in the same second a monstrous
tiger shark rose, swung swiftly around, seized the
young sea-lion and sank. . . . Eighteen or twenty feet
was a conservative estimate of its length, and indeed
these sharks have been killed over thirty feet long.
This was a vivid explanation of the reason for the pup
seals keeping close to the lava ledges.
William Beebe, *Galapagos: World's End*

The Galapagos islands are wonderful breeding grounds for sea-lions. Fish swarm in the seas around and the islands offer miles of rocky shore and fine beaches. Sea-lions will breed among jumbled boulders, on the rocky platforms at the base of sea-worn cliffs or on any kind of sandy beach. We first met them on Plazas, one of the small islands just north of Santa Cruz. The bulls filled the air with bellowing as they patrolled the coast where the females and pups lay. In the evening, several females played around and under the boat with

*Figure 31* The sea-lion beach and our camp, Punta Suarez, Hood Island

marvellous grace in the clear green depths; with a lazy sweep of a fore-flipper they turn, accelerate or decelerate. They sensitively control each sinuous twist of their supple bodies, banking, turning, rolling or shooting straight down with a decisive burst of power. They love play and often seek out the biggest rollers to sport amongst. As the breaker rears before dissolving into a welter of foam, the sea-lions are swept up in a wall of water and hang embedded, cavorting gaily before crashing down with the broken wave. They often played around as we swam, shooting round and under us and leaping clear of the water. Small ones were fine, but the bulls are another matter. Even on land, we fled the first time a huge bull launched itself into a ponderous but ground-devouring charge, urging itself on with lolloping, head-rolling bounds. We soon realised that they would sheer away at the last moment, but when half a ton of bone and muscle bears down with a fearsome grunting, the instinct for self-preservation suddenly takes charge. Even uphill, a bull sea-lion can gallop at ungainly speed and downhill, for a few yards, you have to be pretty nippy to keep ahead. In the water, of course, he moves like a torpedo.

On Hood Island the beach in front of our tent was sea-lion territory with a bull in constant attendance. It was nerve-racking to fetch a bucketful of sea water in the dark for that rock dimly discernible at the water's edge might suddenly rise and charge. It wasn't much better even in daylight. I can still see June standing naked in the shallows, rinsing clothes and saying 'shoo shoo' ever more apprehensively as the bull urges its bulk balefully through the water, then backing hurriedly and retreating pell-mell as it gathers for the final rush. In fact, we never met one that pressed home its attack if you so much as flipped a handful of sand or water in its face; they always made off with an eye-rolling backward look and much roaring. Nobody need pay much respect to a bull sea-lion whatever adventurers say.

Sea-lions were not numerous near our camp on Tower. Sometimes a party of three or four, a bull, a female and perhaps a couple of partly-grown youngsters, came into the creek at high tide and hauled themselves out on the soft sand, to fall fast asleep and snore the tide away, leaving themselves high and dry. We once stole up to such a bull, and gently lifting its enormous flipper, examined the five claws set in their little pockets of skin, without rousing the animal. Its fat, scarred sides heaved and its whiskers twitched as it slept luxuriously on the warm, dry sand; a warrior at rest. But there was an agonising price to pay; the stranded sea-lions had to drag themselves laboriously over the bed of the creek, nearly half a mile to the sea. They made heavy weather of it, shuffling along with their fore-flippers and hunching their back ones forward; shuffle, hunch, shuffle, hunch and then flop as they fell flat, exhausted for a moment, whiskery faces dolefully pressed against the stony ground. They rested like this every few yards, grunting and puffing. Perhaps the sea seemed a long way off, but they knew exactly where it was even if they couldn't see it, and when we approached they made a bee-line for it, scaling awkward jumbles of large boulders and small rock faces with great determination.

On Hood, we were intruders from the start. Our camp on Punta Suarez was pitched just where scores of sea-lions were accustomed to sleep. We didn't have much choice, for the only other suitable beach was equally popular with them. Every rock was polished by the sliding passage of countless heavy bodies and the place stank of sea-lions; excreta lay in whitening piles or revoltingly fresh. Like those of all carnivores, sea-lion faeces contain the noxious skatole and indole which are responsible for the repellent odour, quite unlike the (to me) innocuous one of herbivore excreta. We shovelled the muck away and pitched the tent, now bleached and whitened by the excreta from the red-footed boobies of Tower, though alas, there were none in the colder waters around Hood. The camping place was ideal after we had gathered up the tin cans (left by hash-eaters anonymous) decorating the topmost spikes of the shrubs. The reassuring old *Beagle* rolled gently at anchor and the long boat buzzed back and forth, the one-and-a-half horse Seagull engine complaining harshly. Several hands from the station made short work of unloading and the camp was so quickly organised that Miguel Castro and I had time for a quick trip to the bird colonies on Punta Suarez before dark. A thin July drizzle wetted and darkened the red boulders and there was not much activity among the albatrosses, though there were several groups sitting quietly among the shrub. The white booby colony was practically deserted, the stones sprinkled with the sun-dried corpses of the many starved juveniles. Blue-foots, fortunately, were more active and in evidence and heartened us no end.

Early next morning, the *Beagle* slipped away with a farewell toot on her lung-powered horn and left us to the sea-lions. The procedure was always the same. After a day of constant noise from the tireless bull patrolling his stretch of beach, darkness fell and a short period of silence followed. Then the procession began. Just beyond the feeble range of our paraffin light, we would hear snuffles and snorts and dull thuds like somebody dragging a sack of potatoes. If we were lucky, it would be a female or a partly-grown youngster; not too bad. Inevitably, sooner or later, came a short bellow and a much more impressive crashing and slithering. This was a bull who had slipped past the beach master in the darkness and gained the sanctuary of the bushes and sandy clearings near our camp. Camp? It wasn't there last time he came ashore and he behaved exactly as though it wasn't there this time either. One evening we were petrified by an enormous crash and the whole tent twanged and quivered as a large bull, roaring testily, snapped our guys like strings, to rid himself of their annoying entanglement. Even when the tide was such that sea-lions were feeding in the first few hours of darkness (which they often did), they came slithering up into the bushes in the small hours, ready for a few hours' noisy sleep a few inches from our heads. Or a baby started yelling for its mum like a lost lamb and a cow-pup duet ensued. The bulls took hours to settle down and usually gave a few bellows first. This invariably brought the master charging up the beach, roaring in reply, upon which the intruder kept quiet till things had settled down and then roared again. Sometimes chases and fights, with the most frightful snarling and roaring, went on just outside the tent. The effect in the blackness of the night may easily be imagined. We lay rigidly in our sleeping bags, waiting for the tent to collapse with a rib-cracking bull sea-lion or two on top of us. Sometimes, in desperation, I crawled out with a torch and anything that came to hand – once the detachable alloy table legs which ever after were crazily twisted. The torch blinded them and a few whacks on the backside bewildered and sent them crashing off through the bushes. Then there was peace for a while until a newcomer arrived knowing nothing of humans who dazzled and belaboured sea-lions. But morning always found a few sea-lions sound asleep near the tent. More in hope than expectation we tried to keep them out with a barricade of boxes and cans, but their circus instincts led them triumphantly over all obstacles.

The harem in our rock garden numbered about thirty cows, and there were two more similar groups just along the beach, all within about three hundred yards. Each had its beach master who patrolled back and forth just offshore, calling monotonously and progressing in a series of smooth, slow dives typical of patrolling bulls – head out, roar, blubbing noise as the head goes down, rear flippers appear elegantly apposed and slide smoothly under, head reappears, roar and submerge again. They patrol sometimes for hours and then rest, perhaps on their backs in the shallows, great fore-flippers folded neatly on their chest, or maybe flat on the sand, like a great mound of rubber. Sometimes they slept in this position under water, blowing streams of bubbles and occasionally lifting their heads to breathe. Elephant seals do exactly the same, and the act of rising to breathe seems fully automatic.

Bulls, besides being much bigger than cows, are enormously thicker in the neck and shoulders and have very steep, high fore-heads which give them an unmistakable profile. Individuals vary in this character and in colour and often can be recognised even by a human observer. As in many other gregarious mammals such as red deer, elephants, kangeroos, zebras and our own seals, the 'owner-ship' of females is decided and maintained by fighting and the females have very little say in the matter; presumably one bull is as good as another to an oestrous female. We were curious to know how long one master could keep his harem against the challenge of intruder bulls and kept records of all the encounters we saw. The results revealed a complicated series of coups, counter-coups and dictatorships of variable duration. First, it was obvious that there was a considerable surplus of challenger bulls. It could hardly have been otherwise if, as happens in most seals, equal numbers of male and female are born and neither sex is much more likely to die before breeding age. Later, as in fur seals, there is a considerably higher mortality among males than females. We often saw three or four massive bulls lying out just a few yards beyond the limits of a bull's territory, and in one or two cases, we recognised unsuccessful challengers amongst them. The discrepancy is less than appears at first sight, since several bulls eventually serve one harem. Bulls look much fiercer when hauled out and dry; the fur fluffs up and gives them a strong facial resemblance to a wolf or husky. When wet and shiny, they look rather like old men with the formidably domed forehead of the intellectual, like, I always thought, the late J. B. S. Haldane.

It was quite common to see at least four scrimmages involving five different bulls in one day, all, of course, in the one territory. There was another complicating feature; territorial bulls used to slip away for half a day or more, presumably to hunt. In their absence, a conflict involving two or three bulls might be settled only to be thrown open again by the return of the old master. It is often assumed that during their period of sexual activity territorial bulls live solely on the fat deposits laid down in their enormously thick necks, as Darling (1947) thought to be the case in Atlantic seals. In some instances, as in the fur seals of the Pribilofs, it is certain that during their fifty days ashore, the bulls do not feed at all. This is apparently not the case with sea-lions unless my bulls went to sea for some reason other than to feed, which seems unlikely.

The bull in charge when we arrived on Hood probably lasted about a month – certainly not more. He was replaced in late August by a bull which received a forehead wound on 9 September and disappeared on 13 September, on which date two new bulls scrimmaged before one took over the territory. It wasn't a real fight; after a galloping chase along the beach, the pursuer caught its rival, gave it one bite on the neck and then galloped straight on in pursuit of a cow that was taking its calf out to sea. He seemed more intent on cutting it off than chasing the other bull. He didn't last long in any case; later the same day, a bull with a long neck wound drove him away. This neck-wounded bull was a prominent character in ensuing events. He lasted until about 30 September during which time he occasionally left his territory, returned and drove away whoever had taken over in his absence. He seemed to have one long absence between 22 and 24 September. There was a great fight full of blood-curdling sound and fury during the night of 21 September, and on the morning of the 22nd, a bull was lying up in the bushes with a nasty wound – a deeply lacerated patch several inches square – on the lower back. There was nobody patrolling the territory and the wounded bull eventually went to roll in the shallows. About mid-day, a large bull approached very purposefully from the open sea and made straight for him. The wounded one fled abjectly and was pursued out to sea. This new bull remained in control till the 24th driving away two or three youngish ones in the meantime and we thought he was the new 'master'. At mid-day on the 24th, a bull approached from the left of the breeding beach. He swam steadily in and then stood up and gazed at the big bull who was rolling on his back in the shallows. The latter soon looked up, saw the newcomer and immediately moved menacingly towards him. Nothing daunted, the incomer moved forwards equally threateningly. At last, I thought, I shall see a battle royal, but after one lusty clash, with snarling and biting, the newcomer was victorious and chased the other out to sea. When he gave up the chase and returned, he showed the long neck wound of our friend who had disappeared on the 21st. We assumed that he had been away longer than usual and then returned, fortified, and polished off his new rival. The next day a bull with no scar was in possession. The day after that, old neck wound was back. On the 26th, an unmarked bull was patrolling and was driven away by a large, light-coloured one with the remains of a circular neck wound, who in turn was beaten after a short struggle by our friend with the long neck wound. By now he seemed rather spent, with the skin looser on his neck, but still apparently able to drive off bigger and fresher bulls. However, he didn't last much longer, and we last saw him on 30 September.

Territorial clashes between males, though usually bloodless, are exciting affairs, partly because sea-lions seem so human in many ways. They haven't much in the way of elaborate threat postures, but show every subtle gradation of aggressive behaviour and are able to react appropriately without the need for the highly ritualised and distinctive postures shown by many birds. Indeed, there is a case for thinking that in general, the more intelligent animals have less ritualised behaviour than the duller ones. Intruders are well aware of the risks they run and approach stealthily, low in the water and swimming gently, perhaps with long stretches underwater. They recognise the meaning of everything the master does. If he sits on his haunches, with his whiskered snout pointing vertically up in the air and wavering rather uncertainly, whilst he utters muted, half-finished calls, they know he is very sleepy and unlikely to notice them. Watched closely through field glasses, he blinks owlishly, seems about to fall asleep where he sits and gives a heartwarming impression (quite false) of an old gentleman who is really not so fierce after all, but rather lovable. On the other hand, if he is poised alertly on his flippers, head well back and up, or lying on the beach with his head supported by a convenient rock and gazing around at intervals, intruders know he is watchful and often slide back out to sea as stealthily as they came, probably to haul out on a stretch of no-man's beach. If he is patrolling actively, they are lucky to get close inshore at all before they are spotted and chased. The chase is an interesting sight, combining great power with marvellous athleticism. Accustomed to our own laborious progress through water, it seems almost impossible that such heavy and bulky creatures as sea-lions can accelerate so smoothly and vividly. Usually they did not set off in pursuit at full speed, but swam behind for some distance keeping pace with the intruder. Then, as though galvanised into activity, they both surged forward, throwing up enormous waves. The intruder reacted so quickly that the two appeared to accelerate simultaneously. When swimming at full speed, sea-lions brought their enormous fore-flippers into full play and submerged their heads so that only the smooth curve of the humped back showed above water. A sinuous motion of the hind quarters and movements of the hind flippers in the vertical plane added further power and the hurtling bulls shoved walls of water aside as though it were no more substantial than air. Often they chased in a series of dives, jumping clean out of the water in graceful arcs, leap for leap, as porpoises and occasionally even our own seals will do. The heavy bodies plunged into the sea, sending up a cascade, and if the intruder was overhauled there was a turmoil for a few seconds as they leapt out of the water in contorted postures and bit savagely at each other. Then one broke away and the chase went on. A bite wound on the rump was a badge of ignominy, showing that the bearer had been overtaken and helped on his way with a good nip.

Bull sea-lions spend enormous energy in constantly chasing away intruders besides routine patrolling and inspection of everybody leaving or entering the group. If an intruder bull that slipped ashore during the night or whilst the beach master snoozed, was seen trying to regain the sea, a special sort of contest followed in which the beach master used the curve of the bay to cut off his rival. The intruder ambled towards the sea at a tangent to the master's line of patrol. The master, at great advantage in the water, swam slowly along parallel to the shore until the intruder gained the shallows. Then he turned and moved at an angle to the shore-line, heading slightly out to sea and parallel with the intruder, who all the time, was trying to get into deeper water but fearing to move directly towards the master. In effect, the master kept him penned in the shallows, knowing that ultimately he would have to make a dash for it. When he did, the master judged the angle so beautifully that he just intercepted the fleeing bull and got in a nip. Then the two went leaping and plunging out to sea for a few hundred yards before the master returned at a leisurely pace, and resumed his watchful patrolling and calling. Meanwhile, the females remained, supremely disinterested, yawning and scratching and snoozing as though this rivalry had no connection with them. In effect, of course, it hadn't; one bull is as good as another so far as they are concerned. The old tyrant remembered if any other bull that got ashore during the night showed itself or bellowed. He did not hunt it out but watched for its departure, biding his time till it came down to the beach and ran the gauntlet.

Bulls inspected females and youngsters entering and leaving the group, rushing up and thrusting a whiskery face at them to get a good sniff, for scent is their main identification cue. As they nuzzled, their heads moved excitedly and rather jerkily in a slight head-shaking manner, conveying a clear impression of uncertainty and some hostility. This, and the laying back of the head, with a pronounced side to side sway, were about all they essayed as behaviour apart from the easily interpreted overt hostilities and sexual behaviour patterns. They sometimes chased and bit partly grown youngsters, presumably if they did not belong to the group; quite often they went right up the beach to sniff at the sea-lions hauled out there. Occasionally they played with them just offshore, not too weighed down with their responsibilities to enjoy a gambol.

The beach master's social interaction with members of his group was a noticeable feature of its organisation and marks an important difference between the role of the sea-lion beach master and that of say the elephant seal or fur seal. The latter take no interest in the young, though they quickly resent any attempt by females to leave the harem. The sea-lion's duties are not confined to mere fertilisation of females and his discrimination between his 'own' group and young from another may be a valuable means of preventing his charges from becoming too numerous. Thus, one of the first things a new beach master does is become acquainted with the members of his group and they often reciprocate his interest. At least one valuable function of his guardianship is to prevent small youngsters from straying into shark-infested waters, and for this there must obviously be an optimal group size.

The group was constantly changing, some coming ashore to sleep and others setting off to fish. The wet ones lolloped up to the ranks of nicely dry and sandy sea-lions snoring peacefully in the sun and fell on top of them, dragging wet bodies and flippers over their warm dry fur and causing much bickering, snarling and occasionally irritable snapping. The wet youngsters seemed to nuzzle and paw the others deliberately as though to get a reaction, rather than merely in an effort to find a nice spot amongst them. It is hard to imagine anything more contented than a line of corpulent sea-lions, fast asleep in the sun on a clean sandy beach. They breathe heavily, sigh with exquisite pleasure and occasionally scratch themselves delicately with the long nails of their flexible fore-flippers or rub the flies off their faces. The sand forms rims around their eyes and adds a comical element of surprise to their soulful gaze. Sometimes we crept up to one and scratched it gently; eyes closed, it lazily lifted a flipper for us to scratch in the angle, but one blink and with a sharp startled 'woof' it scrambled madly down the beach, generating a wave of alarm.

Despite the constant territorial activity of the bulls, I saw actual mating only twice. The first time, on 18 August, it occurred around dusk in two or three feet of water. The female was under water most of the time and kept rearing her head to breathe and bite the male. The huge weight of the bull seemed to pin her down and the supple curve of his hindquarters held her firmly; he didn't grip her with his mouth. When released, she fled over the rocks, dragging her hind quarters firmly along the ground. The bull chased her, even following her into the camp area. Eventually she lay down, but shifted and squirmed restlessly and the bull retired to the sea. We saw another mating on 28 August around mid-day and this time we also saw the preliminaries. A female was ambling along the beach in the ordinary way when the bull showed interest and came ashore, giving me the impression that his initial reaction had been olfactory; oestrous females of other seal species are known to stimulate males by scent rather than by performing pre-copulatory or 'soliciting' behaviour. The female fled and the bull followed without really trying to catch her. When she stopped at the edge of a jumble of boulders he didn't approach her. This seemed to stimulate her; perhaps her flight had been sexual play, for she now gambolled up to him. A long period of play followed, in which the male nuzzled her, particularly at the base of the fore-flippers which made her jump as though tickled. He often flopped his enormous bulk on top of her and she reared her head and firmly seized the skin on throat or chest. The male seemed thoroughly good-tempered throughout, frequently sounding a subdued version of his aggressive patrol call. Eventually he managed to wrap his hind quarters round the female and complete the mating. He left her immediately after coition to chase a young bull that had meanly entered his temporarily unguarded territory. It seemed that the pressure of challenger bulls was so great that even momentary inattention to the territory, when the master was engaged in higher matters, encouraged trespass.

One wonders for how many successive seasons bull sea-lions maintain their reproductive activity. Californian sea-lions are not among the most intensively studied seals, but there is a lot of information on other species. Bull Atlantic or grey seals live ten to

GANNET
18 A fierce territorial fight. No boobies fight to any comparable extent

19 The gannet's ecstatic meeting ceremony

WHITE BOOBY
20 Sibling murder (reduction of brood-size from two to one) on Tower Island

21 Members of a pair approach prior to their hostile-looking meeting ceremony—vigorous mutual jabbing

22 Mates peer at each other in a fixed, long-necked posture. This behaviour often precedes movement towards each other and bill-touching or mutual jabbing. It also precedes the sexual display (advertising) in the male

23 Two postures associated with movement. The bird on the right is in the bill-up-face-away position which precedes movement away from the partner. That on the left is bill-tucking (pelican posture), which accompanies walking around the territory

WHITE BOOBY

24 Symbolic nest-building. Notice the large numbers of twigs brought by the partners

25 A red-foot chick, tumbled from its nest in the bushes, finds itself attacked by a white booby chick (right) into whose territory it fell

ALBATROSS

26 The commonest part of the 'dance of the albatross' is a bill-circling movement

27 A ritualised threat posture used in the dance. This wide gaping is also used against rivals in aggressive encounters

28 'Bill-clappering' from the bird on the left and flank-touching by the partner

29 'Sky-point' (with accompanying moo-call) from bird on left

30 Bird on left 'sway-walks' whilst partner walks normally

31 At the end of a bout of dancing one or both birds 'forward bob' as the partner on the right does here

32 Among the worn red boulders and dry scrub of Hood Island nests the world's entire population of waved albatrosses

33 Marine iguanas on Tower. The island is occupied by a particularly small, black iguana

SEA-LION

34 Waiting for the crunch

35 Bull inspecting cow by scent

36 Young bull after a rest on the dry sand. Notice the wet fur beneath the eye: copious secretions flow over the eye and emerge here

BLUE-FOOTED BOOBY

37 The usual clutch is two, laid about five days apart. One chick is therefore much larger than the other

38 Male blue-foot's advertising display—accompanied by a plaintive whistle

39 The male goes into his bill-up-face-away posture while the female bill-tucks and 'parades' (notice the raised left foot).

fifteen years and fur seals about the same, though marked females
have been known to live twenty-six years. Male elephant seals may
live fifteen years before obtaining a harem, though six to eight is
probably about the average age for attaining the enviable status of
beach master. Similarly, in the grey seal puberty may be attained at
five years but full sexual activity not until six to seven years. Sea-
lions probably show a steep drop in survival rate once they reach
sexual maturity, and if they are at all comparable to elephant seals
in this respect, over eighty-five per cent of 'old' males (in the case
of the elephant seals, eight years or more) die in any year. So, once
big enough to survive shark attack, the sea-lion has a carefree life
for several years, with plenty of food, pleasant sunshine and soft,
secluded beaches to laze away the day. But it seems that bulls
rarely survive more than a few – in most cases a very few – years of
breeding activity.

The main pupping period on Hood was between August and
October, when about twenty pups were born in the two nearest
colonies. Baby sea-lions are extremely attractive, rather like black
labrador puppies and about as long. Their heads are a bit too big for
their bodies at first and their skin full of folds. The female gives
birth either on sand or among rocks and leaves the placenta where it
drops, for the lizards to feast on. I suspect that the Galapagos hawk
will also take them, but there is nothing to take full advantage of this
food supply and most placentas simply rot away. Soon after birth the
mother moves the pup away from the area, which is usually slightly
apart from the main resting place of the harem and the playground
of the pups. The mother grips the cub in her mouth by the scruff of
the neck and may swim a considerable distance with it. The first
time we saw this we felt sure the pup would drown, for she apparently made absolutely no attempt to keep it above the surface. At
intervals it managed to poke its head out and bleat piteously before
going under again – an altogether hair-raising baptism. However,
when she brought it ashore it seemed none the worse, though it
stumbled and sneezed for a long time. It is delightful to watch a
bunch of youngsters playing in the sunlit shadows. They chase each
other under the water, climb onto boulders and knock each other off
whilst the old bull cruises restlessly up and down, roaring and
keeping a wary eye on them and occasionally even herding them

back if they move too far out. Care of young is an important part of a male sea-lions duties, for when the females are away fishing, he alone stands between them and any danger from the open sea. Sharks doubtless find baby sea-lions highly acceptible. We once found a partly grown sea-lion, still alive, but with the whole of one fore-flipper and a great piece of the shoulder torn away, leaving a raw gaping hole; very probably the work of a shark.

The pups gambol ecstatically on the beach, falling flat on their faces, and giving themselves sandy goggles and noses. Often they sleep with one fore-flipper sticking vertically up in the air, which may be a way of losing body heat and so, to a slight extent, regulating their temperature. June made friends with one new pup and after a wary start, it began to rub against her, lift its head to have its throat tickled and seemed delightfully tame and affectionate. Unfortunately, its mother's fright reaction so alarmed the pup that it became distrustful again, this time for good. We were never fortunate enough to come across sea-lions as tame as Beebe's charming consorts; they occasionally swam up and risked a touch when we were in the water, but no more.

As in the case of fur seals, and no doubt all others too, female sea-lions find their young by a combination of sound and scent, though the problem is nothing like so formidable as that facing a fur seal coming ashore on the Pribilofs, where over a million

*Figure 32* Female sea-lion carrying pup

animals form close-packed rookeries. When the female sea-lion comes ashore she calls and the pup recognises her voice and answers it. It is very funny to hear the anxious bleating of the pup and the deeper calling of the mother gradually homing onto each other and to watch the ecstatic greeting when they meet, the mother nuzzling the pup and the pup stumbling and falling against its mother. Strange cubs, though they may approach a newly-arrived female, are bitten. Grey seals are said to show a certain amount of foster-parentage, but the usual rule, as in the sea-lions, seems to be each to her own. Sea-lions suckle their young until well advanced in the next pregnancy and it is common to see a great big youngster sucking noisily at his mother's teat for hours. Eventually she turns snappish and I suppose gradually slackens the maternal bonds, though there is nothing like the rapid fattening and sudden desertion of young shown by some other seals. By then the young sea-lion is well able to look after himself and has even a place in the companionable group. He may wander extensively during this period, now virtually secure from predators because of his size and strength. He can lie like a fat torpedo, side by side with others or perhaps pair up with a bull, swimming with him and hauling out by his side. I never gained any information about the nature of this rather charming association, which reminds one of the 'squire' to 'master' stag relationship in the red deer and perhaps in the elephant – nor do I know if it has previously been recorded for the sea-lion. In time he becomes more and more solitary; finds a favourite hauling out place to which, probably, he regularly returns until he becomes fully mature. Then he becomes one of the powerful young challengers for territory and a harem. No doubt he loses his first battles, but eventually he finds a spent old bull which has to give way. Then the once wobbly scrap of sea-lion becomes, in his turn, an old tyrant and beachmaster.

The end probably comes peacefully. Spent old bulls often die comfortably stretched out in one of their resting places, as shown by the huge skeletons we found. Maybe such remains are those of defeated and wounded bulls, but we saw hundreds of encounters and none were serious, certainly not enough to kill a bull. There is evidence that the southern sea-lions of the Peruvian Guano Islands used the island of South Chincha as a cemetery. At least two writers believed that decomposed sea-lions were numerous enough to be an important source of the guano there. It was said that thousands of seals (here sea-lions) could be seen climbing the slopes of South Chincha and tradition was that they did so when about to die (Peck). Apparently, the seal population then (the first half of the last century) was much higher than at present. Animal graveyards are subjects of unfailing fascination; old elephants making their last journey to some hidden valley where untold wealth of ivory lies among the bleached bones, or Galapagos donkeys picking their way to some lonely spot where several skeletons already lie. But there is no reason to disbelieve the seal account and I like to think that when an old bull sea-lion begins to fade he will seek the sanctuary of one of his quiet hauling out spots, and there enjoy his last sleep close to his element, the sea.

*Figure 33* Sea-lion

# Portrait of a Blue-foot                                    11

Nothing could be more comical than the manner
in which the male, with his tail cocked up like a wren's,
goose-steps and waddles about, raising his bright
blue feet as high as possible and thrusting forth his
chest.
Robert Cushman Murphy, *Oceanic Birds of South America*

The small island of Daphne Major is one of the most exciting spots
in the whole of the Galapagos Archipelago. Its precipitous flanks
are riddled with the holes of red-billed tropic birds and dotted with
nesting pairs of white boobies – straddling the attractively flattened
though narrow and indistinct route to the summit. They signify their
objections to trespassers in no uncertain fashion, shouting or
whistling vehemently, hair standing on end, and orange bills
flashing. There is a fine atmosphere of height and steepness about the
place, but the thrilling aspect appears at the top of the island, or
rather where the top was before a volcanic eruption blew it off. Now
the rim encircles a great crater, the 'broiling and insufferable ancient
crater' of Beck. There in the flat bottom of this immense amphi-
theatre, hundreds of pairs of blue-footed boobies form a dense
colony. The crater floor is entirely smooth; in fact, there is so little
disturbing its surface that every booby stands out in sharp contrast
to the white background. The whole scene resembles a model, in
which the flour-covered bottom of a bowl is thickly sprinkled with
currants. The crater is actually in two tiers, separated by a scarp
some fifty to a hundred feet deep and bounded by almost sheer walls
on which cling scattered shrubs holding a few pairs of magnificent
frigate-birds. When we first climbed up to the crater colony, the sun
was already fierce. By mid-day, the heat in the bottom of that
enormous pit was excessive. The boobies looked pathetically

175

*Figure 34* Male blue-footed booby 'salutes' on flying in to his nest site

uncomfortable, gaping and fluttering the gular skin to dissipate heat. The floor was too hot to bear and they kept lifting their garish blue feet or rocking back on their 'heels'. The crater was clearly a most uncomfortable nesting place in some ways, but obviously a great favourite; the colony was extremely dense for this species and there was hardly any unoccupied space. Beebe called the crater 'cool' and remarked on the convection-caused breeze; neither the boobies nor I found it so on this occasion. His delightful fancy took flight in imagining the feelings of a crater-born blue-foot on seeing the outer world; 'Here on this sunken crater floor, the young boobies during all the first months of their existence see only the dry lava and half-baked vegetation, and overhead the unbelievably blue sky. They probably have to remain a full three months or more before their wings are strong enough to carry them around and up, and if a booby has any imagination or ability to be surprised, with what emotion must he experience his first rise above the crater's rim, and see the ultramarine sea stretching away on all sides. Up to that time salt water has not existed for him, and the outside world has been represented only by passing clouds, the trips of his parents and the semi-digested fish which he has plucked from the capacious throats of his mother and father.'

Not a single pair of white boobies nested within the crater, but this species formed a separate colony around the rim. If for no other reason, they were debarred from the crater bottom by difficulty in taking off; they are ponderous compared with the agile blue-foot.

However, there is a marked tendency for boobies to form colonies predominantly or entirely of their own kind and two or more species are never randomly and equally mixed. This social tendency, encouraging a booby to nest alongside its congeners rather than equally near to another species, is probably of advantage to it, though the nature of the benefit remains to be shown. Probably it lies in the value of social stimulation, a topic which will raise its head later.

Murphy sympathises with the blue-foot as an inept species which, in some parts of its range, hangs itself when clumsily attempting to settle on bushes, or is buried alive in land-slides for nesting in dangerous areas and which allies to its misfortune a peculiarly clownish behaviour – a mixture of pomp and drollery. Some birds, like the puffin, have the knack of exciting amusement and sympathy and the blue-foot is certainly a comical bird as he goose-steps on parade, lifting high his brilliantly blue feet, or throws up his head, swivels his wings and whistles in a high piping tone to attract a female. Sympathy we had in plenty for the suffering boobies in the broiling crater.

There are times when the naturalist, or for that matter, anybody, perhaps stimulated by exceptional beauty or interest, sees, registers and interprets more in an hour than he often does in a week or a month. Almost all the things we later puzzled out on Hood Island made their impact, even though fleetingly, in that first morning's observation on Daphne. It was my first real meeting with a booby and my interest and excitement were abnormally high. Everything it did was tantalising; somehow familiar but different. It was like trying to pin down the identity of a face seen dimly yet obviously not a stranger. The blue-foots of Daphne's crater in December 1963 will serve admirably as a framework for most of the points to be made in this chapter.

Blue-foots have blue legs and feet of a quite ludicrous hue, ranging from pale turquoise to deep ultramarine; actually younger birds have lighter feet and males tend to show a slightly lighter blue than females. They are agile walkers and fliers and make great play of parading around their territory, showing off their bright webs. Their agility and flexibility finds expression in many ways, strikingly in demonstrative use of the elongated and pointed tail, now cocked so far that it leans over the back towards the head (males cock their tails further than females) and now sticking out at forty-five degrees. Wings, too, undergo the most extraordinary flexures in display. Head movements are rapid and expressive; far more so than in the larger, slower gannet or the white booby. More than any other booby, their mannerisms and bearing remind one of the sinuous and contortionist shag. Plumage is moderately drab, with back and wings a deep burnt brown relieved by a conspicuous pale patch at the base of the neck and another on the rump, and lightened, overall, by pure white underparts with a neat little dark patch on the thigh. The head and neck are striking and, in fact, diagnostic; the spiky look, like a variegated chrysanthemum, depends on the presence of two structurally different kinds of feathers, perhaps simply old and newer ones. The tips of the old ones are frayed and split, whilst the newer ones are entire and wedge-shaped. The bases of both are dark and the outer part paler. The neck feathers do not lie in a smooth sheet, as they commonly do in birds, but project separately, giving the spiky appearance of wet fur. The formidable, though rather slender, spear of a bill is darkish blue and the keen looking eye bright yellow. Murphy long ago described the intriguing difference between the sexes in the appearance of the eye. Females have a huge and irregular dark centre whilst males have a tiny pin hole and a much larger area of yellow. This is not, as might at first appear, a difference in pupil size, but a difference in the extent to which the dark coloured iris pigment overlays the yellow – extensively in the female and less so in the male. Differences of this kind are probably functional, although we may rarely be able to discover their adaptive value; this particular case, I suspect, is but one of a battery of sex differences connected with sex differences in hunting behaviour. Male and female blue-foots do not fish in identical ways, nor are they exactly alike in their choice of fishing localities. This interesting difference will be discussed later, but I must confess I can offer no good explanation of the way the eye difference works, and my hunch that eye difference and fishing-habit difference are connected may be entirely wrong. Mix this combination of gaudy feet, cocked tail, spiky head, penetrating eye, formidable bill and piping whistle, with sundry bizarre movements and you have a male blue-footed booby. Mix a third as much again by volume and weight with a raucous shout and you have the female.

In the chapter on the red-footed booby, I described in some detail the fact that breeding went on more or less all year. The same is true of the blue-foot, but in this species, possibly because of the stimulating effect of the greater interaction between neighbours, local groups are more closely synchronised than the colony as a whole. Social stimulation, as I seem to remark with great frequency, increases the degree of synchronisation in a breeding group; that is the eggs of different pairs are laid more or less simultaneously instead of spread over a long period. In the Daphne crater, there were virtually no 'local groups' because there were no barriers – only the sudden drop from the first crater to the second formed a natural separation. Hence we found that most of the birds in the upper crater had young of roughly comparable age – no free-flying young and very few eggs. The same was true of the lower crater, but the young were, on average, about three weeks older. We, therefore, got a slightly false impression of the normal situation, in which the breeding habitat is much more diverse than the billiard-table crater bottom. It looked rather as though the blue-foots really had some degree of synchronisation within the *entire* colony and it wasn't until we saw Hood, where the ground was broken, that it became clear that the synchronisation was merely within small groups and not within the colony as a whole. In November 1964, practically a year after our first visit, we returned to Daphne and gained striking confirmation of our hypothesis; the entire crater was filled with fully feathered young and nothing else. The impressive synchrony was rather more apparent than real, since fully-feathered young can range in age from sixteen to thirty weeks. However, we had just left Hood, where we knew that on Punta Suarez there were small groups in which most pairs had an egg, others with fluffy young, yet more with free-flying dependents and so on. There was clearly a marked difference between the two situations and it seemed likely that the factor synchronising the Daphne birds had been the greater social interaction in that unusually open environment, effectively turning the whole colony into a 'local group'.

In December 1963 the Daphne crater contained young which would become fully feathered by about February 1964. Yet in November 1964 there was another crop of fully feathered young. This clearly shows that the months in which the eggs were mainly laid were very different in 1963 and 1964. There is the same absence of a predictable season for egg-laying that we found in the red-foot. Further, if the adults responsible for the two batches of young were more or less the same, as they almost certainly were, the breeding cycle must be considerably less than twelve months. We later found that it is in fact between eight and nine months.

Another arresting feature immediately obvious from the crater colony was that many pairs had two lusty youngsters and a few even had three. We had not, at that point, any knowledge of the extraordinary vicissitudes of growth in the single red-foot chick, but we knew that one was the rule and it was well established that white boobies also had to jettison one of their two chicks early in its life. There was certainly food for thought in the blue-foot's ability to rear two or three, although several pathetic chick corpses lying in the crater suggested complications in the story.

By the time we settled down among the blue-foots of Punta Suarez, we had benefited both by preliminary soundings on Daphne and by comparative knowledge gleaned from the red-footed and white boobies of Tower. The environment of the two blue-foot colonies could hardly have differed more. Punta Suarez, a low peninsula of blackened lava, projects into the often rough complex of ocean currents, dominated by the cold Antarctic waters of the Humboldt. Despite its position within a degree of the Equator, the chilly waters at 65 °F, not much more hospitable than the North Sea in summer, make one gasp. The surf breaks thunderously on the northern shore, where a gigantic blow-hole channels the surging waves before shooting the pressured water in a mighty column of spray as much as a hundred feet into the air. The muffled explosion booms across to the opposite side of the island. A mist of salt spray sweeps across the hinterland of Punta Suarez, killing every blade of vegetation, encrusting the boulders with salt and leaving scores of salt pans in the hollows. Over most of its area, the peninsula is a waste of smooth, reddish boulders which, looked at from ground level and into the setting sun, convey an overwhelming impression of desolation and the feeling that man is an intruder here.

The boobies nest between the boulders and every site is marked by a patch of whitened stones used as vantage points. Altogether about five hundred pairs hide themselves amongst the litter of stones and the area is further divided by lines and patches of scrub. This gradually thickens towards the southern edge and a few boobies on that side nest amongst dense scrub where they are completely isolated from neighbours. This, incidentally, makes one ask exactly what the term colonial means and whether a species can be both colonial and non-colonial. I think one must include the notion of frequent behavioural interaction between the members of the group. Although a blackbird interacts with one, two or possibly three neighbours during delimitation of its territory, it cannot be considered colonial because it interacts relatively infrequently if one regards its breeding season as a whole. It is usually not in visual or auditory contact with its neighbours and is normally subject to stimulation by only one or two simultaneously. In an extremely colonial species like the gannet, members are constantly interacting with each other, constantly stimulated by somebody landing, taking off, fighting, displaying or mating, and constantly seeing and hearing tens, scores or even more of their neighbours. Where a species shows both colonial and spaced nesting in these terms, it must be put in the category to which it most typically belongs. So we must call the blue-foot colonial, even though the eminent Cushman Murphy declined to do so.

Returning to Punta Suarez in July 1964, under typically cheerless grey skies, we found the blue-foots in a gloriously mixed-up state. That suited us; we would get a bit of everything – courtship, egg-laying, growth of young and post-fledging behaviour. The first chore was to mark our birds and nests. We still lacked paint, so we improvised markers with strips of different materials, hence the obscure field note book references to 'Red pyjama', 'June's pants' and 'old sock'. As with other boobies, it was often possible to catch breeding birds by hand so we could colour-ring a few. We marked scores of nests, and many empty sites (in case they acquired tenants) and tramped up and down the entire peninsula counting nests; 282 were occupied, of which 230 had eggs or young. Then we selected our victims for regular weighings, prepared the clean new attendance sheets which would soon be tattered, smeared and covered in hieroglyphics, made our prejudices explicit (not as good as exorcising them, but better than nothing), and began the old routine all over again.

However, we were a bit premature; the colony soon began to wear that neglected look that comes towards the end of a breeding season. There were no pairs performing their aerial flighting over the colony, no 'beseeching whistles' betrayed the whereabouts of ardent little males courting the larger females and the chicks began to see less and less of their parents and their food. The pairs that had been in the early stages of breeding when we arrived mostly disappeared and one or two that did produce eggs soon deserted them. We immediately consulted our barometer of chick growth, and sure enough, there was a storm brewing. Fortunately, we collected enough information to give us a fairly accurate idea of its effects. This temporary drying-up of the food resources of the Punta Suarez blue-footed boobies hit the colony hard. Of forty-seven pairs which had healthy twins at the end of July, not one managed to keep both chicks alive. After the period of food shortage, only sixty-four out of 198 nests that previously contained eggs, or chicks less than six weeks old, still held any. The rest had died. In terms of individuals, rather than nests, the story was even more dramatic. If all the chicks alive before the shortage had survived it, and the eggs had hatched and survived, there would have been four hundred and sixteen chicks after the 'squeeze'. In fact, there were only ninety-two; seventy-eight per cent had died. In addition, most other pairs temporarily stopped attending their sites, obviously far too busy keeping themselves alive. All the chicks we weighed regularly lost weight or practically marked time for three or four weeks, growing far below the normal rate. It was a convincing demonstration of the effects of a suddenly impoverished food supply, reinforcing all the lessons we had learnt from the red-foots of Tower. A pair which lost their two-week-old chicks by starvation, laid again four weeks later when things began to look up. This was unusual, since red-foots and white boobies had never, in our experience, done so, nor does the gannet ever replace a lost chick, though it will replace an egg. We also caught several birds ringed previously and from these and the record of their status (with egg or chick) when ringed, estimated that they breed once every eight to nine months and not once a year, as does the white booby. Every case for which we could glean enough detail supported this. The lack of an annual cycle means that potentially the population could breed either as a whole or in part, in any month of the year, a reflection once again of the non-seasonal nature of the food and climate in the Galapagos. As we found for the red-foot, food seemed important in timing an outburst of breeding and was certainly influential in curtailing one.

There were several major differences between the red-foot and blue-foot with respect to food shortages, and the most obvious was that blue-foots as a species were not fully used to this sort of thing. They had not had to evolve a breeding regime solely or even mainly to cope with such emergencies, though when it came they had several lines of defence. First and foremost, though, they had not evolved a one-egg clutch; as mentioned earlier, most pairs had two and many laid three eggs. Nor had they evolved the habit of invariable brood reduction by sibling murder, as the white booby has; it is common for blue-footed boobies to raise two young and not infrequently they raise three. It was true enough that during the Punta Suarez famine, the younger chicks in broods of two were supplanted at feeding times by their elder brothers and thus, in effect, murdered, but this was a stress reaction, not a normal one as it is in the white booby. Our interest in the blue-foot's ability to rear more chicks per brood than could all other boobies except the Peruvian was, there-fore, still very much alive, despite the demonstration that it by no means always applied. On the face of it, there seemed but little dif-ference between the various booby species so far as their feeding habits went. All were plunge divers, bringing food back in their crop and stomach and delivering it by regurgitation directly into the chick's mouth. So far as we knew, all were principally fish eaters, though no doubt the composition of the catch varied with the species. But it dawned on us that blue-foots differed from their relatives in two important ways – the first, indeed, was known before our study, though not to me, and it had not been connected with brood size; the second had not been suspected.

First, we became deeply impressed by the blue-foot's amazing dives into shallow water. There were hardly any blue-foots on Tower, but occasionally one or two used to fish in Darwin Bay. One day I watched one flying along the shore line where a complex pattern of rocky ridges ran out into the sea, when suddenly it uptilted and went into a power dive, apparently straight into the rocks. After it had risen and resumed its hunting. I waded out and found that it had dived into a small enclosed arm, almost a rock pool, exactly two feet deep. This is by no means the first record of such a feat; Verrill records that he saw one dive from a height of fifty feet into less than two feet of water. Subsequently, these acrobatics were a commonplace sight and we often saw a blue-foot shoot down into shallows fanged by menacing reefs. Yet we hardly ever saw a red-foot or white booby diving except occasionally in the open sea off the north coast. Again, on Hood it was common to see blue-footed, but never white boobies, plunging into shallow offshore water in the little bays and indentations. The habit seemed so important as a trait of the species that I began to wonder if it went further and had anything to do with the accentuated sexual dimorphism in the blue-foot; was the male even more specialised than the female for shallow diving? The male blue-foot weighs only two-thirds as much as the female, whereas the red-foot male weighs about nine-tenths and the white booby male about eight-ninths as much as their respective females. The gannet even goes the other way and the male is slightly larger than the female. We also found that the blue-foot has the longest tail in relation to its overall length and that males out-tail females. Thus, although females are so much larger and heavier than males, the tails are the same length (237 mm) in both sexes. Relatively, therefore, males have much longer tails than females. Such an elongated tail should help the blue-foot to convert the vertical momentum of its plunge into a horizontal or upward direction by acting as a sensitive and powerful rudder. So by virtue of its extreme lightness and its elongated tail, the male blue-foot seems excellently adapted for diving into shallow water. Exactly what this difference meant in detailed terms of the blue-foot's breeding biology we had no clear idea and it was more by luck than planning that we found out. However, we did try to confirm by direct observation that the male does in fact feed closer inshore than the female and feeds inshore more often than she does, and although our figures were inconclusive, they went the right way.

It was perfectly straightforward to show that the blue-foot's inshore tactics had a marked effect on the duration of their hunting trips – they were substantially shorter than those of the red-footed or white booby. Indeed, one bird that we knew from continuous observation had been on duty all day, left its chick in the evening

*Figure 35* Blue-footed booby diving

and within half an hour was back with a full crop and able to feed its youngster. There was quite a shuttle service compared with the red-foot, with its frequently long absences even when the chick is tiny. The very young blue-foot did not face the threat of prolonged starvation, as the young red-foot often did, and we felt that this was an important factor in enabling the blue-foot to feed its two chicks as against the red-foot's one and also to rear them more quickly than the red-foot. In fact, this particular example fits nicely into a much wider pattern, in which birds feeding far away from their nest generally have much smaller clutches, usually only one egg, and slower growth of young, than birds feeding near to the nest. In comparing different families for this correlation, one immediately runs up against the possibility that differences other than the length of feeding trips may be responsible for different clutch sizes and growth, but in comparing the blue-foot and red-foot one looks at two very similar species. So the chances of a correct interpretation of the difference in feeding habits are much increased. In the final chapter of this book, the four booby species and the gannet are compared for differences in feeding rate, length of incubation stints and other related matters. The blue-foot and the red-foot are the two extremes; the former averages seventeen hours' incubation duty at a spell, compared with about sixty in the red-foot.

The next discovery dovetailing with the blue-foot's shallow-diving and sexual dimorphism was that a distinct division of labour existed between the sexes. Both parents, as normal in the family, feed their youngsters. We were so used to this that we never even suspected that the blue-foot regime might be different. But whereas all other male boobies continue their share of parental duties right to the end of the chick's dependence on them, the male blue-foot feeds his young in the first half or so of their growth and then gives up and leaves the rest to the female. Once we knew this, it was clear that the blue-foot's whole system of feeding was highly adaptive; first the species's overall specialisation in inshore fishing, then the sexual dimorphism allowing the male to specialise even more in this respect whilst the larger female can go further and carry more and finally the division of labour, the young helped through the difficult early stages by the quick trips of the male in particular and sustained in their later heavier demands by the larger female. As in all other boobies, the chicks continued to return to the nest for food long after they were capable of flight and this subsidy was vitally important in helping them over the difficult transition to full independence. We were doubly fortunate in recording the effects of food shortage and in discovering some of the factors controlling clutch size in the blue-foot.

Again, the complexity of the interactions between different aspects of a bird's life was striking. The aerial agility of the male blue-foot may have developed primarily in connection with inshore fishing – who knows? – but it has also strongly fashioned other parts of its behaviour, particularly the displays involved in territorial and pair formation behaviour. Because it is so light and agile, several patterns of behaviour closed to other boobies are open to it. The evolution in such fine balance, and simultaneously, of all the interacting systems of an organism, furnish the most impressive evidence of the power of natural selection for which one could possibly ask.

It seemed as though the sudden curtailment of activity in this particular group had finished our chances of seeing much courtship behaviour; the few adults sprinkled about the colony were dismally quiet. But things improved and the colony was soon alive again. A walk through it stimulated a chorus of female grunts and 'aarks' and male whistles, whilst spiky heads nodded furiously and bright blue feet goose-stepped. The great agility of the blue-foot finds expression in its displays as well as in its hunting behaviour. Even on flat ground, the male can spring neatly off the mark, and they frequently take off, fly round the colony and land back on their territory again. Each circuit and landing effectively proclaims their right to that spot and they emphasise this signal by throwing up their feet in an acrobatic vertical salute, so that the widely-spread blue soles flash out against the white belly. The result is a most striking display of site-ownership; females also salute, but less often and less dramatically. The gaudy blue feet are conspicuously displayed in another behaviour pattern, used during movement around the territory. Essentially, it is an exaggerated form of walking, in which the fully spread webs are raised high with extreme and ridiculous deliberation. 'Parading' birds waddle around with cocked tail and spread feet; and again, there can be no doubt that in pair interactions, this display makes good use of the most colourful structure the booby possesses and effectively conveys the message 'I am about to move'. Droll though the blue-foot's parading and saluting may be, he can do better. Murphy's artist depicts a courtship posture of the blue-foot so bizarre and apparently anatomically impossible that one could think he had imagined it, or at least combined two different displays in one

*Figure 36* Blue-foot parading on the spot (*right*) and assuming bill-up-face-away (*left*)

painting. A blue-foot, neck stretched, tail cocked and bill pointing skywards, has opened and swivelled his wings so that their backs are presented to the partner; his wings look broken, twisted out of all relationship to his body. The artist has, in fact, done a good drawing of a blue-foot in his sexual 'advertising' display and it is a pity that he could not reproduce the beseeching whistle that accompanies it. Although its main function is to attract a female, the latter is prepared to do a bit of advertising herself, either to a passing male or to her mate in the territory and her gruff voice undertones the male's piping. Blue-foots are great advertisers and a bird of the opposite sex flying over may be quite enough to set them off. You may often see a male suddenly throw up his head and whistle to such a female or turn with his comical goose-step and repeatedly and passionately advertise to a nearby female, who usually remains entirely aloof. The pair continue to advertise long after they have first established the pair bond; commonly, as one mate adopts this odd position the other goes into a mirror-image performance and the two stand opposite each other, displaying in turns. (fig. 37). The male often displays to his mate after he has moved to some other part of his territory and wants to attract her to him. She may be busy preening or fast asleep and the male may then decide he must go to the mountain if the mountain won't go to Mahomet.

*Figure 37* Blue-foots 'mutual sky-pointing'

Although the decision is invisible, you see the chain of events leading to actual take-off. First he briskly rattles his wings, giving them a brief but violent shake whilst still folded but slightly loosened, and with a curious upwards and sideways tilt of his head, turns away in goose-stepping fashion, walks or runs to a boulder, tucking his beak repeatedly as he moves, and then springs into the air and flies swiftly away. A glance at the chapters on red-footed and white boobies will show how closely related is their behaviour in a similar context. Maybe he goes right out to sea, but often he will do no more than a couple of circuits of the area before dashing in, calling quickly and landing with that impressive flourish of his unreal feet. Then, having gained the attention of the female, he may continue with his advertising display. Often he performs a rapid and vigorous up and down nodding after landing, rather like the white booby's 'yes-no head-shaking' but with the 'no' component missing. This is an aggressive display used mainly against rivals and intruders. The rivals, usually neighbours, stand a little apart nodding vigorously and occasionally striking out at each other with a mighty jab and a violent opening of the wings. Such contests may go on for hours, but rarely lead to anything more serious, though there is a chorus of outraged whistles and grunts and many a brave stab.

Real fighting is not part of the blue-foot's territorial behaviour. Occasionally the male will 'nod' at his mate and there is clearly the same kind of relationship as in gannet and red-foot pairs where the mate evokes some aggression as well as sexual interest. The blue-foots have a rather attractive bill-touching ceremony in which they delicately appose the tips of their dagger-like beaks. Sometimes they go through a brief bout of mutual jabbing, but it is not a common part of their behaviour together. Like all other boobies,* they have failed (or should one say not needed) to evolve a complex greeting ceremony, the territory being large enough to give the pair plenty of room for withdrawal. But it will be clear, even from the brief mention of postures in the preceding paragraphs, that the blue-foot has a variety of ritualised displays in his repertoire and indeed if one sees them in quick succession his performance is impressive. Imagine

* I later studied Abbott's booby and found that it has a long and complex greeting ceremony.

them at real life speed; fly swiftly in; fling up your feet and land neatly; run towards your mate, bill tucking repeatedly; nod at her; on approach, jab at her; touch her bill; throw up your head, swivel your wings and whistle; walk away with a goose-step, head tilted obliquely; rattle your wings and jump into the air; circle the area and return again. The meaning of these various displays is perhaps not so objectively decided, but probably runs something like this in terms of motivation and function – that is, what the bird 'feels' and what message it conveys:

*Salute:* What the booby feels (in terms of aggression, fear, sexual motivation, etc.) when it salutes is not easily interpreted. Functionally, however, the salute indicates site-ownership.

*Run towards your mate, bill-tucking:* The booby approaches because it is sexually attracted (also, perhaps, because attracted to the centre of the territory, which is where the female usually is) but bill-tucks because it is slightly afraid (bill-tucking is probably appeasement behaviour, reducing the chances of overt aggression between the mates).

*Nod:* It nods because it feels slightly aggressive, regarding the female as a territorial 'intruder'; nodding is aggressive territorial behaviour.

*Jab:* This occurs because decrease in distance brings mates close together and elicits close-range hostile behaviour. However, because jabbing is ritualised, it doesn't lead to more intense aggression, but may serve as a simple greeting ceremony.

*Touch bills:* This is a slightly more formalised pair interaction, with the balance swinging rather more towards sexual behaviour and away from aggression.

*Advertise:* The booby advertises because more strongly stimulated sexually, 'advertising' synchronises the sexual behaviour of the pair and probably strengthens the pair bond.

*Walk away with goose-step, etc:* This is slightly less obvious, but part of the complex of sexual behaviour in sulids involves frequent departures and returns by the male, between more overt sexual behaviour such as copulation. The behaviour patterns accompanying this departure (parade, bill-up face-away and wing-rattle) all have to do with communicating the intention of movement and in the case of the bill-up face-away, of turning away in an appeasing manner, since departing pair members are likely to elicit some aggression from the partner.

I do not mean by this interpretative list to make the blue-foot seem entirely mechanical, but to show that the form of its behaviour can give reasonable clues both as to how it feels and why it behaves so, in terms of the function of particular behaviour patterns. It is more interesting to watch once such a framework has been erected. Few people, I should think, could go on watching an animal intensively, hour after hour, with a mental approach compounded entirely of naturalistic benevolence and aesthetic appreciation. Some effort to understand must creep in and should certainly be welcomed and disciplined.

One of the blue-foot's nicest activities is symbolic nest-building. The male often picks up a scrap of material and 'shows' or 'presents' it to the female with a high sweep of his head, before daintily placing it on the nest where the pair bend their heads together and busily 'build' in this fragment. I have already described the significance of symbolic nest-building in the white booby and swallow-tailed gull, and no doubt it occurs in many other species. Before the eggs are laid, the blue-foot may defend and use in turn two or three sites separated by as much as fifty yards. We discovered this by seeing one of our colour-ringed pairs on three different sites, though they began to prefer one of them more and more in the week or two before the female laid her eggs.

The eggs, laid about five days apart, take forty-one days to hatch. The chick has a much bluer skin than that of the red-foot, though it is not much different from the white booby chick; it is equally ugly and helpless until rescued by its snowy down. The adults guard it for the first few weeks of life, unless the family economy forces the parents to hunt simultaneously and it may then fall victim to the Galapagos short-eared owl. Even when almost fully feathered, it is still not completely safe; six of our chicks were killed when about twelve weeks old, in a sudden outburst of owl depredations.

A continuous forty-eight hour check on behaviour and feeding of young showed that the chicks averaged 1.8 feeds a day. At that stage, most were a third to two-thirds grown, so the phase of relatively frequent feeds was over. Their average feeding rate at this age compares with 1·4 per day for the white booby and 0·9 per day for

A Male 'salutes' on flying in to nest site: showing off bright blue webs

B Male 'pelican postures' and parades: lifting fully spread webs

E A pair mutual jab

F The female (right) turns in bill-up-face-away prior to leaving the nest site

*Figure 38* Blue-footed booby

the red-foot. We exchanged a few neighbouring chicks to see if they would be accepted by foster-parents, but they all returned to their original territories. Gannets will readily accept foster-chicks, either instead of or in addition to their own, though only as a *fait accompli*; they will not let them wander up of their own accord and in fact chicks remain strictly on their own nests for two good reasons; if they moved about on cliff ledges they would fall and if they moved among nests on flatter ground they would be violently attacked and probably killed by neighbours, so they stay where they are. In

C  Male parades in the bill-up face-away posture whilst female assumes pelican posture

D  Male sky-points or advertises to female

G  Female wing rattles: the next stage prior to flight

H  The pair parade and 'pelican posture'. Both are wanting to move

gannets, this probably explains why adults so readily accept substitute chicks – they have no need of a rejection mechanism because normally chicks never attempt to get onto a stranger's nest. If they did, it would be necessary to evolve some way of dealing with the situation in order to avoid the wasteful division of labour which would result if one pair had two or three chicks to rear and other pairs none. Similarly, red-footed boobies accept foster chicks and again there is little chance of this happening in nature. Where it is easily possible, as in the blue-foot, for chicks to wander onto a neighbour's territory one might expect adults to reject them and I suspect they would. In those species, such as eider ducks, where 'aunts' look after anybody's babies, or mothers collect (and lose) ducklings indiscriminately in '*crèches*', the problem of feeding does not arise because the ducklings are self-supporting and need only to be protected against predators and perhaps led to the best feeding areas.

Blue-foots are partly nocturnal, though not quite so much as red-foots. Birds returned from fishing trips up to six hours after dark, though we never had any evidence that they actually set off, caught fish and returned all in the dark. If their powers of night vision are not much, if at all, better than those of man, as Pumphrey believes to be true for most birds (even owls probably have much poorer night vision than commonly supposed), then they must have found landing difficult because we could hardly see a thing. The guano-whitened boulders were, in fact, the most visible objects, though I do not suggest that the birds whiten them for this reason.

One of the blue-foot's most interesting habits eluded me altogether. Carl Angermeyer has often seen blue-foots fishing as a group and relates that upon a signal (a whistle) from the 'leader' they all dived. Fritz and Gus supported Carl's account. Quite independently a fourth person corroborated the main facts; that there would be a group obviously looking for fish and that all would suddenly dive, though he could not be certain about the whistle. Later I found that Murphy quotes Delano's account of blue-foots diving at the Galapagos: 'These birds collect together in small flocks for the purpose of diving. They fly around in a circle and continue to rise till they get to the height of from sixty to a hundred yards in the air when one of them makes a pitch to dive, at which motion every one follows, and they fly down with remarkable swiftness, till within four or five yards of the surface, and then suddenly clasp their wings together and go into the water with the greatest velocity that can be conceived of, exceeding anything of the kind that I ever witnessed. They go into the water with such force as to form a curve of thirty or forty yards in length, before coming to the top again, going to a great depth under water. They glide under water at almost as great a degree of swiftness as when flying in the air.'

There are other examples of group co-operation in feeding birds and animals: for instance, white pelicans herd fish inshore by advancing in a crescent, beating the water with their wings, and then fall among the concentrate and scoop them up. There are no other records of co-ordinated group fishing in boobies; if one accepts the above narrative, the blue-foot becomes doubly interesting in its fishing habits and throws up some interesting questions. Why is the signal always a whistle? Do females never initiate the concerted plunge? What constitutes a 'group'? Certainly two or three and probably even a score can fish in close proximity without combining in the above way. Perhaps it is a feeding method adapted to a special set of conditions. It seems pleasing that the blue-foot, most ludicrous of all boobies, and in Murphy's eyes rather pathetic, should have far more tricks in its chrysanthemum head than the rest of its family.

The gulls, family *Laridae*, together with terns *Sternidae* and skuas *Stercorariidae* form a closely related assemblage. Their position within the diverse order Charadriformes (sixteen families) seems problematical.

The forty-two or forty-three species of gulls are now well distributed in both hemispheres, though originating in the north. The ivory gull reaches 85°N. in the polar sea and the Dominican gull well into the Antarctic. Gulls range in size from eleven to thirty-two inches. Nearly all are birds of the shore or littoral zone rather than truly oceanic. A diagnostic characteristic is the gonyx of the lower mandible. Feet are webbed between three toes.

The swallow-tailed gull *Creagrus furcatus*, endemic to the Galapagos, is genuinely oceanic in its feeding habits. It may be distinguished by its forked tail and diagonal wing pattern plus, in breeding plumage, the dark hood and red orbital ring. It disperses south to Peru out of the breeding season.

The dusky or lava gull *Larus fuliginosis* is sedentary in the Galapagos. It is apparently near to the ancestral 'type' of all Pacific forms (Murphy) and has close relatives on the mainland of South America.

The thought is unoriginal, but it has often struck me that gulls are a uniquely well-equipped family. Their powers of flight are unsurpassed; think of the agility of the trim little kittiwake and the strength of the greater black-back. No cliff face is too awkward or its updraughts too unpredictable for the kittiwake and it regularly crosses the North Atlantic in the stormy days of late autumn when the seas are terrifying. Greater black-backs and the other large gulls are immensely powerful and wide-ranging; almost independent of weather and to a large extent environment. On the Bass Rock, I recently picked up an immature greater which had been ringed as a juvenile in Russia.

Gull plumage is waterproof and they don't have to stand like a

*Figure 39* Swallow-tailed gull preening

line of Monday washing, waiting for their wings to dry as the shag must. They can drink salt water and get rid of the excess salt through their salt gland. They can swim and walk with equal ease, unlike so many web-footed species, and they can dive after a fashion. I have seen a herring gull dive and catch a healthy half-pound sea trout to whose excellence I can testify; I robbed the gull. The word omnivorous should really be defined by reference to gulls. Refuse from the local tip; kittens from the canal; grain from the wheat fields; earthworms from the ploughed land; starfish or mussels from low tide scavenging; fish; helpless, ailing or dead flesh of any kind; eggs of their own species; bread from bountiful trippers on MacBraynes steamers – all come alike to the herring gull. Other species have much the same catholicity, and the statue of a Californian gull in Salt Lake City commemorates the gulls that destroyed many of the locusts threatening the Mormons' fruit crops. They are not too big (like a condor or albatross) nor too small to inhabit a vast range of habitats, fresh-water and marine. The forty-three species of gulls live in every temperature from the polar wastes to the baking lava deserts of the Galapagos. Ross's, ivory, Sabine's, glaucous and Iceland gulls live in ice and snow amid sub-zero temperatures. Andean gulls grace the lonely lakes of the high sierras; black-headed gulls are at home far inland among the fields and moors of the English Pennines and the dusky gulls of the Galapagos breed on the hot black lava. Behaviourally they are flexible, dropping shellfish to break them, treading mud to bring invertebrates to the surface, following ships and ploughs, scavenging in warehouses, docks and parks, waylaying puffins emerging from burrows; a variety of behaviour so much greater than that of terns. Yet a gull is easily seen to be a gull; their adaptive radiation has not meant so much change in form and structure that the family has become a vast, diffuse assemblage of basically related but superficially dissimilar species. They have done very well for themselves as a tightly knit family, though they have also, of course, their more specialised relatives, the terns and skuas.

On Tower, we lived with two extremely rare gulls on our door step. They were a great contrast in character. The dusky or lava gull was a typical member of the family in its alert, scavenging, even predatory ways, whilst the highly specialised swallow-tailed or fork-tailed gull showed not the remotest interest in scavenging; it fed nocturnally, often on squids, judging from its regurgitations.

Adult lava gulls are lovely birds, about as big as a black-headed gull, sooty black beneath, grey above with a brilliant white spot behind the eye. The bill, legs and feet are black and the gape is a beautiful flame colour. Their sooty plumage and lurid mouths are eminently appropriate to birds of the black lava, spewed from fiery volcanoes. A number of unrelated birds in the Galapagos have brightly coloured areas around their eyes; the doves have bright blue orbital rings; swallow-tails bright red ones; female great frigates red ones; magnificent frigates blue ones; and some of the boobies have brightly coloured skin on the face. It is very likely that brightly coloured face parts and gapes are often part of the bird's equipment for display and in combination with movements and postures help to make a conspicuous signal, but the exact signifi-cance of coloured orbital rings is not known. They are not acquired solely in the breeding season, but again there is no reason why they should be, unless there was selective pressure against retaining them at other times. In two closely related species of flycatchers with differently coloured orbital rings, it has been shown that these probably help the species to recognise each other and avoid hybridising, but again this is an interpretation from which one cannot generalise to other species. However, it is true that the two sympatric frigate species in the Galapagos have differently coloured eye rings.

Young lava gulls are duller and rustier, with brown edges to their feathers and no white spot. They are practically invisible on the dark lava, although I do not believe that their dark colour has evolved to protect them from predators. Black colour may protect the little ground finches, since these are hunted by owls and hawks, but the hawks are themselves black and nobody preys on them. Their colour is probably adaptive in other ways, perhaps connected with the equatorial position of their native islands. Birds and animals in general tend to become smaller and darker towards the Equator, and their appendages – beaks, legs, tails, ears, etc. – tend to become shorter too. Or it may be, as Hailmann suggests, that their black colour, by making them hard to see against the lava, saves them from at least some persecution by frigates, which are always on the look-out for birds with food. Cryptic colouration as an anti-predator device usually acts by saving the life of the camouflaged species, but if Hailman's interpretation is correct, the lava gull's plumage is cryptic in a rather similar sense. Extending this, the Galapagos hawk's black colour would certainly help it to approach feeding doves, mockers and finches unseen against the lava. Its hunting habits, however, have been so little observed that it is not known whether it hunts in the appropriate way, that is against a dark background such as a steep slope, or a cliff face, or very low over the ground.

Like the mocking birds, lava gulls were insatiably curious; they also possessed greater lifting power and several movable articles such as socks, brushes, pan scrubbers, string, spoons and cups mysteriously disappeared. Any unusual activity drew a small crowd of lava gulls; they watched critically as June waded into the lagoon with the week's wash and ran up with interest when I cleaned a fish. They had an endearing habit of perching on the stem of our rowing boat as we crossed the bay, which swallow-tails would never do, bending low to give the aggressive yodelling 'long call' if another gull flew towards them. Despite their scavenging habits, they were third-rate bolters. A herring gull would have bolted anything within reach before a lava gull could have moved. Parker says of a herring gull: 'When the bird was quite small in the down, it one day seized from my hand an entire mutton-chop bone and bolted it before I had time to take it away. The bone was so large in proportion that it greatly distorted the bird.' The chick looked like an animated chop bone.

Lava gulls were rather fastidious and, for gulls, dainty eaters and usually ran down to the sea to wash their food, for the call of the running tide was strong. So was the running tide, and they often lost their morsel in a welter of water and looked rather witless peering round for it. Even when they caught a fish, they seemed to have difficulty dealing with it. One bird snatched a small but lively fish from the sea and ran up the beach with it. He hammered away ineffectually for several minutes, almost lost it three times by washing it when it was still very much alive and eventually after ten minutes and several abortive attempts to swallow it, lost it to a frigate who sailed overhead, saw the fish, swooped, snatched it from beneath the gull's nose and swallowed it competently, finishing off the operation in the usual way by swooping to take a few sips of water in flight. Equally, with crabs and eggs, the lava gull was a bungler. The red crabs that swarm everywhere in the Galapagos are frequently stalked successfully by the yellow-crowned night herons, but the lava gull ran after them too openly and childishly and usually missed. It did a little better with eggs because they couldn't run away, but it

*Figure 40* Lava gulls as camp followers

cracked them none too expertly and I never saw one drop an egg from the air to break it as herring gulls drop molluscs. When feeding in shallow water, they upended and often turned repeatedly in half circles, rather like very clumsy phalarope spinning.

Despite my disparaging remarks, the lava gull continues to exist, though in numbers rather less successfully than most members of the family *Laridae*. In one thing they have done very well; they were until about four years ago, I think, the only gull, perhaps the only sea-bird whose nest and eggs had never been discovered. The ivory gull and Ross's gull used to hold that distinction too, but fell before the lava gull, whose solitary nest was difficult to pinpoint in a jumble of cinders and lava in some remote part of an island, usually uninhabited. Also, the lava gull has the distracting habit of making a fuss long before one is anywhere near the nest. They breed on Tower and we once found a young one but never an egg, though several times we drew their full alarm attack.

Lava gulls behave in many ways much like our herring gull. Aggressive territorial behaviour included the well-known 'long call' in which the bird, with head and neck held low and parallel to the ground, gives a loud, repetitive call something like a laugh or yodel, starting with a chuckle like a cock red-grouse just before it calls 'go back, go back' and gradually working up to full intensity calling. It was strikingly similar to the long call of the herring gull and the lava gull's alarm call 'klee-ow' was sometimes, to my ear, indistinguishable from the equivalent call in the herring gull. The threat posture is a low hunched position with neck retracted and beak horizontal. Territorial defenders walked or ran towards intruders in this posture, calling in a low key or alternating with the upright threat posture in which the bill is held ready to peck downwards. Scared birds showed the anxiety upright position with feathers sleeked and neck vertical. Lava gulls frequently bend their heads down and minutely examine their feet. This 'foot looking' behaviour is typical of all gulls but its meaning seems not yet clear. The immature birds showed one curious trait that intrigued us. Sometimes they seemed to go mad, jumping into the air and squawking and snatching at invisible objects – perhaps small flies. They reached a pitch of great excitement and frequently stumbled or hopped on one foot.

Somehow the lava gull fits the Galapagos. A settler there said he
thought that only escapists or those who could not make their way
adequately in the more competitive and high-powered world outside
settled in the Galapagos. I believe he was wrong, but maybe the lava
gull is a bit low-powered as a gull and ekes out its living in the
Galapagos, away from interspecific competition in the most arid
parts of the most arid islands. However, to do that is itself no mean
feat.

The swallow-tailed gull, endemic to the Galapagos though
closely related to the Andean gull, is an integral part of Tower. Its
wild alarm calls are often the first greeting as you step ashore on the
most outlandish corners of the islands. It is far more colonial in its
breeding habits than the lava gull and adjacent pairs are noisy and
tireless in territorial display. Their most impressive feature is perhaps
the huge dark brown eye surrounded by a scarlet orbital ring and
beautifully set off in the black hood of breeding plumage (the hood
is lost out of the breeding season). The black beak has a polished
grey tip and a large white patch at the base of the upper mandible
and a small white spot just where the lower mandible runs into the
cheek. Chicks, incidentally, peck at these white basal patches rather
than the grey tip when begging for food. The deep grey mantle,
black wing tips with white mirrors, pure white underparts and bright
pinky red feet and legs confer great elegance. The tail is deeply
forked and the gull's flight easy and buoyant. Juveniles are strikingly
different, with a dark spot around the eye, which consequently
appears much enlarged, and a dark diagonal bar stretching across the
wings, giving them a distinctive appearance in flight.

Swallow-tails were at home on sand, shingle, rough lava and cliff
ledges, though cliffs may be their most typical nesting habitat and
perhaps the one in which they breed most successfully. Certainly, the
breeding success of thirty-odd pairs around our camp was extremely
low. In fact, between December 1963 and July 1964, only one
juvenile fledged; all other nests lost their egg or in most cases their
small chick. As a species, the swallow-tail, like many Galapagos sea-
birds, breeds throughout much of the year instead of showing a
single annual peak; this has been known for a long time. Whilst we
were on Tower, there were two small peaks of laying around
January and June, and David Snow has recently shown that their

internal cycle is in fact about six months. Our own gulls, of course, all show annual breeding cycles.

In January 1964 the birds at the head of Darwin Bay showed all stages of the breeding cycle; some were just establishing territories, others had eggs or young and one or two had free flying juveniles. All the eggs and small young perished and an extensive tour of the island in April revealed no signs of laying whatever. Indeed, we could find only one chick, about four weeks old. The next burst of laying began in late May and carried on into June and July. As with the red-footed booby, each period of laying continued for quite some time, eventually leading to eggs and young at different stages of development, but the birds within small local groups were rather more closely synchronised, several neighbours producing their eggs within a few days of each other. I have already mentioned this phenomenon and will do so again when discussing the Peruvian booby; it is partly due to the exciting effect of social stimulation acting on close neighbours and to some extent telescoping the natural differences (due to age, date of return and other factors) in their individual breeding conditions. We saw it in all the boobies and the frigate birds. In fact, although Darling's original ideas (1938) on social stimulation were based on ambiguous evidence – the effects he described could have been produced in ways other than the ones he postulated – it has still proved a stimulating hypothesis. A great deal of detailed work has been devoted to the subject of breeding in different kinds of colonial sea-birds; what factors affect the date on which a female lays her egg (for instance, age, density of group); whether any survival value accrues to the individual pair by breeding in a group at more or less the same time as the others and if so how; what are the advantages of faithfulness to nest and mate, and so on. I would even suggest that in fairly dense colonial species, the effect of social stimulation via the displays and activity of nearby pairs, in bringing about some local synchronisation, is inevitable and occurs even if there is no significant survival value attached to it. However, it is equally possible that in fact there is always some advantage, even if it lies only in a reduced likelihood of interference by neighbours when they are equally busily engaged in the same phase of the breeding cycle. This has recently been shown to be true for three-spined sticklebacks (van den Assem).

The early stages of the breeding cycle are the most rewarding to watch, for then the gulls are busy establishing their territories and forming pairs. The hours around dawn and before dusk are full of activity and noisy with the thin, aggressive 'scree-ee' calls of contiguous pairs. Swallow-tails defend territory as a defined area and not as an individual distance around themselves, moving with them. Territory owners will tolerate neighbours at very close quarters so long as they are on the right side of the boundary, but may fly to drive away a more distant bird if it trespasses. As with most gulls, fights are relatively infrequent and inflict no damage. However, the fighting method is interesting. As two males clashed near the top of a small cliff, I clearly saw one bird grip the other's bill and with a twisting movement reminiscent of kittiwake fighting, force him off the edge. The interest lies in the fact that kittiwakes are specially adapted for nesting on cliff ledges and are the only gulls known to fight in this way – others peck downwards or grip each other's bill and pull. This scrap of evidence is a slight clue indicating that the swallow-tail's adaptations may be towards cliff nesting. If so, it is certainly not nearly so specialised as the kittiwake, but may be rather more crudely adapted as in its fighting method. After an aggressive encounter, swallow-tails often 'display flight' above their territory, flying buoyantly with slow, floating butterfly wing beats. Display flights are common in gulls and terns and probably originated as pursuit flights against intruders, though now released by the sexual stimulus of the female. When swallow-tails land, they shuffle their wings in typical gull manner and utter the faint 'scree' and a snore-cum-rattle note, difficult to transcribe. The voice of the swallow-tail is one of its most curious features; it has a bizarre un-gull-like vocabulary, snoring, rattling, screaming and whistling. The composite effect of a thorough-going swallow-tail medley is quite indescribable.

In aggressive encounters that do not lead to fighting, the attacking gull, like other larids, shows several different displays. The 'upright' threat with long neck, sleeked feathers and widely parted mandibles and the thin 'scree' call, is similar to that of the herring gull and occurs when the rival is at some distance and there is a strong probability that the owner will fly or run to attack; birds even try to do it whilst butterfly flighting. Alternatively, they may run at an opponent with arched neck and downward pointing bill. This resembles an aggressive posture of the herring gull just before it pecks downwards at an opponent or the ground, or gives the aggressive long call. A striking posture in many gull species is the 'long call' posture, perhaps most familiar in the herring gull. (It is the striking forward and upward leaning position in which, with thick, powerful-looking neck, the gull delivers its loud yodelling call; telescope and binocular manufacturers find it makes a striking advertisement.) It is of great interest to behaviourists to discover how widespread is any particular display within a family and how, if at all, it has been modified in the various members. The lava gull has a long call very similar to a herring gull's, but the swallow-tail is a much less 'typical' gull and its long call is less obvious. Nevertheless, I have seen what seemed to me a perfectly recognisable long-call posture in this species, accompanied by the swallow-tail version of the actual polysyllabic call. The circumstances were always similar to those that would evoke a herring gull's long call – namely intrusion of its territory by a neighbour. The long call itself was a squeaky polysyllabic 'co-week, co-week' and the forward-flung posture was preceded by the upright – a sudden change of posture which enhances its visual impact. Once the procedure was gone through silently. Finally, common aggressive behaviour on land or water directed against a short-range rival involves the assumption of a most menacing-looking forward-oblique posture, neck thickened and bill pointing slightly upwards, accompanied by a snoring note. After successfully running or flying against an opponent, swallow-tails often remain momentarily with their beautiful wings held, tern-like, aloft – a most graceful posture. Then they shuffle them into position and do the 'upward choking', a display mainly performed on the nest site by the owning bird. In this, the bill is pointed vertically upwards, neck retracted, and then the gull makes swift up and down pumping movements of the head, at the same time calling gutturally.

Choking is another display which has an equivalent in other gulls. In the kittiwake, it is a rhythmical downward jerking with the yellow beak opened to reveal the striking red mouth. In the swallow-tail, choking, as I have said, is usually done with the bill pointing upwards. Usually it is followed by a very odd piece of behaviour in

A Butterfly flight of swallow-tailed gull

B Aggressive displacement of intruder

E The right-hand bird is in the aggressive forward oblique posture used against intruders. The left-hand bird is also somewhat aggressive, but has adopted the thin-necked aggressive upright posture

F Upward choking: performed on nest site

*Figure 41* Swallow-tailed gull

which the bird suddenly bends its head and minutely inspects its feet. If it performs the upward choking from a sitting position, it still tries to follow it by looking at its feet which, of course, are totally hidden. Obviously this behaviour has become highly ritualised and is no longer concerned (if it ever was) with an inspection of its feet; its signal function, as I mentioned, is still obscure. Choking is

206

C The mate flies up to reinforce its partner in an aggressive territorial encounter: a form of the forward oblique is performed by the standing bird

D Anxiety upright. Bird calls thinly and shows tongue

G Foot-looking

H Members of a pair preen each other

essentially a signal of site-ownership, performed at the nest site after displacing an intruder or bringing a pebble to add to the 'nest'. Pebble-bringing is a symbolic form of nest building – symbolic because the nest certainly cannot have any real importance as a structure, being just a neat patch of small pebbles, bones and oddments. Still, the birds spend a considerable amount of time in this pursuit. Carrying their pebbles they run to the nest in the long necked position, beak pointing down, calling 'kerr-er', or sometimes it sounds more like a high-pitched 'ss-coya, ss-coya'.

Copulation is preceded in both sexes by a long bout of upward nodding or head-tossing behaviour, from a hunched position. This is just like the head-tossing of young herring gulls begging for food and is accompanied by a similar note too – a plaintive 'phee-o, phee-o' repeated over and over; it is probably derived from the food-begging behaviour of the young bird. During head-tossing, the female usually stands slightly in front of and a little lower than the male, repeatedly reaching up and grasping his grey bill tip, whilst he occasionally grasps the white base of her bill. Sometimes the female half turns and plucks at the male's breast feathers. The male mounts and stands with spread wings, calling. Then he begins to patter up and down and the female lifts her tail. The male's note now changes to a low throaty rattle or snore 'or-orr-or' whilst the female continues her 'phee-o' calls and keeps reaching up to grasp the male's bill or breast feathers. As usual in the family, the male achieves several contacts and ejaculations before dismounting.

Courtship feeding in birds is always appealing to watch. Nothing is more graceful than the agile hawking flight of a male little tern, pure white against a blue June sky, a silver fish dangling from his beak, whilst the female chases him with shrill screams, pestering him to deliver the prize. The swallow-tail's bribery, though not so prettily conducted, is adequate. The male regurgitates his offering actually on one of the nest sites (he may have two or three within the territory) or walks to the site with the food held in his bill. Often he precedes the feeding by courtship or even copulation away from the site and then 'leads' the female to the site before lowering his head and with choking movements and widely parted mandibles, regurgitating the fish or squid. The female, perhaps recognises some slight intention movements of regurgitation, or feeling hungry enough to beg for food, sometimes upward nods and pecks repeatedly at the base of the male's bill. She does this from the side and in the submissive, hunched posture of the young chick. The food is deposited on the ground for the female to pick up. After feeding, the male may lead the female up to thirty yards away from the feeding spot. This probably reflects the male's initial fluidity with respect to the choice of nest site. Some males even made their pebble-lined scrapes in spots which were submerged twice daily by the tides, though we never found an egg on such a site.

A pair of swallow-tailed gulls were unfortunate enough to hatch their egg just where we pitched our tent. Despite our terrifying intrusion, they continued to guard the egg during the two days it took the chick to emerge (later we found that incubation takes about thirty-five days). As soon as it was dry and fluffy and steady on its feet, they led it several yards away from the tent, to the edge of the lagoon, where there was unhappily no cover. That night we were startled by a scalp-tingling laugh, a weird, old man's cackle that came from the darkness just outside the tent. The voice belonged to the Galapagos short-eared owl, the only predator known on Tower, and I'm afraid it boded ill for the swallow-tail chick. It disappeared and I suspect it formed the penultimate link in a food chain ending in the owl. It was the first of several chicks to vanish; in fact, our growth records for young swallow-tails never got beyond 200 gm at fourteen days (a newly-hatched chick weighs about 45 gm).

The fluffy grey chicks, marked with black, were guarded constantly for several days after hatching and then they sheltered in a crevice or beneath an overhang. Around our camp, only a single chick survived to the juvenile stage and it used to while away the daylight hours in the depths of a shady recess containing the spring through which sea-water flowed into our lagoon. Beneath it the gaudy orange-bellied fishlets guarded their territories; above, boobies squawked and screeched in the shrubs and juvenile frigates caterwauled in frenzied supplication each time the adults dropped from the hot sky on buoyant black wings. They were all part of its Galapagos world and it ignored them, interested only in preening and the next squid, fresh from the crop of its elegant parent.

*Figure 42* The 'wings aloft' position of the swallow-tailed gull

# The Man o' War

The family *Fregatidae* contains five closely related species (*Fregata minor;
F. ariel; F. magnificens; F. andrewsi* and *F. aquila*) occurring in tropical and
subtropical waters. *Fregata minor*, the great frigate-bird, is the subject of
this chapter. Frigates often replace each other geographically, but *F. minor*
overlaps slightly with *F. magnificens* in the Galapagos, and on Tower,
though the main colonies of *F. minor* are 'pure'.

Frigates are placed in the Pelecaniformes, and a special relationship
between frigates and pelicans has been postulated though they are now
known to share certain 'primitive osteological characters' with tropic
birds, and these two groups may be more closely related than either is to
the Pelecani.

Frigates are highly specialised for an aerial life, showing special skeletal
characters (furcula or wishbone fused to keel of sternum and shoulder
girdle) and unusually low skeleton weight (about $\frac{1}{4}$ lb). Wing area is
greater, relative to body weight, than in any other bird. They have reduced
legs and feet adapted for perching, not swimming. They are usually
reckoned to be inshore feeders feeding from the wing, and specialising in
piracy. They breed on small oceanic islands, usually in trees or bushes but
sometimes on the ground. They lay single egg clutches.


Then another emotion obsessed him; he bent his head
back until it sank between his shoulders, the red
balloon projecting straight upward, and the long
angular wings spread flat over the surrounding bushes.
The entire body rolled from side to side, as if in
agony, while the apparently dying bird gave vent to a
remarkably sweet series of notes, as liquid as the distant
cry of a loon, as resonant as that of an owl. In our
human, inadequate, verbal vocality, I can only record
it as kew-kew-kew-kew–kew-kew! In a higher tone the
female answered him from the sky, oo-oo-oo-oo-oo-oo!
William Beebe, *Galapagos  World's End*

*Figure 43* Female frigate in flight

Although the reasons are far from obvious, frigates and boobies are placed in the same order, Pelecaniformes. They do not have much in common. Frigates are entirely and superbly specialised for an aerial life. They have an eight-foot wing-span but weigh about a quarter as much as the waved albatross, of similar size, and less than a third as much as a gannet with a wing-span of slightly under six feet. Even the small and light male blue-footed booby weighs almost as much as a frigate which, in fact, is lighter in relation to its wing area than any other sea-bird. Palmer states that frigates have forty per cent more wing area than other sea-birds of similar bulk. Their huge wings are deeply cambered to grip the air and the enormous forked tail, like an earwig's pincers, is a sensitive rudder and stabiliser. Because they are so light and carry such a spread they fly with leisurely, buoyant wing beats suggesting deep reserves of power, or soar and glide effortlessly. They have been recorded at a height of 4,000 feet. Their plumage is not fully waterproof and they rarely settle on water, though contrary to some opinions, they are certainly capable of rising from the surface even in a flat calm. I saw frigates splash into calm water in an attempt to seize a sinking fish, and then rise from the surface. Their tiny, unwebbed feet, with the vestiges of a fringe between the toes, are useless for walking or swimming but extremely flexible and prehensile and therefore very useful among the twigs and branches in which frigates usually nest; they can perch with two toes forward and two back or three forward and one back with equal ease.

A great frigate-bird's beak is about four inches long and deeply hooked, with a sharp tip. With it, and in full flight, they snatch fish from just below the surface, delicately pick up floating scraps, drink, lift twigs from the ground or tear them from the living bush. That beak and the exquisite nerve and muscle co-ordination with which it is wielded is everything to the frigate. Other birds may survive with grossly deformed mandibles, but a frigate works to clearances measurable in thousandths of an inch. Just how fine is the margin of error we appreciated by seeing a frigate swoop at full speed and without pausing bend its head and clean the thinnest smear of spilt fish from a rock surface, making a faint click as the bill tip whipped over the rock. Another observer saw one pick up a fragment of food from sand, so cleanly that its bill tip left no trace. Still more impressive a frigate will actually take fish which is being passed from booby parent to offspring, or from frigate to offspring, for that matter. Just as the youngster inserts its head into the mouth of its parent, the frigate swoops down and in one movement knocks them apart and takes the fish. When a frigate is itself the victim of such an outrage, it calls hoarsely and lunges at the retreating marauder – usually a male. One would suspect that frigates must have specially modified neck vertebrae or muscles to enable them to withstand the stress imposed by their method of feeding.

However, frigates live on the whole honest lives, occasionally ranging several hundred miles from land in the extensive forays for fish, perhaps mainly flying fish and squids, though also jellyfish, plankton, scraps and whatever else they can catch. Nearly every ocean voyage account mentions frigate birds, up to 1,000 miles from land. But the image of the frigate as an honest fisherman snapping up the flying fish as they leap to evade their underwater predators, easily fades before the piratical and predatory frigate. It is hard to estimate what proportion of their food comes from other birds; under some circumstances it may be substantial and it might be more than coincidence that they always nest among large numbers of potential victims. The skies above Tower were never free from frigates, their distinctive silhouettes poised watchfully above, waiting and waiting. From first light to beyond the brief tropical dusk, the air was likely to rend with the harsh, agonised squawks of red-footed boobies, and a glance would reveal a brown form desperately trying to evade the vengeful black shadow or shadows, for the frigate often hunted in small bands, probably not in co-operation but rather in competition. How the boobies fled, flat out, but not nearly fast or agile enough to shake off their persecutors! They came flashing over the beach, the booby glancing fearfully behind and the pursuing frigates, relaxed even in chase, coming up fast with deep muscular strokes. We cheered the booby on, sorry that he might lose his hard-earned catch, but his only chance was to come in low over the ground or pitch headlong into a tree – there was no time to land elegantly. Sometimes he ended in a tangle of legs and wings and had the devil of a job to extricate himself. Maybe crash landing in trees was too dangerous to become a routine escape tactic; we saw two or three corpses hanging in forks and it was a fact that in the last resort they usually regurgitated rather than chance it. A booby hemmed in by several frigates and stubbornly refusing to throw up was seized by the tail or wing tip and capsized. This usually encouraged him to give in and he then began to regurgitate, pointing his bill downwards to aid the process. The frigates snatched eagerly at the fish as soon as the slimy bolus appeared, catching it in the air or following it down to the sea. I think they must have snapped at the booby's beak; some of our marked red-foots came home with pieces chipped out and I cannot imagine how else this could happen; certainly not by territorial fighting in these cases. We never saw frigates seriously attack a booby, although Alexander says they may break the wing of their victim. However, they certainly manhandled them, and the poor booby was usually left, empty and highly agitated, on the comforting bosom of the sea. Almost all the piracy that went on around Darwin Bay was carried out by adult males. Another observer, on the other hand, found that in the magnificent frigates of the British Honduras, females invariably were the pirates (Verner). Frigates will chase each other when one of them visibly carries food, but they will not chase other frigates in order

*Figure 44* The chase – frigates hounding a red-foot

to make them regurgitate. Once the loot had been swallowed, the group separated amicably and each went their own way. It appeared that the frigates had initially no way of telling whether their chosen victim was full or empty – they began the chase on a hit or miss basis. However, it was also apparent that after a short chase they knew that certain boobies had fish, for they stuck to them and were always rewarded. We came to suspect that the frigates might detect a difference in the calls of full and empty boobies. We could ourselves hear that certain boobies called in a wheezing, strangled voice which could have been caused by pressure of food on the windpipe. If the frigates could also associate this noise with fish they could use it as a cue. Probably because they often chose an 'empty' one, a relatively low proportion (twelve per cent) of their chases yielded results and even when they did, only one out of the gang got the fish; the others had worked for nothing. All in all, it did not seem a particularly easy way to live, but no doubt it was a useful supplementary source of food. Also, one should remember that sustained flight needs very little energy expenditure for a frigate. They rarely bothered with anything other than boobies. The swallow tails were too agile for them, despite the frigate's reputed ability to fly down any other sea-bird, and they didn't molest the tropic birds much.

Chasing was instinctive in frigates. Audubon's shearwaters nested

*Figure 45* Frigate up-ending a white booby

on the north-east coast of Tower and several times we saw frigates fly down a newly fledged juvenile and repeatedly pick it from the sea and drop it until the shearwater was dead. They were never swallowed, probably because they were too large. Even a warbler flying from bush to bush sometimes released chasing behaviour in frigates – a ludicrous sight – and they would swoop onto a ball, tossed high into the air. This instantaneous reaction to a falling object must be vital to a species whose existence depends on catching flying fish, or dropped food.

The frigate's feeding methods are clearly highly specialised and not likely to be acquired in a day. In December 1963 there were scores of free-flying juvenile frigates on Tower, probably from eggs laid in March of that year; they were still being regularly fed by their parents. In July 1964 some of those same juveniles were still receiving food from their parents. This astonishingly long post-fledging feeding period – six months or perhaps considerably more – puts the frigate way ahead of any other sea-bird in the world so far as the period of dependence of free-flying young on their parents is concerned. It also means that a complete breeding cycle takes considerably more than a year, since incubation of the egg requires fifty-five days, the rearing of young to the free-flying stage takes about six months, and then one must allow about a month for the period of display and nest-building prior to egg laying. Altogether fifteen to eighteen months are probably required for the complete cycle.

Successful pairs cannot breed annually or less than annually as other members of the order apparently do. This was an unexpected discovery, which we interpreted to mean that the food situation enforces slow growth on the young and that after fledging, a frigate needs many months to acquire the tricks of its aerial trade; until practically a year after hatching it first needed feeding and later subsidising by its parents. More startling still, we found that even after this long apprenticeship, many juveniles began to starve when their parents stopped feeding them. It is possible that in April, May and June of 1964, fish were unusually scarce and to that extent our juvenile frigates may have suffered additional handicaps, but the salient point is that some of them lost weight and died after falling to the starvation weight of around 600 gm; one and a quarter pounds for a bird with an eight feet wing-span. They accepted their fate apathetically, sitting around on the bushes instead of scouring the seas for food. Of course, we could not follow the fate of any that did die at sea; maybe the sea-farers, if any, were no better off. Like a gannet's plunge diving, a frigate's forage-feeding and piracy are not entirely built-in; they are partly learned and there is ample time and scope for disaster before proficiency comes.

Long before the juveniles from the 1963 season were fully independent, the 1964 breeding season began. We never estimated the entire frigate population of Tower, but nests were built in the shrubs of our camp colony, one might truthfully say in the back-garden, and we followed their fortunes very closely. The story became far more complicated than we had expected; the courtship displays of birds beginning a new cycle, alongside the (not *their*) juveniles of another cycle, is a good beginning point. Incidentally, the presence of juveniles sitting alongside displaying males or newly-formed adult pairs has been noticed before, but wrongly interpreted. Beebe remarks how a youngster sat 'close to the new home of his parents.

Lonesomely he perched, hunched up, for hours, sometimes all day, content to be near his parents who now were absorbed in one another, in a renewed courtship or a new egg or chick.' The mistake was understandable, but in fact the juvenile belonged to the pair who *had* nested where the new pair now were. Its real parents were away gathering food for it.

On 5 January, the first frigate display livened the scene; the fashion spread almost overnight and by February, displaying males, ardently vying for females, dominated the scene. Even though I filmed the whole performance and can check the details as often as I want, it still seems unreal because it is so bizarre. The display is built around the frigate's enormous scarlet throat sac or gular pouch, just as the peacock's centres around its tail. No real bird should possess a sac like the frigate's. It is creative licence gone mad. Outside the nuptial period, the black plumage is relieved only by the glossy, elongated scapulars which form a fancy cape and the shrivelled pink strip of gular skin running down onto the throat. But for three or four weeks at the beginning of each breeding season this innocuous pink strip turns scarlet and can be grossly distended, blown up like a balloon, until the frigate fades into insignificance behind the glory of his fantastic pouch. (fig. 47).

*Figure 46* Male frigate displaying before second male and juvenile

Naturally he is not saddled, or chinned, with this ornament for longer than he chooses; he can blow it up and deflate it at will, though it takes about twenty to thirty minutes. The pouch is connected with the bird's air-sac system, and inflation is accomplished without visible effort. The walls of the sac are covered with a network of conspicuous capillaries and when it is fully extended it feels soft and warm to the touch; a useless fact which we felt compelled to discover, and he, so impeded, powerless to prevent!

The scarlet sac is couched between the frigate's huge black wings, which in display are fully spread. In this position the male stations himself on a perch and waits, bill resting on top of his sac or pointing upwards as he scans the sky. He is looking for a female and as soon as one flies over, even at a height of 200 feet or so, he unleashes his full display. Although the males of different frigate species are in some cases extremely similar, the females all have distinctive patterns of black and white underneath. Furthermore, the juveniles have completely different patterns from the females, being dark on the throat and upper breast and white on the belly, whereas females have white breast and black belly. There seems little doubt that these diagnostic patterns enormously help the males to pick out females from juveniles and their own species from close relatives that may breed on the same island. They clearly have this ability and can spot the right females from a considerable distance; a female magnificent frigate flying over a group of great frigate males, will not elicit their display, but let a female great frigate appear and they respond immediately.

Swivelling on his perch so that he is oriented towards her, the male turns the undersurfaces of his great wings upwards and trembles them violently, making their silvery surfaces flash in the brilliant sunlight. He throws back his head and turns it from side to side, revealing the full size of his sac, and utters a high, falsetto warble, imitable by emitting a steady, high note from tightly rounded mouth and rapidly blocking and releasing the sound with the hand. Sac, wings or warble; any single one would draw attention; in combination they must hit the female like flak. A displaying male attracts others and nuclei of a score or more flower exotically on the bright green shrub or among the sun-silvered branches of the pala santo trees. When they all throw back their heads, tremble their wings and

*Figure 47* Male frigate in full display before a female

warble in concert the effect is best left to the imagination. The whole display is one of the spectacular sights of the animal kingdom.

The female descends, attracted by this display, and sends the males into a frenzy of warbling and head waving, often now interspersed with a fine drawn rattle exactly like a fisherman's reel. All their attention is concentrated on the female and even though they may cluster so closely that they are in actual contact, they do not jab or threaten each other. They are in strict competition, but in this instance, it is purely sexual and not hostile; they are not on territories which they will defend. The female chooses one of the males, though it is impossible to say what guides her choice. One may see her descend as though to land near one displaying male, then rise again and fly off to some other part of the colony. Or she may actually land and perch opposite the male, almost literally embraced by his outspread wings. The successful male keeps his wings out, indeed it is such an effort to furl them that he may sit for hours like that, and continues waving his head from side to side and warbling, but he also frequently utters the fine rattle, like the inwinding of a fisherman's reel. The rattle and warble may follow each other in quick succession whilst the male slowly waggles his head, gradually tending more and more to incline his bill down to the twigs. At this stage he has no nest, for the simple reasons, first, that he may move his display site elsewhere if another nucleus springs up and he has

R

been unsuccessful, and second, no nest material would survive more than a few minutes if left unguarded; as I have already mentioned, he has not even a territory at this stage, but I will defer that point. The existing accounts of frigate display are brief but confused, particularly on the vocal part. The grating squeals and 'kekking' sounds are not used in display, but occur in aggressive encounters between rivals. The 'chuck' call is given by birds coming in to their nests. The 'drumming', 'chattering', 'muttering' may all refer to the falsetto warble described above. A variety of horrible gakkering squeals are produced by young birds when frightened, and a hoarse, repetitive monosyllable by alarmed adults.

The female seems mesmerised by the male's display and stands opposite, looking exceedingly vacant. Eventually she too begins to waggle her head and call in a hoarse counterpart of the male's falsetto. So the pair stand, reaching down to the twigs, passing their heads over and around the other's and calling. Mutual head-waggling may go on intermittently for hours, flaring up and dying away again at intervals. If this happens, the female has attached herself to this male and the initial part of pair formation is over. But she may stand for a few minutes, stolid and unmoved, and then open her great wings and beat away, rejecting the male for at least that occasion.

*Figure 48* Early stages of frigate pair formation: the pair perch close together, frequently passing their heads over the other's neck – a sinuous mutual head-waggling

After the frigates had been displaying for a few weeks, we became aware of a number of very puzzling loose ends. First, it seemed difficult to understand how mates that had paired and bred together in previous years managed to re-establish their relationship. There was nothing to suggest that old pairs quietly came together again, as happens in many species that pair more or less for life. On the contrary, every male that came into breeding condition began displaying, either alone or, more likely, with several others. This could only mean that experienced as well as new males were 'in the market' for any female that would respond to their display; it would be entirely wrong to suggest that they would display but accept only the female with whom they had previously mated; we never saw a displaying male reject a female, though the reverse happened. Furthermore, displaying males were not always, or even usually, on old nests. We longed for a few marked birds and nests, with known histories; they would have given us the answer in the most direct way, but unfortunately we had only one season in which to unravel the tangle.

The situation was this: males that had bred before, that is experienced males, had only a slight tendency, if any at all, to stick to their previous site; they might start their new season's display on it (or at least on or near the remains of a nest), but were more likely to be attracted by other displaying males in the general area. Only so could one explain the growth of these nuclei of display rather than scattered males displaying singly, and the observed situation in which a male moved from one display site to another. Even if they did go back to their old nest, it would probably have disintegrated or been dismantled by other birds. Then even if we made the reasonable assumption that the experienced females would probably return to the area in which they had bred (after all, they would know every small detail from their countless visits to feed their young; the area would be firmly imprinted on their visual memory) and if they also returned more or less at the same time as the males, there would be only a *tendency* for old partners to pair up again. The chances of changed pairings would be vastly more than in the gannet, where the nest is a fixture and the meeting place for the pair each season; both male and female are strongly attached to it and whichever comes back first goes immediately to its nest and is there when its mate returns. Such a departure from the strong tradition of the entire order of birds to which frigates belong, and indeed of almost all long-lived sea-birds, of keeping the same mate and nest site from year to year, was puzzling and certainly called for an explanation. Then it became clear that the whole business of territory holding and aggression was somehow all wrong in the frigate. For one thing, the males showed absolutely no aggressive territorial behaviour after taking up their display station. It was not the usual story of a male first finding and establishing a territory, possibly against some opposition, and then, once established, looking for and displaying to females. So far as the male frigate was concerned other males could, and did, come and display so close to him that they were in actual bodily contact. This was at least consistent with another fact that puzzled us – that if several males in a displaying nucleus obtained females, the remainder might pull up their anchors, reef their pouches and float off to join another nucleus some distance away, so far as we could tell always within a few hundred yards. Obviously there would have been no point in the aggressive defence of a territory if this were so potentially temporary; later, after pair formation, defence would be necessary and did in fact occur, though at a relatively low intensity compared with boobies.

This total situation meant that both nest site and pair bond were far less permanent than in the boobies, if indeed they endured at all. Summing up so far, we supposed that the clusters of displaying males were a mixture of experienced birds and those breeding for the first time, and that the displaying nuclei started where they did probably because that general area was the previous breeding spot of one or more of the experienced males. We also made mental notes of the great difference between frigates and all other Pelecaniformes in territory defence and pair formation and in subsequent fidelity (over the years) to nest site and mate.

These matters all turned ultimately on the problems posed by the long breeding cycle. How often did frigates breed? Every second year, twice over three years, or what? Only existing records could throw light on this and they were precious few. They indicated that around February was the main period for displaying males and we knew by the presence of juveniles in December 1963 that there had been a laying around February/March of that year, (of course, there is considerable spread of laying in any one year, and eggs may be found in June or even July, but laying on Tower is definitely discontinuous). Since there was another laying in February/March 1964, there were obviously not alternate years in which there was no laying by the frigates on Tower. If this is a true picture, and since frigates cannot breed annually, the only inference is that the population is divided very roughly into two halves which breed alternately. This basic situation is bound to be vastly complicated by individual variability leading to staggered cycles, and by failed breeders beginning their next cycle in the following year instead of the next but one. As we found with the boobies, failed breeders do not take the full period between cycles – that is, they are ready to breed again before they would have been had they been successful. This point is particularly important since such a large proportion of frigates *do* fail each year and will probably try again the next year. Thus the population will certainly not be divided into two neat halves.

The situation, in terms of the long breeding cycle and the ensuing complications, is not particularly difficult to interpret. There is abundant evidence to show that frigates suffer from the irregularity and often downright poverty of their food supply, indeed they are classic examples of this. Therefore, it will be advantageous not only to have a population in which the individual pairs are not too closely synchronised in their breeding, so that there is a fair spread in any one season, but also to have part of the population breeding one year and part the next year so that the bad effects of extremely unfavourable years are halved. The fact that this would in any case be forced on the species because of its long breeding cycle means that this regime is doubly advantageous; the bad effects of the erratic food supply are minimised by the adaptations of the young to a slow, long and interrupted growth, whilst the very length of their growth enforces the alternate year cycle which is itself adaptive in the way suggested above.

These points begin to make rather more sense of the frigate situation than at first appeared. In response to their peculiar problems of feeding their young, frigates have evolved a regime in which a permanent attachment to mate and site is of secondary importance. Indeed the effects of the long cycle, complicated by individual variability, both normal and in response to failed breeding, will inevitably make it difficult for pairs to stay together in successive cycles. So the male's habit of displaying anew each year and being ready to accept any female is to be expected.

This apparently resolves one of the things that puzzled us – the male's habit of changing his display site and perhaps joining a new group elsewhere. Clusters of displaying males sprang up everywhere and as one died away, most of its males now paired, another came to life and there was no doubt that the same male might display in two different groups. This was a totally different procedure to that of the boobies, who first got themselves a site and then stuck to it, defending it against other males until they acquired a mate. With the frigates, apparently, the site was of little importance until after they had paired – hence the remarkable tolerance of other males, even to the extent of actual bodily contact during display and the facility with which they changed from one display site to another. Site and mate fidelity being relatively transitory in the frigate the only important thing was to obtain a mate that particular season. Since the female-attracting effect of combined display would almost certainly exceed that of a solo performance, an unsuccessful male would leave a group in which display was waning to join a newer one. Thus frigate nests tended to occur in clusters, where displaying males had performed, but the clusters were not necessarily located where those of previous seasons had been.

So much for the frigate's anomalous mating system. Once the pair has really formed, nest-building gets under way. Frigates build flattish platforms of twigs, sometimes substantial but often rather flimsy, depending on the supply. Each twig is won by a hard chase or laborious scanning. Once or twice I saw a frigate stoop to artisan level and pluck his own material, and even then he did it in flight; but they prefer to rob a booby or another frigate. To the flight-adapted frigate violent aerial chase is probably no more tiring than wrestling with a stubborn twig is to a rook. But their chases are spectacular. Frigate against frigate employs every imaginable trick of flight. One of the most spectacular, used by the male trying to get back to his nest with a twig, is to descend in a screaming, ever-tightening spiral that gives his over-shooting pursuer no time to recover. The pair build the twigs into the nest with the customary side to side head movements that roughly interlace them. The female does not contribute nest material until the egg has been laid and even then she brings relatively little, though she does most of the actual building from material brought by the male.

Before egg-laying, sometimes for as long as ten days, the pair sit together on the nest, the male occasionally leaving to gather nest material and returning for bouts of head-waggling. They make a pleasing picture, the male with his high metallic sheen, the scapulars positively iridescent, and the female matronly respectable in her more sober black, lightened by the white breast. They look gentle though the impression is misleading and due mainly to the effect of the dark eye; they cannot seem gentle to the unfortunate frigate chicks which adults occasionally peck to death. They are in fact less prone to attack a human intruder than are boobies and we were rarely bitten. Their beaks have no great ripping power, although the hooked tip can impart a respectable cut in a peevish, snapping sort of way. They find it such a trouble to take off that they usually prefer to sit tight and with a cautious approach one can feel for eggs beneath the sitting birds without suffering so much as a scratch.

The first egg of 1964 was laid on 1 February and the last around 24 June. Frigates lay a single large white egg which weighs on average 85 gm or about twice as much as a hen's egg and constitutes about 7·5 per cent of the female's weight. The female usually hands over to the male relatively soon after laying, though even her first incubation spell may last for eight days. Since she usually spends about six to eight days more or less continuously on the nest prior to laying a first incubation stint of that length means that she probably went at least fourteen to sixteen days without food or water; fourteen to sixteen baking days. No wonder she looks listless and drooping at the end. It must be a great relief to lift her wings and float off into the familiar spaciousness of sky and sea after the cramping confines of a small twig platform. The average incubation stint lasts about ten days and since the egg takes fifty-five days to hatch this means that male and female take three stints each; there are only five or six occasions on which nest relief need occur. This may sound an odd kind of emphasis but it became clear that nest relief was a significant hazard to the egg and anything that reduced the number of times the pair changed-over thereby reduced the risk.

This may not be the only advantage of such long incubation stints.

Frigates probably need a substantial time to find food and the most economical way of ordering things is to take a long spell off duty and feed as heavily as possible. This, in turn, probably enables them to build up reserves of fat upon which they can then exist during the equally long spell of fasting. If they were away just long enough to fill their stomach and crop they would not be able to endure such long fasts and the whole system of long incubation spells would break down. Even so, frigates lose up to twenty per cent of their weight with each incubation spell – that is, three times during the incubation of the egg male and female each lose a fifth of their weight, despite weighing so little to begin with. Probably this is about as much as they could stand, so the incubation periods are in that case as long as they could reasonably be. Other birds, for different reasons, order things quite differently. A gannet sits only about thirty hours at a spell though, on other evidence, I know it could easily manage at least a fortnight if it had to. However, frequent nest reliefs are no disadvantage in the gannet and the whole economic situation is of course quite different.

A number of new problems sprang up as soon as egg-laying got fairly under way and it became obvious that something was sadly amiss; nest after nest lost its egg. Soon the ground was littered with frigates' eggs, many of them entire and fresh, though some had been broken by mocking birds. Some nests had two or even three eggs lodged in the twigs below or on the ground. Egg loss was not caused by predation, but by one of two things. The first, as already hinted, was nest relief. Because the nest is so flimsy and often has an extremely shallow cup, the egg is in some danger of rolling out when the off-going bird disengages itself. Frigates have extremely short legs and cannot spring into the air. Instead they raise their wings and beating them with mounting vigour, gradually lift themselves into the air. This tends to sway the twigs cradling the nest and the egg can easily roll over the edge.

A more important cause of egg loss was interference by other frigates. We never discovered why there were such destructive goings on within the colony, but this was the story for the frigates of Tower Island in 1964. I doubt if it is fully representative of the species as a whole. Of 315 eggs laid 205 were lost before hatching and in many cases a third party was clearly involved. As one could only expect we were never lucky enough to see the entire sequence of events from the beginning. On one visit the nest was intact, with male or female incubating peacefully, and on the next, sometimes only an hour or two later, the egg was beneath the nest, which was occupied either by a male with full display sac, a female, or a pair – the male with inflated sac. Those were the facts.

The 'explanation' was far from obvious. Everything depended on the identity of the bird(s) on the nest following the loss of the egg. Unfortunately, the males were not individually recognisable either by natural features or by rings; their legs were too small to take the size we had, and we shortsightedly omitted to take plastic wing tags, which would have made identification easy without hurting the birds. Various measures, more optimistic than informed, failed to mark the birds for long. One was a code of sticking plaster bill-adornments which made the frigates look like stretcher cases. However, circumstantial evidence was surely enough to show without doubt that in many cases these males were intruders. Where the rightful male had been away for only a small part of his recuperation spell, it was probably safe to assume that he would be at sea and not hanging around the colony. Ordinarily he was never seen at the nest between the end of one incubation spell and the beginning of the next.

Secondly, who was the female, either alone or with the intruder? Probably females alone at the nest soon after egg loss were the rightful ones, returned after the disturbance or incident that led to the loss. Females with the intruder males were in some cases known, from absence of dye markings, to be newcomers and the conclusion must be that they had quickly joined the intruder male displaying on the site. In two instances, the rightful female was actually sitting nearby. Where egg loss occurred almost at the end of a female incubation spell, and we did not discover it for a day or two, it was possible that the male had returned and the pair had recommenced courtship activity prior to laying a replacement egg; we found that frigates will replace a lost egg in one to three weeks and in all cases, the male regained his sac and displayed again before coition and egg laying occurred. Allowing, however, for cases of this kind, the most significant point remains, that there was a great deal of intrusion causing heavy loss of eggs. And not only eggs, for small chicks often went the same way, evicted by intruders after inter-ference had displaced their parents or in some cases, evicted after the parents had stopped guarding the chick, which they do when the latter is about thirty-five days old. Altogether forty-five per cent of the 110 chicks that were lucky enough to hatch were killed by predation or frigate interference before they were six weeks old.

The reason for such massive interference remains obscure; the facts show that there were both spare males and spare females in the population and there were certainly plenty of nest sites. There seems no good reason why such birds should not have paired up and nested in the usual way without upsetting the affairs of established pairs and drastically reducing the breeding success of the colony. However, we can at least partly understand why breeding frigates were so easily displaced. If the territorial behaviour and pair bond is that much weaker than in most sea birds, for reasons given earlier, it follows that territorial invasion and the disruption of the pair bond will be correspondingly easier. Indeed, we had striking proof of this in two cases, where an owning male returned to find an intruder actually attacking his chick and yet simply stood by and did not attack or displace the intruder – we had to do the job for him, whereupon he then went to and fed his chick. It seems that the factor of over-riding importance in the frigate's life history is the scarce and erratic food supply, and the complicated results of coming to grips with this have by indirect means led to the long breeding cycle, widely-spaced breeding (once in two years) and indirectly, through this, to his unusual territorial and pair formation. Given these, the apparently stupid and inefficient behaviour in the matter of intrusion simply follows – his behaviour apparatus is not tuned to deal with them. This still leaves open the question 'why the intrusion' and open I'm afraid it must be left.

The frigate chicks lucky enough to hatch were unimaginably ugly. Even a newly hatched booby was beautiful by comparison. Apart from their sickly colour, they had heavy down-bent bills, and enormously thick eyebrow ridges. Apparently reluctantly, they sprouted white down and began to look more tolerable, especially when the precocious scapular and interscapular feathers grew, giving them neat black shoulder capes. We often puzzled about this, and concluded (apparently as had been suggested before we were born) that they protected the young against the weather. However, we went a little further. Perhaps black is specially useful in absorbing heat from the sun and so warming the chicks after the shivery Galapagos nights! Frigate chicks have a very old-mannish look as they squat, hunched up, on their guano-whitened platform. When approached by man, they open their livid blue beaks to the widest extent and, mandibles trembling with the stress, produce the most piteous caterwauling, snapping and lunging among the squeals, till they almost tumble from the nest. Their weight rose slowly from the birth weight of 61 gm to 85 gm at one week, then 127, 209, 281, 343, 486, 480 and 632 gm at two, three, four, five, six, seven and eight weeks respectively. They are fed by regurgitation, inserting their heads into the parent's gullet. At the approach of food, they set up a curious bobbing movement, in the hunched posture accompanied by a grating squeal like an angry pig. Oddly, they do not flail their wings as young red-foots do, although they often spread them and continue bobbing from between their great vanes. Fully feathered juveniles, as big as adults and capable fliers, squat by the hour on their favourite perch, scanning the hot sky for their parents. They cock one eye upwards, rather than looking binocularly as gannets and boobies. Hunger often compels them to intervene when a luckier juvenile is enjoying a feed, but they are soon pecked off. Unlike the adult males, who will try to snatch food being passed from frigate to offspring, the juveniles do not attempt such advanced piracy.

In April and May, the frigate colony looked far from healthy; besides the many nests with whole or broken eggs lying outside there was a growing number of dead youngsters or their remains. Some had fallen from their nests and been unable to climb back, though they had crawled pathetically far along the ground beneath the canopy. Many had fallen prey to the Galapagos short-eared owl but, it seemed, quite needlessly. Their parents had stopped guarding them, so at the very tender age of about five weeks, still clothed in down but for their little black capes, the chicks were left to cope with whatever marauder chanced along. The owls chanced along quite regularly and hardly a night passed without another frigate victim. Considering that simply by extending the guard stage for another three or four weeks, the frigates could have given their offspring a chance to grow big enough to defend themselves, it seemed crazily inefficient behaviour, explicable only on the supposition that the parents were experiencing such difficulty feeding their young that they could not afford to have one adult as nursemaid any longer; both were needed for hunting. In fairness, I must say that we had good evidence, from the growth of frigate and red-footed booby young, that food was in fact rather scarce at that time. Maybe in better years the guard stage is extended. By November when we returned to Tower, the juveniles with their characteristic rusty-coloured heads and white bellies, were squatting stoically on or near the same perches that had held juveniles when we first arrived in December of the previous year. A few were already dried carcases on the ground, whittling down the number of potential survivors still further. The stage was almost set for the beginning of a new cycle. We would have liked to stay and see it; there were so many points to settle. However, we are sure of the essential fact that the scarcity of the frigate's food supply in the Galapagos has had many effects on its breeding biology. In evolving mechanisms to cope with this, the frigate has found that drastic alterations to all sorts of inter-connected behavioural systems have necessarily followed, territory and pair formation among them. No doubt the story is much more beautiful and complex than this sketchy essay has told; the frigate is a mysterious creature and will still generously reward curious naturalists.

# Predators and Scavengers 14

The barn owl is one of the most widely distributed birds in the world, reaching even the Galapagos as *Tyto alba punctatissima*, the Galapagos barn owl, which is very like our own, though smaller and darker above. Apparently it is restricted to Santa Cruz, James, Albemarle, Narborough and south Seymour, though there seems no reason why it could not spread to others. It is one of the least known Galapagos birds and only the scrappiest information exists about its habits. It eats mainly mice and rats, now present in the form of its familiar prey *Mus musculus*, the house mouse, and *Rattus rattus*, the house or black rat, though originally it preyed on the endemic rat *Oryzomys* or *Neoryzomys* spp., of which several races occur in the Galapagos. Galapagos rats are now regrettably rare. Eibl-Eibesfeldt points out how nicely they fitted into the Galapagos fauna, whereas the introduced species 'ravages the natural flora and eats lizards' eggs'. Against it, the Galapagos rat is totally inadequate.

The most detailed analysis of the barn owl's food* showed that of 390 warm-blooded animals only 9·7 per cent were birds. Remains of two bats were found in the pellets, one of them, *Lasiurus cinereus*, widespread on the South American continent but known in the Galapagos only since 1964 (Niethammer).

On Santa Cruz I saw a barn owl in the great cave which runs beneath the road about two and a half miles north of Academy Bay. The cave opens as a large hole only a few yards from the road, but the entrance lies in a subsidence jumbled with boulders, and unless you knew exactly where to look you could spend hours in the search. A few yards' error in the Galapagos can be as good as miles. At first the roof of the tunnel is comfortably high but deeper underground it becomes low and narrow. After a long stooping journey it becomes so low that further progress means squirming flat on one's belly

* Abs, Curio, etc. (1965).

until the cave ends where floor and ceiling meet. It is vaguely alarming to press on and on, squeezing through narrow slits in the absolute blackness, with an awful feeling that the earth which presses so insistently on all sides, is ready to slip. That would be nothing fresh in the Galapagos.

About three-quarters of the way along, a narrow chimney rises vertically towards a chink of sky. Roger Perry, my companion, wanted to climb the crack. The ascent was not difficult, but still the incident sticks in my mind. Roger is that hypothetical beast, the 'type' Englishman, dryly humorous, imperturbably well mannered and impeccably dressed (perhaps I should have written the Englishman's idea of the 'type' Englishman!). When duty or inclination indicate a visit to an outlying island Roger goes along as he went to his job with the B.B.C., in suede Chelsea boots, faultlessly creased trousers, long-sleeved shirt, bow tie and pork pie hat; and of course, the pipe. The first time he came to Hood, dressed like this he placed one elegant foot on a block of lava and tied his shoe lace in front of an interested and respectfully grouped audience of sea-lions and iguanas. After his arrival in the Galapagos the islanders, amazed and, who knows, perhaps impressed, waited for the supply of shirts, bow ties, trousers and boots to dry up and the workday garb of the field naturalist to appear; in vain. Sartorial elegance was but a minor expression of his perfectionist nature. Serene among lava, cacti, sea-lions and iguanas, Roger picked his precise way. To return to the cave chimney – he climbed it without removing pipe or pork pie hat and emerged into daylight amid the scrub and lava. To my deep regret no thunderstruck Ecuadorian was there to goggle as this impossible apparition squeezed up from the bowels of the earth and out through the tiny crack in the hot crust of lava, buried among the scrub and cacti. That way legends grow.

The other owl of the Galapagos, the short-eared owl, has already forced his predatory habits on our attention. It is widespread in the archipelago, occurring on practically all the main islands – a measure of its ability to live on a variety of prey. Unlike the barn owl, it is largely a bird-eater. Even on islands such as Santa Cruz and Champion, where there are rats and mice these formed only about thirty per cent of the prey taken. The rest were birds, and usually the species most common on the island in question – petrels on Tower and finches on Santa Cruz. Two German scientists, Curio and Kramer (1964), studied the reactions of ground finches and mocking birds to predators, including owls and hawks. Their interesting conclusions, based on the birds' reactions to stuffed predators and non-predators of various kinds, were first that Darwin's finches fear carnivorous mammals substantially less than avian predators or snakes. Since there are no mammalian predators in the Galapagos this seems adaptive and to be expected. Then they found that avian predators often provoked a fright response, but, often, so did similarly-sized, harmless species. However, predators were feared more than the harmless birds, except in the small finch *Geospiza difficilis* of Tower. A somewhat puzzling feature, though, was the absence of a hard and fast correlation between fear of a predator and its presence or absence on the island concerned. Fear of avian predators and the distribution of these were only loosely correlated. On Tower, for example, there are many short-eared owls and yet the finches show hardly any fright reaction to stuffed owls. Curio believes this is because the owls on Tower prey almost entirely on petrels and therefore, so far as finches are concerned, there are no predators. This is not a fully convincing interpretation, since the petrels are confined to one corner, whilst the owls occur all over the island. In any case, we saw for ourselves that they commonly attack several species other than petrels and there is certainly no guarantee that finches will be spared. On the other hand, Wenman specimens of *G. difficilis* do show fear of avian predators, even though there are none on the island. So there is obviously much more to be discovered about this intriguing subject.

One conclusion does seem to be that in the relatively short length of time, measurable in thousands rather than millions of years, that the Galapagos mockers and finches have been separated from their mainland ancestors they have in some cases entirely lost one of their basic, inborn anti-predator reactions. In the finches with fear responses, the specific releasing mechanism underlying the recognition of avian predators matures, even though the finches have had absolutely no experience of predators. Experience of the predator has little effect on the functioning of the mechanism, which is probably inborn. The differences between islands are, therefore, largely genetic. The loss of reaction to predators is in some ways analogous to the celebrated tameness of Galapagos species, which no Galapagos visitor ever fails to remark. It seems that the land birds have become warier than they were a hundred or so years ago when, as Darwin's (1890) quotes and personal observations show, doves, finches, mockers, flycatchers, etc, were killed in large numbers with switches and sticks. However long it took the finches to lose their innate predator response, it has apparently not taken very long for some Galapagos species to acquire an innately enhanced though by no means complete fear response to man.

Like our own species, the Galapagos short-eared owl hunts partly by day, but mainly rests quietly in dark holes or roosts in trees. The Gifford expedition in 1905–06 recorded more than twenty in one day on Tower and claimed that they preyed extensively on giant centipedes, a habit which made them welcome visitors to our camp. The centipedes didn't disappear, but the swallow-tailed gull chicks did. The owl population of Tower was certainly high, which may be linked with the enormous number of petrels, in particular, and with the absence of all other predators that might compete.

*Figure 49* Galapagos short-eared owl

SWALLOW-TAILED GULL
40 The alarm call of the swallow-tail, a thin high note followed by a rattle, is one of the most evocative Galapagos sounds

41 A day-old chick crouches in the shade, its drab colours blending with the lava and coral fragments. But short-eared owls still find almost every one

FLIGHT
42 Juvenile frigate chases male to
steal his twig

43 Adult blue-footed booby

44 White booby just air-borne

FRIGATE
45 Male with fully inflated sac, displaying in a mangrove

FRIGATE
46 Juvenile taking food from the female's mouth—often a bolus of flying fish

47 An energy-saving sleeping position of juvenile frigate

PREDATORS
48 A handsome black buzzard with yellow talons

49 Galapagos short-eared owl, which preys on young boobies

50 An immature pelican with skeins of guanay cormorants above

**PERUVIAN BOOBY**

51 Peruvian boobies and guanay cormorants on the slopes and buildings of Guañape Norte. Boobies and cormorants nest cleanly separated from each other

52 Male (right) 'advertises' to female. Foot-lifting, as here, is commonly associated with advertising

53 Mates often perform vigorous mutual jabbing

54 Calling loudly they bend forward to touch the ground. Symbolic nest-building is common pair behaviour

PERUVIAN BOOBY

55 Peruvian boobies nest densely but regularly spaced. The nest is made of excreta, dried like cement. The chick on the central nest is begging for food

56 Male 'advertising' or sky-pointing

57 Distance between nests is maintained by jabbing or threat display

The Galapagos hawk, a most beautiful raptor of the near cosmo-
politan buzzard or *Buteo* genus, is similar to the group of New
World species including the red-tailed hawk, Swainson's hawk and
the zone-tailed hawk (to which it is most closely related) which
between them cover North and Central America and part of South
America. The Galapagos hawk is also very like our own common
buzzard. It has for me that subtle quality (perhaps its blackness)
which makes it far more of a special Galapagos bird than either owl
species. Tower surprisingly lacks Galapagos hawks, which are, in
fact, absent from several islands to which its powers of flight could
easily take it. Hood held two pairs on Punta Suarez, where we
camped. For a while one pair seemed about to build on a lava
outcrop near the tent and may have been deterred by us. The pair
often swept in together, screaming and calling wildly, shooting
their legs forwards to clasp the knobbly black lava with their ochre
talons. There they shuffled their powerful wings and settled into a
hunched posture, black lumps against the sky as though carved out
of the lava. We could almost always find a pair near the tip of the
point, sitting on top of a bush or rock, watching the sea-lions
sporting in the shallows.

The Galapagos hawk is not common in the archipelago and has
decreased in the last thirty years. Rambeck told me that it was
common prior to 1930, when he left Santa Cruz. He returned in
1935 to find it had become much scarcer, partly because of persecution from settlers, but also he thought owing to the virtual disappearance of the native rat, which could not compete with the
introduced rat. The hawk breeds on Santa Cruz, James, Barrington,
Hood, Isabella, Culpepper, Narborough and Baltra. It takes quite a
wide variety of food, and among birds the remains of young
penguins, albatrosses, frigates, blue-footed boobies and shearwaters
have been found at its nest or seen taken. It is reputed to prey
extensively on marine and land iguanas, which, if true, makes its
absence from Tower all the more mysterious since there the marine
iguanas are a particularly small and convenient size and incredibly
numerous. In fact I would suspect that only the very small lizards
would be available to hawks; medium or large specimens would be
too strong and well-armoured. Darwin recorded that the buzzards
were important predators of newly-hatched tortoises, as well as the

small Galapagos land birds (doves, finches and mocking birds). The hawk is also a scavenger, eating carrion and probably sea-lion placentas. Goat entrails which we left on the rocks soon attracted their attention and Castro found the remains of a kid which he thought had been attacked by the hawks. On Santa Cruz it used to feed largely on the native rat, and no doubt the Galapagos mouse, and Mr Rambeck recalled that it would take one offered by hand. We found them fairly tame but not remotely to that extent. Like other species they are learning to mistrust man.

*Tropidurus* lizards and small birds form a large part of their diet and the mockers, at least on Hood, have evolved a dramatic response. If a hawk sails over when a group of mocking birds are feeding, one member, presumably the one that first spots the hawk, gives a short, loud chirp and they all vanish like magic beneath the nearest bush. We saw this several times and never knew the signal to fail in its effect. It is not uncommon for birds to utter warning notes which other members of the flock, even other species, will heed. For example, a mixed party of tits feeding in a wood, or chaffinches and bramblings at the edge of a field, will flee when they hear the special alarm call given by a bird that spots a hunting sparrow-hawk. But a main feature of such warning signals is that they are attenuated, high-pitched 'see-*ee*' notes which avoid any abrupt changes in pitch and amplitude and are extremely difficult to locate. It is believed that this kind of note has evolved because it is best suited to act as a warning without pin-pointing the whereabouts of the author. By contrast, brief, loud chirps with a sudden rise or fall in pitch or amplitude are easy to locate (because they are picked up sooner and louder by one ear and therefore give a directional cue). This kind of call is given, for example, by a hen which wants to gather her chicks. By using a brief, loud chirp the mocker theoretically betrays its position, but presumably its sprinting prowess is such that it can afford this more emphatic signal without endangering itself.

Even so, there are puzzles associated with this kind of apparently altruistic behaviour. Why should one bird warn another, unless that other is its own young or possibly its mate? In those circumstances it is enhancing its breeding success and so will enjoy the favour of natural selection in the normal way; its behaviour is an adaptive part of parental care or pair relationship. But by what mechanism could a bird benefit from warning an unrelated individual at some risk, however slight, to itself? Perhaps by reducing the hawk's chance of catching anybody, including itself. Where a group of birds flees simultaneously rather than dispersing singly, the hunter presumably finds it more difficult to snap one up. There would certainly seem little future for the individual born with the tendency to cry 'look out' for the benefit of others but at the cost of its own life. Another odd point is that although the call acts like magic in clearing a spot of mockers, we never heard one give it as a false alarm to clear the others away from food and give itself the chance to grab it. It seems by no means obvious why such a situation has not arisen. One might have expected that an individual or two would eventually learn to connect his alarm chirrup with the disappearance of his food competitors and, perhaps being a trifle bolder than they, would begin emerging sooner and sooner after calling until eventually he did not hide at all, but merely called and claimed his reward when the others ran. It is no argument to say that such misuse would destroy the value of the signal; this is true, but one needs to know how it can be avoided without invoking

*Figure 50* Galapagos hawk carries off a Darwin's finch

mystic phenomena, altruism, intelligent behaviour and other attributes which mocking birds are unlikely to possess in high enough degree.

The Galapagos hawk lays one to three eggs, usually one or two, in a substantial nest of twigs, the cup lined with finer material and with fresh greenery added, as in our buzzard. The Punta Suarez nest in August 1964 was built on top of a commanding crag but trees are also used. The season is ill-defined; although eggs seem to be laid mainly in the first half of the year there are records of eggs for practically every month. The incubating female on Punta Suarez slipped off her egg long before we reached the nest. The only danger lay in the nosey-parker mockers, which arrived within less than a minute and would certainly have taken a stab at the egg but for our intervention. With difficulty we managed to keep them away whilst ourselves retreating far enough to encourage the hawk's return. Despite successful efforts on this occasion the egg later disappeared.

It seems rather remarkable that the Galapagos should be as free from predators as they are, and particularly that, except for the Galapagos hawk, all the scavengers of Central and South America should be absent. In Central America and Ecuador black vultures are as common as crows, often scavenging in groups like barnyard fowl, in the small towns and villages. Turkey vultures soar overhead and there are plenty of other predators or predators-cum-scavengers such as king vultures, several kites and a hawk or two. Why shouldn't black vultures scavenge in the Galapagos or a small insect-eating kite fill the vacant aerial niche? Competition between species could probably be largely avoided by subtle specialisations. Kruuk has recently shown that even where five vulture species feed on the same prey species in Africa, they all have their specialised feeding habits. One tears large chunks from the carcase, another picks up the scraps flung aside, a third takes splinters of bone and so on. In the Galapagos there is no lack of prey or carrion, but few birds to eat them, especially the carrion. The mere 600–1,200 miles of sea are not much of a barrier, though there is no migratory route taking birds in that direction, so colonisation depends on strays. Presumably too few individuals of such species ever strayed there to become established. This general lack of predators must have contributed to the tameness of Galapagos species, just as the lack of human persecution on the hawks had until the last thirty years or so made it unnecessary for them to fear man.

There were no tracks to our bird colonies, but we soon found our feet wandering precisely the same way each day, threading automatically across the stony flats, through scrub and over heaps of lava. Here was a slab that always cockled, there a complete goat's skeleton every bone *in situ*, in this bush a half-finished finches' nest; maybe it belonged to the Darwin's finch I saw carried off in the yellow talons of a hawk. These and similar landmarks were our milestones. Like wild animals we had our home range mapped and used the easiest routes. In its way such familiarity, especially when extended to animals, is as satisfying as more dramatic experiences, though less spectacular and harder to communicate. It is fascinating to know individual animals, as people prove by their strong emotional identification with the animal *dramatis personnae* in Tarka the otter, Elsa the Lioness, Goldie the eagle and many others. Every naturalist is rewarded for living a while in one spot by getting to know his neighbours. We could hardly keep pace with ours. Besides our colour-ringed boobies and albatrosses, our dyed frigates, tame finches, mocking birds and doves and battle-scarred bull sea-lions, we had a nodding acquaintance with individual snakes, lizards, owls, flycatchers, iguanas and goats.

Fortunately for the vegetation there were no goats on Tower and one hopes there never will be, but they are everywhere on Hood. More than on other, mainly larger islands (Santa Cruz, Barrington, San Cristobal, etc.) where they have been introduced, usually to provide fishermen with a source of meat, they have played havoc with the vegetation. Their tracks criss-cross Hood and it is almost impossible to examine a square yard of ground without finding a dropping. It is miraculous that they can exist at all in this lava desert. They are phenomenal vegetable scavengers, eating the thick, fleshy leaves of the *cryptocarpus* shrub when they can get them, but also turning to a filamentos lichen (*Ushera plicata*), as dry as tinder, seaweed or tough corrugated bark which, I imagine, contains about as much nourishment as steel shavings. Elsewhere I have seen goats persistently eat cardboard. We often saw them drink sea-water and they also lick the stones and twigs wetted by the fine Galapagos mists.

On the whole they seemed in good condition, though some were painfully emaciated and obviously diseased. One weary female, doubtless riddled with parasites, collapsed whilst feediug, rolled on her side twitching convulsively, then lay still. Her puzzled little kid ran jerkily away from and back to her, clearly showing his conflicting feelings of fear and attachment. Eventually she climbed shakily to her feet, but died within a few days. The kid tried to join a slightly older one, but the nanny gave it short shrift and it never found a foster-mother.

Most of the goats were a dun brown variously marked with white, though there were some rich chestnuts, strawberry roans, yellows and handsome blacks. They were genuinely wild and, like deer, the Hood ones went about in tightly knit groups, usually a female with one, two or even three generations of young, probably her own. Sometimes two or three nannies led a group of younger beasts. Youngsters often split off or were driven away from the family units and moved about together. The old billies had separate groups, always the same individuals together like old men in their exclusive park-bench groupings, and never showed any hostility to each other. Beebe, however recorded ferocious fights among the billies of Seymour island and no doubt, as in related wild forms, there will be reproductive fighting among them. Maybe ours were senile. The goats on Barrington have increased to such an extent that, apparently, there is real food shortage among them. At least, the many specimens shot (for conservation reason) in 1964, were, overall, in extremely poor condition. This, if the food factor really was responsible, is an interesting example of a herbivore over-exploiting limited food resources.

By August we had battened some eight months on a basic diet of tinned tuna and sardines etc. eked out by the odd langusta and parrot fish. The goats were certainly a pest and a danger to rarer and more valuable animals so we earmarked a fine youngster for the pot. Every day he and his mother, a saddleback, wandered down to the tip of Punta Suarez browsing as they went. Then they turned and came back past our camp at midday. All the goats followed fairly well-defined paths and time-tables like this, as a lot of animals do. When I tried to get really close they became wary and kept a respectable distance with a few shrubs as a shield. One morning whilst watching blue-footed boobies I spotted saddle-back browsing towards the point. I ran for the gun and began my version of stalking, though it was mid-morning and baking hot, not the weather for crawling under spiny shrubs and over uneven ground. The goats were coming straight towards me so I waited five minutes before raising my head, only to see their distant backsides – an appropriate gesture. After a detour and more sweating I settled down again, but when I looked saddle-back was gazing straight at me, ears forward and head high. She couldn't see me and there was hardly any wind, but she was suspicious and took the kid away out to open ground. At the next abortive attempt, when I was scuttling along bent double, a blue-foot exploded beneath my feet like a rocketing pheasant. It was most unusual to find a solitary blue-foot squatting unsociably amongst dense scrub and it made enough commotion to rattle the dry bones of the goat carcases littering the ground, victims of previous campaigns to clear the island. Eventually I got fairly close without being seen; saddle-back and the kid settled down to rest under a dense cryptocarpus canopy, within fifteen yards. When I stood up they both immediately rose and stood still, presenting a perfect target. But after all that I simply let them go, because I knew them too well.

The eventual victim had to be a complete stranger. Within an hour it had been skinned, cleaned and quartered and the succulent joints hung temptingly from the veranda roof. The mocking birds got to work instantly and clinging, tit-like, with their strong feet and legs, hammered away with their serviceable beaks, tearing off strips of flesh. They were so intent that I easily plucked them off the carcase as they fed. That goat was really good, quite as good as young mutton and better than old.

Most animals of course are perfectly edible if properly cooked, though James Fisher tells me that boa constrictor is tough; he sampled one of the Regent's Park specimens that had to be killed on the outbreak of the last war. Healthy grain-fed rats are as good as rabbits and squirrels are well known to be extremely tasty, though few people bother to eat them. Even venison is ridiculously scarce in Scotland, apparently because there is no demand; many of the hills are swarming with deer and plenty are shot, but they are mainly exported to Germany. We did not try sea-lions (our own seals are quite edible); I suppose young ones would have been quite good. They were far too intelligent and playful to shoot, anyway, though we were not above pulling their legs as they slept. Iguanas are reputed to make good eating to those, in Darwin's words, 'whose stomachs soar above all prejudices', and turtle steaks are extremely good, whilst the edibility of the giant tortoise was one of its fatal liabilities. Very few birds are distasteful and even old gannet and shag is delicious, whilst young gannets or 'gugas' have been famous for centuries. One or two thousand of them used to be collected annually from the Bass; they fetched about 20*d*. each in the second half of the eighteenth century but dropped to 8*d.*–10*d*. by the late nineteenth century. The fat from these solan geese was considered to have remarkable curative properties: 'Within the bowels of these geese there is a kind of grease to be had of singular force in medicine and fleaing likewise from their bodies with the fat, they make an oile verie profitable for the gout and menie and other diseases in the haunches and groines of mankind.'* Advertised on television with one of those irritating ditties, there is no telling what gastronomic adventures could be initiated. Mass advertising that can persuade us to like what the bread factories want to turn out – that is, soggy cardboard – has an open field.

Turtle steaks are good, but I would rather do without them; few animals can be more difficult to kill. With the crew of the Beagle we caught and despatched one in Turtle Bay, but it was a disgusting blood bath. To my mind it is literally degrading when one has to struggle to extinguish an animal's tenacious hold on life. The end result may be the same as an instant kill, but the effect on the butcher is not.

The chase, however, was exhilarating. We cruised around in an outboard powered dinghy, the warm water turbid with suspended particles of mud licked from the twisted mangrove roots and the vegetation-smothered banks, and agitated by the rushes of many feeding sharks. The helmsman held the critical post, since he must manoeuvre the boat into position so that the gaffer can hook the turtle by its leathery skin or under the anterior tip of the carapace. Then it is the brute strength of the crew that hauls the threshing reptile over the gunwales amidst flying spray; the camera is unfortunate whose eye seeks to record the event.

* Hector Boece, *History of Scotland*, translated by Hollindshead.

One of the most efficient marine scavengers is the Galapagos 'dragon', the marine iguana. These lizards have turned back the evolutionary clock and returned to an amphibious life. Thus there are now aquatic, arboreal, burrowing, aerial (gliding) and terrestrial lizards. The age of the greatest flowering of reptiles, though, ended more than a hundred million years ago; now there are only the remnants of this order, which sprang from the primitive amphibians during the Carboniferous and dominated the middle or Mesozoic era with such a profusion of fantastic forms. Even today, whilst giant tortoises, turtles and iguanas remain in the Galapagos, the reptiles will not lack notable examples. The literature is unkind to the iguanas, from Colnett's 'the most hideous appearance imaginable' to Darwin's 'a hideous-looking creature of a dirty black colour, stupid and sluggish in its movements'. We found them amusing and by no means unattractive.

It is not known when the now distinctive Galapagos marine iguanas (closely related to the iguanas of mainland South America) reached the islands, but they are obviously strong candidates for an early assisted passage from the mainland, capable of clinging powerfully to flotsam, surviving prolonged immersion in salt water and long periods of starvation. Beebe's specimen survived a hundred days' complete starvation without weakening. They could doubtless swim from the continent if lucky enough to escape predators. When they arrived they would not need land vegetation or any other forms of land-based life, so they would stand an excellent chance of survival. At any rate they and their relatives, the land iguanas and tortoises, have successfully filled the large niche occupied elsewhere in the world by mammalian herbivores. That is, they had filled it until man introduced donkeys, goats, pigs and cattle.

Marine iguanas are readily distinguished from Galapagos land iguanas by their tail, strongly flattened in the vertical plane and now a powerful swimming organ. The tails of land iguanas are more or less round in cross section. The marine iguanas are corpulent lizards with exceedingly tough, sagging hides and immensely powerful five-fingered feet equipped with sharp curved claws capable of clinging to a slab of greasy marble. At least they easily cling to the equally slippery, wave-scoured, slime-covered surfaces of the intertidal zone, where they feed on the glutinous algae, or to the sea bed where they browse on *sargassum* or others of the three hundred sea-weeds found in the Galapagos.

The largest specimens, from Santa Cruz or San Cristobal, may reach a length of four feet from nose to tail tip and weigh, according to Beebe twenty pounds. Tower iguanas are a coal-black, pygmy race, never more than eighteen inches long and usually less. Hood's iguanas are much more colourful, brightly decorated with red and green patches. It is perhaps not surprising that Hood and Tower should show two markedly different forms; they also provide the most extreme forms of certain birds. The Tower representative of the large-billed ground finch has the biggest bill in the archipelago, whilst the Tower mocking bird is the smallest. As Beebe points out, there are two prominent features of Galapagos races or sub-species – they have several very marked characters distinguishing one from the other, but they also possess unpredictable blends or combinations of characters either in the race as a whole or even in individuals. This phenomenon sorely taxed systematists trying to arrange specimens in some sort of sensible linear order. In the absence of the fuller mainland range of selective pressures, many characters that on the mainland would have provided material for differences of species status, in the Galapagos have not realised this potential. On the other hand, the few characters with special survival value have been markedly pressured and developed strong race-specific features. Both points are well shown in the range of forms of the Galapagos snake, marine iguana and mocking bird.

Furthermore among the Galapagos islands Tower and Hood seem to have proved peculiarly difficult of access; consequently there are both odd omissions from their fauna – like the hawk and snake absent from Tower – and strongly differentiated local populations of several species, probably reflecting the infrequency with which individuals from other islands have infiltrated the population. Frequent introduction of specimens from elsewhere would have encouraged a blending of characteristics and opposed the development of specially distinctive forms, which prolonged and more or less complete isolation has favoured. Nevertheless, it may seem remarkable that the marine iguanas, with their great swimming power, have remained in more or less isolated island populations which, as Eibl-Eibesfeldt shows, are now racially distinct. Something, probably sharks, has prevented iguanas from establishing the habit of inter-island crossings, though in the absence of any biological gain there is, of course, no reason why they should have done so.

The sophisticated tastes of Carl Angermeyer's semi-tame marine iguanas, conditioned to come for household scraps at the rattle of pots and pans, have already been mentioned. On Tower we could rarely entice them into the camp area, though their natural feeding grounds were only a few yards away. Occasionally we came across them as much as a quarter of a mile inland and wondered if they were beginning to appropriate the niche of the land iguana, which does not occur on Tower. We also found them many feet up in trees. Mainly, though, the marine iguanas stick to their sea rocks, retreating a few yards beyond high tide to sunbathe and rest on the dry lava. Stick is just the right word for a feeding iguana. The little black beasts crouch low on the slimy boulders, applying their blunt muzzles closely to the minute growth and cropping to right or left, or laying their heads sideways like a dog with a bone, the better to graze with their sharp, tricuspid teeth. Their sturdy limbs move in the dogged crawl typical of the primitive land-walking animal before the further evolution and improved joint mechanism of the pentadactyl limb allowed the mammalian way of locomotion. The waves break and foam around them, scouring the boulders and their industrious black gnomes, but the gnomes are still there when the water sucks back. Like the red crabs in whose company they so often feed, they can resist enormous suction pressures. Unlike the crabs they are none the worse if a heavy wave does dislodge them, for they wear their skeletons under their tough, scaly hides, nicely packed around with resilient tissues – difficult to break. One often sees a swimming iguana absorb a thunderous hammering on the stormy south-west coast of Hood, hurled violently against the rocks in the foaming water, but unruffled at the end of it. They can withstand prolonged submersion. A member of Darwin's *Beagle* crew submerged one for an hour, after which it was still lively. A member of the 1964 Galapagos International Project frightened one which was in mid water returning to the surface after feeding on the bottom (Hobson). It returned to the bottom and stayed there a further half hour. He also saw them feeding at a depth of thirty-five feet and suspected that they went considerably deeper.

One would imagine that sharks and other large predatory fish would endanger iguanas in deep water and relatively far from land, and Eibesfeldt says that shark stomachs often do contain iguana remains. Yet Beebe concludes that sharks can be only a minor danger and indeed iguanas would otherwise scarcely feed under water so regularly, unless, of course, there were so many that such an extra source of food became essential. I particularly noticed that their tails were always entire, which meant that none had partly evaded a shark attack but lost its tail in the process. As a minor and hypothetical point, one might also expect that if sharks were important predators, the iguanas would have evolved a special break joint in their tail vertebrae, enabling them to cast their tails as many lizards do in order to baffle and distract predators. Perhaps such a tail would be incompatible with the motion used in swimming.

On the other hand, and despite its willingness to enter water of its own accord, the iguana has a well-known dread of remaining in water when forcibly immersed. It will always return straight to land, time after time. I imagine dozens of people have confirmed Darwin's account of this, as we did. Nor will iguanas enter water as an escape reaction when disturbed on land. They persist in hiding in crevices or running over the cliff edge and part way down the face. Darwin's interpretation was that iguanas had an innate fright reaction to sharks and reacted to any form of fright by the appropriate 'shark' reaction, namely flight to land. This implies that iguanas have a single type of fright reaction and indeed it seems that they do not fear much else, even if they do fear sharks. For instance, they completely ignored the hawks on Hood; Eibesfeldt noted this too. Iguanas have been recorded among the hawk's prey, but it seems likely that they are not commonly taken. Certainly the iguanas have no tendency to use their armoury of weapons. Beebe remarks that they would do great damage to any bird of prey with their powerful clawed feet, but in fact they never try either to bite, scratch, butt or use their dorsal spines when handled. Any scratches they inflict are quite incidental. Their potential defences surely suggest that land predators, at any rate, do not bother iguanas. This, incidentally, would make the small Tower iguanas even more suitable as potential prey for hawks, if they ever got there.

Eibesfeldt provides an entertaining account of the iguana's

behaviour on land. He describes their interesting method of finding
their way to their customary resting places by smell, licking the
ground and then testing the result by applying their tongue to an
olfactory organ in the roof of the mouth. Aggressive iguanas have a
vigorous nodding display and discharge spurts of water from their
nostrils, probably the secretion of the salt gland. Then there is the
highly formalised territorial 'jousting' behaviour, in which rivals
push against each other with their formidably spiked heads, but do
not bite. The victor also responds to the submission of his opponent
by suspending his attack and allowing the loser to escape. Eibesfeldt
goes on to a Lorenzian development of this theme of ritualised
aggressive behaviour taking the place of overt conflict in animals
which possess harmful or killing weapons. There are, of course,
exceptions and real fights may be common and damaging even in
species with powerful weapons of attack, as we saw in the gannet
(Chapter 5).

In March 1964 we found a spot on the north-west coast of Tower
honeycombed with the burrows of egg-laying iguanas. Spurts of
sand emerged from the openings as the iguanas excavated with their
fore-limbs and kicked out the debris with their hind-limbs. We
tripped and stumbled as we repeatedly broke through the crust;
the whole of one small sandy area was undermined. Iguanas lay two
or three eggs which they cover with sand and leave to hatch. Like
all reptiles they leave their young to fend for themselves from the
very beginning.

Predators, we have concluded, are a negligible factor in iguanas'
lives. So is starvation. They must die of disease or senility! One day,
in the full heat of the Galapagos sun, with the black lava at a temperature of about 140°F., the ancient lizard, as black and craggy as
the rock, clambers lingeringly to his favourite slab. Nodding ever
more slowly, he directs the last derisive vapour puffs from his
nostrils. Then (looking a little like Muggeridge) with 'his smug
lizard's smile unchanging' he returns to the womb of the island that
spawned him.

The land iguanas are now very much rarer than marine ones,
occuring only on the central islands of the group and in numbers
much reduced since 1834 when Darwin complained that on James
it was difficult to find a camping spot free from their burrows. I

photographed one or two on Plazas, where they are thought to be increasing slightly. The quick vertical nods of the head, common to many lizards, are found in the land iguanas. Perhaps in the family as a whole the movement originated as scanning to aid judgment of the position of prey, though now of course the herbivorous iguanas have no need for such an ability. Lizards, like most birds, lack binocular vision and so find it more difficult to judge depth.

Galapagos land iguanas eat shoots, bark, flowers and fruits and pads of cacti. Beebe in a delightful account of these impressive saurians, records an interesting incident in which a land iguana on Seymour apparently procured *opuntia* fruits by striking the base of the plant until the fruits fell. Whether this really showed the intelligence Beebe supposed, or the foot movements against the cacti were intention movements of climbing, is perhaps doubtful, but the gastronomic prowess of the reptile in swallowing 'spines and all' cannot be queried. Many Galapagos creatures, doubtless 'encouraged', if that is the right word, by the harshness of their environment, have taken to extraordinary feeding habits. I have already mentioned the mocking birds eating faeces, the finches and mockers drinking blood, the crabs picking scales (or ticks) from the marine iguanas and the amazing tool-using finches that probe out insects by using appropriately shaped twigs or spines. Life is hard there and many

*Figure 51* Marine iguanas

empty or near empty niches, though these are often unprepossessing, have encouraged inhabitants to experiment. We could add to the list the amusing crab-eating antics of the Galapagos yellow warbler. On Tower these colourful little warblers, with crimson crown feathers, often stalked the tiny fiddler crabs that formed a dense colony in the sand of the creek, inland from the open bay. As the fiddlers emerged cautiously from their burrows after the departing tide had laid a new supply of detritus at their doors, the warbler dashed and fluttered here and there, snapping feverishly at the crabs, which withdrew in a twinkling. By persistence it would catch several, which it dismembered by dashing against the ground before swallowing some fragments. Perhaps not as impressive as the spine-eating iguana, but another case of grist to the mill in the harsh and demanding Galapagos environment.

Some say that it is soil that God put there . . . and
others that it is the excrement of sea-birds, which are
so abundant along that coast that they cover the
heavens.

Vasquez de Espinosa,
*Compendium and description of the West Indies*

The sea-bird colonies on the Peruvian Guano Islands are without
doubt one of the world's ornithological wonders. They are biologically fascinating, particularly in relation to their food source, but
their first impact is aesthetic and quantitative – the impact of
numbers. The off-lying chain of about forty islands thrust their
barren, bird-carpeted flanks and peaks from the chilly waters of the
Humboldt into a hazy blue sky filled with the harsh sea-bird calls
from countless throats, an indescribable, pulsating gabble that rises
and falls but never dies away until night really comes. The blend of a
thousand discords produces an oddly pleasing harmony. Everywhere the sky is patterned with mobile, interlacing black lines,
skein upon skein, thick and strong or thin and wavering, about to
dissolve. Perhaps nowhere else on earth can one feel a stronger
sensation of sheer, teeming numbers.

We couldn't miss the chance of visiting these islands, since they
lie only about 1,000 miles from the Galapagos, as the booby flies, and
I hope inclusion of the Peruvian booby in this book offends nobody's
zoogeographical susceptibilities. The only problem seemed how
best to get from Guayaquil in Ecuador down the coast to Lima and
out to these populous and carefully administered colonies. The
cheapest way is undoubtedly to travel by night boat from the centre
of Guayaquil down to Puerto Bolivar; by launch to the frontier at
Aguas Verdes and then along the 1,000 miles of desert coastal

strip, south to Lima, by bus and coach. The troubles are minor, like keeping tabs on one's wife and the inevitable heap of luggage, particularly photographic equipment. But we fell for the speed, comfort and cheap fare of the A.P.S.A. air line and rarely can cowardice have reaped a richer reward.

We flew down the backbone of the Andes as dawn broke. The storm-seared, razor peaks of the most venerable Andes, ancient when the Alps were upthrust, blushed a delicate flamingo-pink. Charcoal black shadows clean-etched the ravined, scoured flanks, meticulously emphasising depth. Range after range of snow-capped peaks strode away. The cold distance belittled the contrived cosiness and group-consciousness dear to man, increasingly gregarious and noise-loving the world over and increasingly frightened of his own company. One felt it would be admirable prescribed viewing for Beatle audiences as a healthy antidote to mass hysteria and as a sort of time and distance scale to pit against one-minute wonders. A score of years ago mountain panoramas like this were the sacred preserve of the Himalayan or Andean mountaineer, dangerously achieved. Now, half the passengers dozed in unlovely attitudes, too indifferent to spare a glance, as though jogging through a dreary suburb. Much of this vast mountain range is probably still untrodden by man, and no wonder for the stark crests look utterly remote and barren. By comparison the desert island we had left seemed fertile.

Ecuador and Peru are not, to put it mildly, on the best of terms; their boundary feuds are ancient and bitter. So far Peru has come off best, for it is larger and despite huge tracts of desert and forest (over a third of Peru is dense jungle) it is richer and better organised. Its ancient and dignified capital, Lima 'City of Kings', founded by Pizarro after he had finished off the Incan Empire, holds in its centre the substantial offices of El Corporacion Nacional de Fertilisantes, the guano administration which has succeeded the old Compania Administrado del Guano. They stand near the famous Plaza de Armas with its richly balconied colonial buildings, ancient cathedral and cobbled seventeenth-century fountain square where religious and political offenders were publicly executed. Within twelve hours of our arrival in Lima I entered these ornate Victorian premises and from that moment until we left Peru received unstinted courtesy and help, in particular from Señor Gamarra. The charming Lima custom

T

of tearing up old calendars and throwing the fragments from office windows at mid-day on 31 December, for me symbolised the benevolent descent of the fragments of red tape kindly torn up on our behalf by the administration and showered on our grateful heads; for by 31 December we had just returned from the Guano Islands.

In the president's handsome office stuffed specimens of the major guano-producing species of the islands gazed from their glass cases. There stood our quarry the Peruvian booby or piquero, along with the Chilean pelican and the guano bird itself – the guanay cormorant. My eyes strayed to the booby as we talked, assessing its similarities in appearance to the other members of the family. I could hardly wait to see it in the flesh. To my grateful astonishment the company insisted on providing not only the necessary permission and transport, but food, accommodation and a car to take us to Callao harbour; all this with perfect charm and courtesy. It seemed too good to be true. How many nights we had spent under our Galapagos canvas, planning ways and means of surmounting the formidable hurdles set by our imaginations. What we had feared might be a cumbersome, bureaucratic grind turned out to be an informal chat, a phone call to the docks and an appointment to be picked up from our lodgings at 08.00 hours two days hence.

A week before Christmas we boarded the *Pacific Queen*, a twenty-five-year-old, running to about sixty feet and very solid. She looked as though she would roll heavily in the oily swell common to these waters, and she did. Everything on her was clean, tidy or well-painted – an uncommon phenomenon in our sample of South America. Inca terns, cormorants and laughing gulls clustered on buoys and piers and dotted the placid turquoise water of Callao harbour, backed by the Andean foothills. Hordes of anchovy fishing boats and Peruvian naval vessels flanked our path as we slipped through and out to sea. Meat and vegetables hung from the deck house walls, two comfortable chairs were placed for our use on the main deck, the ship's veteran mongrel overcame his distrust of our peculiar scent and all was set fair for the thirty-hour trip to North Guañape, one of the main booby islands.

Sea-watching can be deadly dull, but I cannot imagine a more exciting and memorable trip than a voyage along the coast of Peru.

Events and species vie for attention and the sheer numbers involved are so astonishing. On this occasion the sun battled against a substantial mist, creating a silvery atmosphere and lighting the smooth, heavy sea with pewter. A constant parade of sea-birds emerged from the mysterious hinterland and streamed across our sight. Heavy, bomber-like great skuas victimised the abundant Peruvian boobies. Just as they harry the gannet over the North Sea and Atlantic, so here in the Southern Hemisphere, the original home of skuas, they harass the boobies. Andean, Franklin's and southern great black-backed gulls stood in for the gulls more familiar to me and Inca terns (fig. 52), incredibly beautiful with their exotic face colours and long white ear tufts, flew gracefully athwart our bows. Hosts of

*Figure 52* Inca terns, Peru

sooty shearwaters angled swiftly over the sea and huge Chilean pelicans lumbered along, vaguely dignified. Occasionally Humboldt penguins flipped smoothly beneath the surface, down into the cool green depths. Above all, countless guanay cormorants, hump-backed and thrumming along with their swift, shallow wing beats, wound across sea and sky in thick black ropes of birds, a single column containing two to three thousand birds. Often a file of cormorants followed a single Peruvian booby or perhaps he stood out like a pearl in a string of jet, as though, in Murphy's phrase, 'a self-appointed lieutenant were an essential part of any successful foray against the fish'. Sometimes the boobies formed their own chevrons, without a single cormorant. The booby's habit of attaching itself to a cormorant skein probably has no special significance and is likely to be simply an extension of the tendency to form flight skeins with its own species. Skeins themselves are aerodynamically economical flying formations enabling all but the leader to benefit from the turbulence created by the bird in front.

As the mist gradually cleared the extent of these skeins became apparent. Here a skein close to the ship; there, in the middle distance, a column perhaps half a mile long winding its way to some sea rock; beyond, faint lines on the horizon, more and yet more of them, moving purposefully over the sea's pathways. They teem in these waters not in hundreds, thousands or even tens of thousands, but in millions. How prolific must be the supply of anchovies that sustains these hordes, one can scarcely imagine. It is like trying to comprehend astronomical space. In 1963 the Peruvians harvested over seven million *tonelados* of *anchovetas*. This probably represents at least two hundred thousand million fish, before the millions of birds, each eating several anchovies per day themselves and also feeding their young, begin to make their inroads. The cold upwelling Antarctic water of the Humboldt, bringing rich supplies of minerals and plankton from deeper layers, must be little more than a thick soup of fish to withstand such phenomenal drains on its resources and still show no signs of over-fishing. If these signs do materialise, as they may do if the annual toll continues to rise, it will be serious for the countless sea-birds largely or in some cases wholly dependent on this relatively local food supply. However, at the time of our journey the sinister slide down the hump of the over-exploitation curve had not begun and men and birds were doing well. The fish meal factories in Chimbote were going full blast and the town lay under a stinking pall. On the islands healthy broods flourished in the dense colonies (see Chapter 16).

Part of this never-ending struggle for food was enacted before us as we ploughed along. A vast raft of guanays and boobies covered an area of some thousands of square yards. Guanays often fish in great flocks, concentrated in the area of a large shoal of *anchovetas*. It is difficult to judge just how far this communal feeding is adaptive, benefiting each individual, and how far it is simply a consequence of the huge fish shoals attracting correspondingly large flocks. Naturally it implies a measure of social behaviour in the sense that the sight of actively fishing birds must draw others to the area, but it is equally clear that there is no mechanism enhancing this process. Fishing guanays are not conspicuous, as fishing gannets are, and indeed their black backs against the dark water even tend to hide them from above. If it had been of marked advantage for guanays to fish in flocks we might have expected a more conspicuously attractive plumage, unless even better reasons forbade. Nor do guanays leaving an island to fish always join a fishing flock even when they could. On the whole I suspect that there may be some slight individual advantage to be obtained from membership of a fishing flock and of course some advantage in reacting to one as a guide to the whereabouts of a shoal, but communal hunting is unlikely to be a specially important mechanism.

A hunting flock of guanays feeds rather like a band of starlings, newcomers usually going beyond and not amongst the feeding individuals and so, no doubt, if there are enough birds and the shoal is small enough, more rapidly encompassing the area covered by the fish. This perhaps supports the idea that individuals, once there, are not benefiting from the presence of others but rather going a little beyond them. It would be fascinating to know more about the precise schooling behaviour of *anchovetas* and what effect hunting guanays have on their behaviour.

Near the raft of guanays hundreds of boobies plummeted headlong into the sea in the dramatic manner which none but other members of their doughty family can emulate. Down they rained, hissing into the spurting water one after the other. How they missed impaling each other amazed me, as it amazes everybody. Yet the dives of the piquero, though so dashing, seemed to lack by a trace the verve of the male blue-foot's. Murphy, on the other hand, gave his weighty vote to the piquero.

I have watched the dives of gannet, red-foot, white booby, blue-foot and piquero and the blue-foot carries off the gold medal. Gannets dive with enormous power and penetration; they are the heavy-weights of the family. Although they will perform relatively cautious slanting dives into shallow water when feeding on sand eels (indeed they will even hunt them on foot) or items such as offal near the surface, they usually feed in deep water, where their prey is mackerel, herring, saithe, codling, etc. It is often necessary to penetrate deeply and to be powerful enough to hold and manipulate the strong heavy prey. Commonly they scan the water with downward pointing beaks, from a height of twenty to fifty feet, beating slowly upwind. They dive in pursuit of prey which they have first marked visually, rather than diving at random into a shoal of fish and then marking their prey beneath the surface. This is obvious from the way in which they adjust their angle and direction until the last instant, even sheering off without completing the dive. When diving deeply they begin the descent from a good height, accelerating with one or two wing beats. Once under way their weight, stream-lining and use of angled wings impart terrific velocity and there is no finer sight than a full-blooded gannet dive; it ranks with the pere-grine's immortal stoop. They strike the water with terrific force, the dull thud of impact travelling far over the sea and the splash spurting high in the air. Then, if the sea is translucent and calm, one can see the white blob and the trail of fizzy water which it leaves during its descent gradually disappear until, some seven to twelve seconds later, the bird bobs buoyantly to the surface. It rarely surfaces with a fish, mainly because by far the majority of its dives are unsuccessful but also, I believe, because it often swallows its prey underwater. I suspect that birds which perform a few excited bathing movements after surfacing have just swallowed a fish. Normally they take off without such displacement reaction, probably following unsuccessful dives.

Mackerel shoals often cruise at about twenty feet or more, as one can tell from echo-soundings and the consistent depth at which they may be hooked, and gannets can easily penetrate that far. There are many records, given in the best of faith, of gannets diving much deeper than this – down to one hundred feet and more – but none wholly eliminate alternative explanations, such as that the birds are trapped in ascending or descending nets. The average duration of dives alone makes it certain that their normal depth can be little more than twenty to thirty feet and often much less.

From the gannet's leaden plunge to the tiny male blue-foot's sizzling dive one traverses in parallel the full range of anatomical diversity within the family. I have already described the blue-foot's astounding ability to dive headlong into shallow water at what seems a suicidal speed. Its lightness makes it buoyant and its extremely long central tail feathers probably help greatly to arrest its downward movement and transfer the velocity to a horizontal or upward plane. Between these two lie the white booby, the red-foot and the piquero. The white booby is rather deliberate and ponderous compared with the blue-foot and yet lacks the power of the gannet, which is about two to three pounds heavier. The red-foot is much smaller and more agile, but the dives I saw were not particularly thrilling. I suspect it takes a good number of flying fish on the wing or snatches prey near the surface. However, it never fed near the islands on which it bred in the Galapagos and my chances to observe it were few.

The bold piquero (Spanish for 'lancer') almost rivals the blue-foot. Coker found its diving skill most impressive of all and thought it occasionally dived from a height of almost a hundred feet, describing a scene in the Bay of Pisco as follows: 'We saw an actual cloud of thousands of piqueros flying over a school of anchovetas, when suddenly they began to fall, hundreds at a time until practically the whole cloud was precipitated into the sea before the first birds had risen from their brief rest after emerging from beneath the surface. Scarcely a bird was seen in the air. The first to fall were soon up, however, and from that time on the plunges were uninterrupted. Changing the course of our boat a little we soon rowed directly through this downpour of birds. Hundreds of birds seemed to strike the water at every instant and even within a few feet of our boat. The bewildering effect is to be imagined rather than described, the atmosphere 'cloudy' with birds, the surface of the sea broken and spattering from falls of animate drops and speckled with reappearing birds; the confused sound of whirring wings and unremitting splashes.' So far as its tendency to hunt in dense flocks is concerned the piquero must take pride of place and certainly its mass dives, like a shower of hailstones, are especially thrilling.

The main breeding grounds of the piquero are the north and south Guañape Islands, though the north island holds even more guanay cormorants than boobies. On this island there is a surprisingly spacious building with a tiled forecourt and an ornate balustrade. It must have been built in a more expansive era late last century to house visiting company officials who expected luxury. It contains several small bedrooms, showers, a dining room and a large common room with a fine table-tennis table. It is flanked by several store buildings and a 'hospital' building whose roof the boobies have gladly utilised for nesting. The entire installation now in some disrepair looks distinctly incongruous here, on this island entirely given over to the screeching sea-fowl, black with their nests and young and fog-thick with the penetrating smell of guano and decaying fish. The buildings stand sea-gazing, silent and empty, with their futile embellishments. The fancy balustrade and tiled forecourt would have graced a verdant patio. Here they were guano-spattered, listening to the clamorous sea-birds rather than the tinkling fountain. Dry guano lies thickly everywhere. Clouds of it rose from our trestle beds when we climbed into them and piles of it, laced with down, feathers and innumerable mites encrusted the window sills.

When darkness fell and the inspiring outlines of the Andean foothills faded, the crescendo of sea-bird voices died slowly away from the high pitch to which the evening arrival of countless mates had raised it. In the painful silence the old building came to alarming life. The rats emerged. I could not understand why they didn't batten on the inexhaustible food and decimate the birds, but apparently they remained relatively scarce. Here may be a problem; on Ailsa Craig, early this century, rats (supposedly) reduced a quarter of a million puffins to practically nil. Perhaps the boobies and cormorants are too fierce in defence of their eggs and young, or maybe there is a 'quiet' season when, with the birds absent, there is virtually no food for the rats, and a large population is thereby precluded.

The labyrinthine sea-caves and passages eaten into the rock beneath the house by aeons of surging swell created rumbling noises. A wind invariably arose, no doubt produced by the rapid cooling of air masses and their consequent motion, and set the doors creaking and rattling. Our small, flat-wick paraffin lamp threw a meagre light on the bare walls. Two comfortable chairs stood in the common room and there we sat with the miserable glow between us, waiting for a reasonable hour to retire. Thus we spent Christmas Eve and Christmas Night, 1964, and wouldn't have changed places with anybody.

The three ordinary *Guardianes* on the island lived in tiny wooden and corrugated-iron shacks, little more than four ramshackle walls and a roof, though Señor Claudio Mendosa, the *Jefe Guardiane*, had a better dwelling. They retired early for there was nothing to do, nowhere to go and in any case their day started at 05.00 hours. For living in the discomfort of a primitive shack, on a barren isolated rock, carrying out various monotonous duties and living away from family and friends for all but one and a half days per month, the ordinary *Guardiane* received, I understood and I hope correctly, about £2. 10*s.* per week. The cost of living in Peru is on average at least as high as in England; many things, such as clothing, food in restaurants and chocolates, cost a good deal more and little, except local products and labour, seems to cost less. Nor did their 'keep' amount to much; every day they had to go fishing for their dinner of lump suckers or octopus, although rice, beans and a very few vegetables were provided. The British lighthouse keeper, who I suppose is the nearest equivalent to the Peruvian *Guardiane*, receives, if my memory is right, over £15 a week in addition to his keep whilst at the lighthouse, a free house or flat ashore, an allowance for coal and electricity and various extras such as some clothing and small items of household equipment. In addition, if he is on a 'rock' he goes ashore for two unbroken weeks after every four weeks away from home, though he remains 'on call' whilst ashore. The very idea of possessing a car was ludicrous to Peruvian *Guardianes* but is commonplace to lighthouse keepers. I might add that this comparison is meant to emphasise the miserable rewards of the Peruvian and not to imply that lighthouse keepers are treated too well.

To us the *Guardianes* seemed to live the dreariest lives, but their courtesy and kindness were unfailing. Every fortnight the two who had been ashore brought back fresh bread. For the rest of the time they breakfasted off sawdust-stale bread rolls, without butter, and black coffee. Whilst the cook remained behind, humouring the villainous black stove in the dim interior of the sooty, cobweb-hung kitchen, the others launched their open boat and rowed out to their fishing grounds. They always rowed, one man to an oar, from a standing position, pushing the oar for the power stroke. They took the boat skilfully close to the rocks, over which the sea boiled and foamed alarmingly. There, clinging to the slimy rock faces, were the lumpsuckers, a kind of fish that clamps itself to rocks by means of a large sucker on its under-surface. We found them mucilaginous and tasteless, but they loved them; each time they hooked one with bent

wire on a stick they grinned with delight. They ate them with practised skill, crunching the heads and by mysterious buccal juggling,
sifting the bones neatly to one side to be spat out. They also ate dried
octopus, although they never gave them to us, perhaps thinking we
might be horrified. Innate courtesy and hospitality so often go hand
in hand with poverty and the hard, open air life and we have the
pleasantest recollections of the Peruvian *Guardianes* of Guañape.

A most astonishing feature of the islands is the way in which birds
nest in cleanly demarcated patches. Not only do cormorants and
boobies form their own pure groups, but the outer limits of these
are sharply defined even where there is plenty of adjacent ground,
identical in all respects. The periodical upsets associated with guano
operations of course creates an unnatural situation. Guano birds
shift their breeding sites, either on the same island or even between
islands far more than do their relatives on undisturbed islands.
Long-lived sea-birds, particularly gannets and boobies, are generally
faithful to the same nest and mate from year to year, but piqueros
and guanays are often unable to return. Both species are highly
sociable and will settle down to breed only alongside others of their
own kind. Thus, if a nucleus of birds return to breed but are forced
to settle in a new spot the colony, or a part of it, grows around
them. The original settlers are mostly in about the same state of
reproductive development and others in a similar state join them.
However, once this group has started to lay, birds in the very early
reproductive stages will tend to set up elsewhere, together with
others at a similar stage, rather than among birds in an advanced
phase. So one gets two related phenomena: discrete groups which
end suddenly and group members more or less engaged in similar
phases of breeding. At least the members of any one group are more
closely synchronised in their breeding activities when compared
among themselves than when compared with members of another
group.

I wondered what decided the birds' choice of one spot rather
than another. The *Guardianes* thought that one spot was too hot, or
was especially infested with parasites, blood sucking ticks, but the
distribution couldn't, I think, be explained as simply as that. It
seems certain that, in general, the guanays do nest mainly in relatively windy areas, though, as I point out later, it seems to me that

they do so for the wind's lifting power rather than its cooling effect, but the finer aspects of distribution within the main areas are probably decided by a combination of factors, including man's activities and the social tendencies of the birds acting in the way described above. It is certain that none of the natural factors could explain why a particular slope, without change of aspect, incline, exposure, temperature or substrate, should suddenly become un-suitable. Yet the colony boundaries are hair-sharp and sometimes occur on such a slope.

Guano is the improbable meeting place of several disciplines: geology, biology, biochemistry, history and sociology (if human exploitation be a discipline, and it has certainly been practised enough) are involved in it. The high grade phosphate fertiliser from the Guano Islands has played a major part in the economy of Peru. At one time the external debt of the Peruvian government was guaranteed by guano and a reliable estimate of the extent of the deposits was therefore a very practical concern. Long before the Conquistadores blazed their arrogant trails the Indians used guano to fertilise their stony arid soil. A fairly recent translation of the early writer Vasquez de Espinosa remarks that 'the Indians would rather go without eating than without buying their guano', so valuable was it in crop production in the Andes (where it was transported by llama) and on the coastal plain (Hutchinson). Since the middle of the last century Peruvian guano has underpinned her agriculture and formed a major source of revenue; for a city built on something less solid than sand Lima has endured remarkably well.

When the Incas quarried guano from the pristine, crystalline deposits they were hacking away with their wooden spades at the slow accumulation of hundreds of years of fossilised excreta. On a geological time scale this is no age at all, but the evidence is firmly against any great age for the deposits. A number of complications prevent a straightforward calculation of age. The rate at which the deposits accumulated during different periods is not accurately known, and it is clear that it was certainly not uniform. For a long time some deposits may have been losing as fast as they were gaining. Hutchinson goes into the historical and other evidence most critically and thoroughly and concludes that the most likely average rate of deposition is about eight centimetres per year and that the guano caps on at least some of the main islands began to form about 2,500 years ago.

The dazzling, glassy caps of guano which existed on some islands covered guano strata forty or fifty metres thick, possibly more. Such ancient deposits depended for their formation on the excessively dry climate; rain would leach away newly-deposited guano. These thick layers represented an astronomical number of tons of high-grade fertiliser, especially in the deep layers which contained as much as ten per cent of nitrogen and over twenty-five per cent of phosphates. The reserves of material on the Guañape Islands alone in the third quarter of the last century were estimated at almost one and a half million metric tons. According to Hutchinson there are about 147 islands and twenty one mainland localities producing guano, so the extent of the Peruvian and to a lesser extent Chilean riches in this valuable stuff were obviously phenomenal.

Nowadays the guano harvest depends on the annual increments deposited by the nesting birds at perhaps two to four ounces each per day, wet weight. The immense deposits have been cleared and the days are gone when gangs of imported labourers, mainly Chinese coolies, toiled in virtual slavery and literally to death on the precipitous, sun-baked crags, whilst the great sailing schooners waited to load their precious cargo. Not only mummified seals and birds were occasionally disinterred from the guano when it was finally unloaded; more than one labourer ended his life horribly in the ship's hold, choking in guano after falling into the polished chute and sliding to his death. Even today accidents occur, though not so grisly. On South Guañape the *Guardianes* had light-heartedly stuck a human skull on a pole – a small memento of an unfortunate worker who fell over the cliff when digging guano. In the guano heyday, say from 1855–67, guano was exported at the rate of over 400,000 tons per year, mostly from the Chinchas; exploitation of the Guañapes apparently began in 1869. However, guano output had been high for years before that and Hutchinson's evaluation of the situation is that about 9,000,000 metric tons of guano were gleaned from the coast of Peru between 1842–70. Those days are now over and the present harvests are merely the biennial accumulation of excreta.

Under the present system each island is visited in turn once every two years by an itinerant squad of guano diggers, acting on the information sent to the head office by the chief *Guardiane* of each island, concerning the numbers, distribution and stage of breeding of the guano birds. These are mainly the guanays, piqueros and alcatraz or pelican. The guanays now produce about eighty-five per cent of the total guano and the piquero is the next most productive species, but pelicans were once a much more important contributor. There is one estimate that two and a half million pelicans (a race of the brown pelican), probably on one of the Lobos islands, produced 10,000 tons of guano annually at the end of the last century. The schedule of visits is timed to cause the least disturbance to the nesting birds. Naturally, it is impossible to co-ordinate operations on more than thirty islands so that each one is cleared only when empty of breeding birds. One finds evidence that small numbers of unfortunate pairs have been caught at the tail end of their breeding cycle and their fully feathered young, abandoned and starved, lie there to tell the tale. This is unavoidable; in their own interests the company guards its birds vigilantly.

The invasion of guano diggers must turn the island temporarily upside down as five hundred men swarm on its slopes. Each pair of birds presents the Corporation with its nest made of hardened, cement-like excreta – really just a substantial rim of guano and a litter of moulted feathers. These nests, together with whatever can be scraped from the stones and ground, annually yield many thousands of tons of fertiliser. When the islands were buried beneath their virgin mantles of guano, like cakes hidden under a mound of icing, they must have been an astonishing sight. Even now, when the bottom of the barrel is being scraped, the guano is still a suffocating layer, piling into every crevice and leaving not a square millimetre of ground uncovered. On the Guañape Islands, at least, except on sheer faces and sea-sprayed ledges, you couldn't find an inch of ordinary rock or earth. There is only the yellowish, excreta-covered substrate, here rocky, there loose and ankle-deep in rubble and detritus.

The Guano Islands and the considerable staff involved in research, administration and maintenance operate with the smoothness of long experience. The *guardianes* fill in routine simple maps of their particular island, showing the distribution and density of the birds. The islands are divided into segments by retaining walls which are primarily to stabilise the slopes and facilitate working, but which also serve as useful group boundaries. By simply dotting or shading areas corresponding to the density of birds in them, so many per square metre, which becomes easier with practice, the total population of the island can be estimated. Although the error is likely to be considerable in absolute terms the numbers involved are so tremendous that, in terms of a proportion, it will probably be unimportant. Most of the areas can be scanned from a boat during the daily trip around the island.

The Compania Administradora del Guano, which was for ages Peru's guardian of the islands, strongly traditional and protectionist, fairly recently gave way to the present Corporacion Nacional de Fertilisantes, perhaps less politically minded and more modern in approach. However that may be, the stupendous growth of the guano birds' formidable rival – the fish meal factory – seems to owe something to the removal of Compania opposition, though the Corporacion is itself by no means happy about some aspects of this growth. Since 1952, when the factories from the collapsed pilchard industry in California were shipped down to Peru and rebuilt to process anchovies for fish meal, the catch of anchovies in Peruvian coastal waters has risen to over nine million tons in 1964 and 1965. Peru became the world's top fishing nation. This phenomenal catch was made possible by a combination of economic factors, such as the injection of vast amounts of foreign capital and cheap nets on credit from Japan.

When we were in Chimbote, the entire town lay under a stinking pall from the fish meal factories which made breathing seem like an intake of solid, rotting fish. The factories, according to the *Economist* in December 1965, convert fish to meal in the ratio of 6:1, whereas the birds can manage only a conversion of 8:1 as a result of their estimated annual consumption of two and a half million tons of fish. The obvious question is what effect will this tremendous human catch have on the fish population and through them on the birds. We know that over-fishing becomes apparent only when the stock has been really hard hit, since up to that time increased fishing effort can always make up for a slight decrease in stock. But it is also reckoned, though it is not clear on what grounds, that less than ten per cent of the primary production (green plant growth) of the Humboldt, upon which anchovies feed, is actually consumed each year. So it is argued (quite falsely) that the increased toll of fishes might just make room for more fish to feed on the endless supply. It is saying, in effect, that one cannot over-exploit anchovies whilst they still retain an abundant food supply, but it ignores the fact that anchovies may already be reproducing as fast as intrinsic or other non-food factors will allow. If so, decimating the population will not lead to faster increase, unless by the reduction in numbers, the inhibiting effect of whatever is limiting reproductive rate is also lifted. And if it is, the question then becomes a very complex matter of relatives – how much cropping can be practised so that the loss to the population is balanced by the gain produced by disinhibition of the limiting factor. It has presumably taken a long time for the anchovies of the Humboldt and the endemic sea-bird populations to reach equilibrium, if indeed they have done so. By the time the anchovy-fishing industry recognisably upsets this balance it may be too late to prevent serious repercussions on the birds. Naturally, some would argue that so long as men take the birds' fish ration all is well and to hell with the birds. Even if one could do so, and there are no grounds for hoping that we would allow natural selection to bring us into balance before we overfish, it would be a rare disgrace deliberately to treat this wonderful population of sea-birds as nothing more than an economic pawn. As described in the next chapter, the guano birds have managed to cope with the incredible natural catastrophes that hit them periodically, but there is no guarantee that they can

*Figure 53* Peruvian boobies and guanay cormorants in flight

continue to do so in a significantly changed environment. Their success depends on an extremely rapid rate of increase following disaster. The disasters will recur, but the increase can do so only if the conditions under which the mechanism evolved (available food resources, for one vital thing) do not change too quickly and drastically.

However much their economic importance may decline, the status of the Peruvian Guano Islands as the home of perhaps the most astounding sea-bird congregation in existence should only increase in a world losing its natural assets far too quickly.

If the stone falls on the egg alas for the egg.
If the egg falls on the stone alas for the egg.
Greek Cypriot proverb.
Lawrence Durell, *Bitter Lemons*

The beamy old *Pacific Queen* wallowed sturdily towards north Guañape (Lat. 8°34' S., Long. 78°56' W.), with a bored crew but at least two pleasurably excited people aboard. The trip had been anything but dull, but we were itching to get onto one of those austere islands towards which the endless processions of sea-birds had been weaving from all directions. The previous chapter introduced the piquero at sea, as a doughty hunter. Now we will meet him in the dense nesting colonies of the Guañape Islands, north and south.

Our arrival took the keepers by surprise; they have no telephone or radio communication and we had embarked at short notice. We saw them hastily launch their heavy rowing boat, hauled out of the water to avoid the swell which pounds the rocky base of the island. They do it at least once a day so the operation was as slick as naval drill. They tumbled in and standing a man to an oar pushed out to meet us. Five minutes later we climbed onto the seaweed-slippery grid at the base of the rickety ladder leading to the upper landing stage, the welcome din of a million sea-birds assaulting our ears.

We dumped our rucksacks on the tiled forecourt of the visitors' quarters and immediately sought the nearest boobies, which meant walking five yards to the edge of the forecourt; piqueros nested a few feet below. Behind the building a barren slope angled steeply to the flattish top of the island, black with guanay cormorants whose exclusive ranks held not a single booby. To the left of the main residence stood several buildings of the guano administration in various stages of decay, smothered in dust and guano, their roofs packed tight with quarrelsomely guarded booby nests. Huddled in corners stood the tiny shacks of the *Guardianes* who, except for the chief, existed in miserable dwellings of planks and corrugated iron. North Guañape takes quite a bit of patrolling and observing; it is over half a mile long and more than a third of a mile wide, bordered by miles of indented coast and cliff. All this, and the interior, must be regularly checked.

Peruvian boobies are neat and unostentatious, about thirty inches long (larger than the male blue-foot but hardly as large as the largest female), pure white below and on the head and neck, and dark brown above with the paler outer margins of feathers giving the back a slightly barred or scaly appearance. The legs and feet are sober, a dark slaty blue, but the reddish brown eyes hold a touch of fire. Peruvians could be confused with blue-foots, but the latter's whitish rump and nape, ashy streaked head and neat brown thigh patches are distinctive in flight and at fairly long range. Juvenile blue-foots, or for that matter juvenile white boobies, could be mistaken for adult Peruvians, being dark above and mainly white below, but the brown head and throat of these juveniles contrasts with the pure white of the adult Peruvian. Juvenile Peruvians are like adults, but dirty buff on head, neck and underparts.

The piquero was of special concern to us. Puzzling out the relationships within the group was becoming more and more interesting and this was a vital piece of the jig-saw. The initial meeting with a species under these circumstances is exciting; rather like meeting some long lost member of the family who holds the answers to questions you are dying to ask. The bird's every action is charged with a special significance and scrutinised with an attention that would seem ludicrous to the ordinary watcher. Of what earthly use is it to know what a bird does just before it takes off, or after it lands, or when it meets its mate, defaecates, copulates or performs any of the scores of behaviour patterns that maintain its life and breeding activity? None, you may think, to the biologist who deals in ecology, taxonomy and distribution, for instance; none, in effect, to the non-ethologist. But behaviour can be a useful tool in working out relationships between animals and this in turn is very relevant to problems of distribution. Similarly, behaviour and ecology are in fact very closely knit and many important ecological problems depend for their solution on information about behaviour, which is hardly surprising since behaviour is the mechanism by which ecological relationships are forged. Spacing-out within a species' range or within a particular breeding group is an ecological phenomenon, since it is a relationship with the environment and with other organisms, but it depends on behavioural mechanisms.

But these and other apparent trivia of behaviour are important to ethologists for a variety of reasons. They provide the raw material by which methods and interpretations can be tested and improved and may teach something about the evolution of behaviour. Tinbergen has pointed out that, whilst the types of analysis developed, for example, in work on the motivation of displays in gulls hold promise also for an understanding of the motivation of man, it is the *methods* and not the results that hold this promise. Yet it is often the results that people apply in this way and understandably they lack conviction. Most people rightly object that because a gull or a stickleback or a goose behaves in a particular way under certain conditions (stress, for instance), it is not necessarily fair to assume that man behaves in an equivalent way under somewhat comparable conditions. Lorenz's recent book on aggression draws heavily on the implications for human communities of the triumph ceremony in geese; as Koestler puts it, 'It is surprising how strong the temptation can be, in otherwise ultra cautious scientists, to take flight on the treacherous wings of analogy, at the risk of sharing the fate of Icarus.'

The methods of behavioural analysis are many; an obvious and (misleadingly) simple one is that of observation. But Tinbergen points out that when some people apply observational methods to human behaviour, they look at the wrong things. Instead of observing the tell-tale signs of a person's behaviour, they often ask the person to describe his reactions and so introduce a glaring source of error, since with all the skill at his command a psychologist can hardly allow accurately for the risk of dissimulation and deceit inherent in inviting a person to describe his reactions. When observing birds one uses perhaps tiny but consistent indications of fear or aggression or sex motivation in analysing and interpreting the behaviour seen. Our close attention to the Peruvian booby was entirely normal and necessary, if we were to build anything on the observations.

The piqueros were nesting densely on the flat top of one big building which the keepers called the hospital, measuring 43 by 49·5 feet and holding 300 pairs, or one pair in 0·8 square yards. A second, thinner group was ideal for our purposes since the members were still in the first stages of breeding whilst nearly all the others had eggs. In yet other areas most nests held part-grown chicks. Local synchronisation of breeding was a marked feature in both Peruvian and blue-footed boobies. As I have suggested in previous chapters, it was probably due at least in part to the effect of social interactions within the group, hastening the maturation of the gonads in pairs a bit behind the others and so producing more uniformity than if all the pairs, early or late, had responded in a standard manner merely to environmental changes (temperature, day length or whatever other factors ultimately act on the reproductive system) but with no differential behaviour effects involved. A bird is reproductively stimulated, particularly in the later stages of reproductive development, by seeing and hearing other members of the species performing breeding activities and it may well be a roughly quantitative correlation; that is to say, the greater the degree of noise, display, mating and so on within a colony, the greater their effect on the birds involved. This is readily apparent in gannets, where the late comers to the colony spend less than two-thirds as long as the early birds between return and laying; the tempo of activity is so high by the time the late birds return that they almost catch up on the early ones. In his erudite work on guano, Hutchinson interprets an earlier account by Murphy as showing that there was no social synchrony in a colony of Peruvian boobies. There seems more reason to believe that the local social synchrony which certainly existed in 1964–65 was typical rather than exceptional, particularly since it is so widespread in booby colonies. The probable answer is that in all years there is the kind of local synchrony that I have described, but not enough synchrony within the colony *as a whole* to justify describing it as 'synchronous'.

Small-group synchrony in piqueros may well be enhanced by the tendency of birds coming into breeding condition to be mainly attracted to groups which are themselves in the early stages; later a group ceases, or almost ceases to attract newcomers. This leads to a greater uniformity of condition throughout the group than if it were constantly gaining new recruits, irrespective of the late stage of breeding reached by early members. If, for any reason, there was a succession of birds coming into reproductive condition over a longish period instead of just a few weeks, and they formed mainly homogenous groups as just described, we would end up with a number of groups in which the birds were more or less synchronised, but there would also be wide differences between groups.

These necessary conditions are created in several ways. The system of gathering the guano, for example, often disturbs a section of the population before they have finished breeding. The interval which such birds spend before beginning their next breeding cycle is shorter than in successful breeders and so a discrepancy is introduced. Again, relatively young birds do not usually come into breeding condition at exactly the same time as older ones. Apart from this there is also considerable variation between individuals, so a supply of birds 'ripening' over a longish period is assured. Under natural conditions it is sometimes adaptive for a population to stagger its breeding effort, for example, to minimise the effects of periodical but irregular environmental disasters of one sort or another.

We were lucky to find a group still in the early stages of breeding. Birds, like men, are far more active in display and aggressive behaviour at this time; later, territorial and mate disputes over, they settle down to the rather dull routine of incubation and chick-rearing. It struck us immediately that fights were much commoner here than among other boobies; piqueros were definitely quarrelsome. The sight of them locked in a struggle amongst hostile neighbours reminded us forcibly of the highly combative Bass gannets. They fought like gannets too, gripping the opponent's beak and stabbing furiously at face and head. A slight but puzzling difference was that the Peruvian's head feathers stood on end as they fought, whilst gannets always keep theirs sleeked. Ruffing of head feathers is common in all boobies but has been mainly lost in the gannet. It is a small example of bird behaviour which we can describe but 'the "why" of which ever eludes'. Some day it may provide a clue in a chain of reasoning. Fights were quite lengthy by booby standards and, though they were shorter and far less damaging than those of the gannet, there was obviously a marked degree of competition for sites.

It would be a mistake to assume that the site competition was similarly based in the two species; there are fundamental differences, which I propose to discuss in some detail. The Peruvian booby, along with a wealth of other species (cormorants, pelicans, penguins, terns, burrowing petrels, etc.) which together total many millions of individuals, is attracted mainly by the anchovies of the Antarctic or Humboldt current, but however apparently unlimited the supply of fish may be there are only about thirty small islands on which the hordes of birds can nest. Also some islands or parts of islands are unsuitable for the guano birds, probably largely because they are too flat or too windless, or even too black and therefore heat-absorbent. Informed opinion seems to favour the idea that the distribution, in particular of guanay cormorants, is governed mainly by temperature and therefore by wind, the birds choosing those slopes exposed to cooling winds. I suspect this opinion over-estimates the part played by temperature and underrates the value of the wind as an aid to flight. Guanays are heavy birds, none too well endowed for getting off the ground and landing again. Wind could be vital in this respect. As one might expect, the Peruvian booby, which is a lighter and more aerial species than the guanay, is less dependent on wind. Yet presumably it suffers equally from heat and its presence in flat areas devoid of guanays is due to lesser dependence on the lifting power of wind.

In any case, by the simple law of supply and demand space is at a premium and the birds are packed into the islands in ridiculously large numbers, more appropriate to insects than higher vertebrates. The imagination boggles at a figure of over five million birds, mainly cormorants, on the one island of Central Chincha, which was Coker's estimate in 1926. There were an estimated 356,340 pairs of boobies on Guañape Norte in 1964 – over twenty times as many as in the biggest gannetry. Consequently, whether they like it or not, Peruvian boobies have had to come to terms with the requirements of dense, colonial nesting. In my view they are descended from blue-footed booby stock and were originally, like all other boobies, moderately rather than densely colonial. However, they have responded to the space pressure by squashing closer together and by re-evolving (as a species) the ability to use cliff ledges ('re-evolving' because I think ancestral boobies were probably cliff nesters but took largely to slopes or flat ground). Even now the Peruvian booby is by no means confined to cliffs. In fact its habits seemed to have changed quite a bit since the beginning of this century. There was some belief that the pelicans, then very much more numerous than now, were driving the boobies from the flat interiors of some islands and it became rather rare for boobies to nest inland on flatter ground, whereas once it was commonly recorded. Now it is again quite common, perhaps correlated with a decline in pelicans and a re-invasion of flatter ground by boobies. As a result of their dense nesting, and also their cliff-nesting tendencies, piqueros have had to develop rather more elaborate social behaviour, for much the same reasons as given earlier for the gannet. But of that, more later.

Nothing remotely similar to the booby space shortage applies to the gannet,* whose numbers are trivial compared with the carrying capacity of the available sea-rocks and islands around the coast of Britain. Yet they pack themselves onto a few rocks and fight fiercely for nest sites as close as they can get to existing nesters, even if much of the rock remains empty. It is hardly worth discussing the idea that from the gannet's viewpoint there is something wrong with most of these unused islands, however suitable they may seem to us. It is doubtless true that an animal's choice of habitat may and probably usually does involve subtle determinants imperceptible to us, and it is clear that precious little is known about the finer details of habitat choice in most birds and animals. But it just does not hold water to account for the gannet's present distribution in terms of available rocks; there are plenty spare, including some that have been gannetries in the past. Yet gannets actually nest more densely even than piqueros and show the strictest competition for nesting sites.

It may seem odd that this, the most obvious characteristic of gannetries, has stimulated very little attempt at explanation, but then the function of colonial breeding in vertebrates is in general little understood. Once the obvious 'explanations' have been discounted (like space shortage, social co-operation against predators,

* See Nelson, 'Population dynamics of the Gannet'.

lack of any important function but persisting as a relic of a habit once useful), there is very little left except to postulate that social breeding leads, somehow, to higher reproductive success and/or enables the population to control its reproductive output. Whichever of these is accepted as a working hypothesis, it immediately becomes imperative to put some flesh on the bones and find out how the process works. It is here that the rather circular offerings of those who say, in effect, that colonial animals just enjoy the company of their own kind, or are gregarious, fall down. Nobody can test such a theory, quite apart from its other shortcomings. But the idea that colonial breeding somehow increases success has provided a few leads and seems me a likely candidate for explaining the adaptive value of this habit in gannets.

Starting from the simple facts that gannets considerably outnumber breeding islands, so that each pair must at least share with some others and (rather more exciting) that breeding in a group tends to facilitate reproduction, that is helps to bring it about, tends to synchronise it and may, in one or more ways, increase the probability of success, one can build a tolerably satisfactory structure as follows. First, and reasonably, assume that the facilitating effect of social nesting acts through behaviour, the various sexual and aggressive displays stimulating the reproductive systems of birds that see and hear them and, it may be, are involved in them. Then, the denser the nesting, the more of this kind of stimulus there is. Second, look for the survival value in synchronised breeding which begins at the same time each year, regardless of transitory variations in weather. Broadly, it could be either before or after the young leave the nest. If there happens to be a particular time of year favourable for the growth of young, there is obviously going to be advantage in having young at that time. Again, if there is one period when independent young survive best, parents will do best to breed so that their young are launched then. There is very suggestive evidence that both these factors operate in the gannet.\* Because the main laying always occurs at the end of April, the young mainly hatch in mid-June and fledge in early September†. Their growth coincides with such an abundance of highly nutritious food, par-

\* See Nelson, 'The breeding biology of the Gannet'.
† *Idem*, 'The behaviour of the young Gannet .

ticularly mackerel in the case of the Bass gannets, but maybe herrings elsewhere, that they are able to complete it and lay down extremely rich fat deposits in about thirteen weeks, which is far shorter than any booby can achieve, even though boobies are considerably lighter birds. It is not fanciful to suggest that the gannet population of Britain may have evolved its breeding regime to fit in with the cycle of its principal food fish. Where seasonally consistent trends in food availability occur, species that utilise it may be expected to become suitably geared to it. In fact, the biology of the herring, which is known in detail, fits fairly well with this supposition. Their main movements and reproductive cycles bring them well within the gannet's fishing range in abundance, at the right time for the bird.

Then, when juvenile gannets fledge they have the best possible chance of survival, taking into account that they go to sea completely alone, without ever returning for food (see Chapter 4). It is obviously extremely difficult for them, since a very large proportion die in the attempt to become self-sufficient. They would not stand a chance under unfavourable weather conditions. Since these deteriorate markedly from late September onwards one can immediately see the great advantage enjoyed by chicks that fledge before that time.

These twin advantages of producing young at the most favourable time for growth and for the post-fledging transition to independence seem enough to explain why it is that gannets have evolved the habit of laying, in the main, at the end of April every year. And social nesting helps to bring about this synchronised April laying. A weak link in the reasoning is the fact that we do not know that fully adequate synchronisation of breeding could not be achieved by purely external factors (such as photoperiodicity) acting quite independently, on each individual. This seems to me unlikely since birds are inherently variable, and age groups more so, and yet such differences are largely ironed out by social facilitation.

If all this is true, then the main advantage of dense colonial nesting in the gannet may be through these effects, and not through utilisation of 'scarce' sites or safety from predation and so on. Since the only breeding sites that provide full exposure to the social stimulus of the colony are either among or hard by nesting pairs, there is obviously going to be a good biological reason for competing for such sites regardless of how much spare, distant ground there may be in the gannetry or how many vacant islands there may be near at hand. So we can suggest reasons for the gannet's dense nesting, biological advantages accruing from it, but these advantages are entirely different from those which the Peruvian booby gains from its almost equally dense nesting habits.

All this stemmed from the reasons for fighting in the Peruvian booby, to which we now return. Having got its square yard of ledge or ground, the male advertises for a mate in much the same way as the other boobies. He has basically the same sky-pointing display and the same pathetic whistle as the blue-footed and white boobies, except that he innovates, quite distinctively, by raising one foot as he sky-points. A glance through the sky-pointing displays of boobies demonstrates how easily a species can modify a display and make it distinctive. A display can be remarkably changed by adding another gesture, like foot-raising, wing-swivelling or tail-cocking. Variations in speed and amplitude can be equally diagnostic. Behaviourally, there are masses of raw material potentially ready to be ritualised.

After the male has successfully negotiated the early stages of pair formation and the female is at least strongly inclined to remain with him, in the invariable sulid tradition he begins the next or 'cementing' stage. He frequently flies a short way out from the island and then returns and the pair excitedly perform the mutual jabbing and symbolic nest-building, calling all the time. As in many other birds mating for life, the meeting ceremony or ceremonies are very important in boobies. Lorenz believes that in geese the triumph ceremony, a symbolic victory of the male followed by ecstatic interaction between the mates, though basically derived from aggression, is the main binding force between pair members, more important than sexual attraction in keeping them together. Among sulids only the gannet has a comparably complex and highly ritualised meeting ceremony and one which is also derived from aggression (here a ritualised form of aggression redirected to the ground or nest). But boobies also have some form of meeting ceremony, more or less primitive. The flight circuiting and returns of the male, followed by the excited jabbing and intimate nest-building, one bird leaning closely over the other, must be significant in strengthening the pair bond.

The gabble of the Peruvian booby *en masse* is hard to describe, yet quite unmistakable. It is somewhat high-pitched and yapping, rapid and voluble, rising and falling in waves and crescendos of sound. There is the same hullabaloo and stimulating atmosphere of intense excitement that one enjoys in gannetries and misses so markedly in some boobies. Like gannets, Peruvian boobies find their neighbours a nuisance and protest by word and deed, and frequently. They jab and menace each other and perform a violent nodding of the head, up and down through a wide swing, which is the ritualised aggressive display of site owners and advertises such ownership. It is, in fact, a slower and more emphatic version of the blue-foot's head-nodding, used in similar circumstances, and again showing how a small difference in tempo and extent can make displays perfectly specific.

Before the egg has been laid, whenever one of the partners leaves the site, it assumes the same sort of posture that one sees in both blue-footed and white boobies, in which the bill is pointed obliquely upwards with the head slightly backwards. Simultaneously it lifts its feet in an exaggerated goose-stepping movement exactly equivalent to the parading of the blue-foot. There is one small difference; the movement is less conspicuous and this may be linked with the piquero's much duller feet. A bright or ornamented structure, like the tail of a crested newt, the red belly of a stickleback, the collar of a ruff, the balloon of a frigate-bird or a baboon's behind, is often connected with a special movement or position which shows it off; where the structure is more ordinary the associated movements may be expected to be less exaggerated. In support of this is the fact that the male blue-foot in particular has a dramatic salute in which he throws up his feet and displays the bright blue soles before landing, but the piquero has only a reduced version of it.

The nest of the Peruvian booby is certainly a useful structure, not only to man but, incidentally, to the birds. It is merely a bowl of excreta with a few moulted feathers added, so nest-building activity, as behaviour in which the pair can co-operate, can hardly be more than symbolic. Like blue-footed or white boobies, the Peruvian booby pair spends a lot of time picking up, depositing and arranging

A Male flies in with salute: a less extreme version of the blue-foot's

B Aggressive yes head-shaking directed towards an incoming neighbour

C Head-shaking as defence of nest site. The partner bends down to touch the nest

D Sky-pointing or sexual advertising

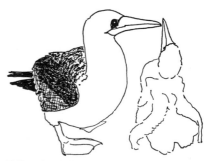

E A version of the bill-up-face-away, in which the bird about to depart assumes a head back posture

F Begging behaviour by Peruvian booby chick

*Figure 54* Peruvian booby

278

scraps of excreta or particles of stone, but the real work is done from the other end. In fact, both the Peruvian booby and the gannet, the only real cliff-nesters in the family, have developed the habit of using their excreta to cement their nests onto the ledges, which are sometimes precarious and would not allow ordinary nest material to stick.

The Corporacion manager specially asked us not to disturb the nesting birds, so we crept cautiously around trying by detours and distance never to flush a bird from its nest. However, the *Guardianes* offered to show us the southern island, where there were even more boobies and, familiarity breeding contempt, the keepers there kindly took us right amongst the birds so that we could catch the full atmosphere of the colony. The experience was unforgettable. As we climbed the steep rocky slope and penetrated the nesting ranks, the numbers became overwhelming. Now there were not only birds thronging the skies above, but also around and below, whilst the living carpet stretched upwards and outwards until the far birds were just innumerable specks. A delicate mist, common here until dispelled by the mid-day heat, swirled softly round the whitened flanks of the island, creating a quite unearthly feeling of birds, space, wings, sky and disembodied life.

Many birds left their nests in mild panic and we saw that this part of the colony contained mainly eggs and small young. Most nests had three eggs, though clutches of two were common and a few held four.* The young were all fat and healthy in their hot, dry nests of dusty, concrete grey excreta. Despite the obvious age difference between first, second and third, corresponding of course to the interval at which the eggs were laid, the youngest were in good condition. In another part of the island many nests held well-grown chicks and we looked with special care for any signs of hostility between them, recalling the determined assault of the white booby chick upon its younger sibling. We saw nothing to suggest such strife; despite their large broods, Peruvian boobies can easily cope under normal conditions. Furthermore, they guard the chicks throughout much, if not all, of their life in the nest so that at least one parent is in attendance and the time available for fishing is

* In a sample of 181 nests ninety-four held three, sixty-six held two, eighteen held one and three held four.

considerably reduced. Apart from gannets, which habitually guard their young throughout the entire nestling period, Peruvian boobies are the only member of the family to do so. The vast fish shoals of the Humboldt are responsible for this emancipation from the desperate food struggle which attends the tropical red-foot, white and brown boobies. Not only are fish readily available, but often they are near the doorstep, whereas the red-foot may face a five-day round trip for, in all probability, a poorer catch. Moreover, although the Peruvian booby is not strictly seasonal in its breeding, it tends to lay mainly in October/November and to rear its young in December/January/February, which is apparently the period in which food is even more abundant than during the cloudier winter of the southern hemisphere (June to September).

Despite its handicaps, the red-foot is a much more numerous species than the Peruvian. Yet both, no doubt, are reproducing as fast as they can and the Peruvian rears at least three or four youngsters to every one that the red-foot gets off. Since they are so nearly equal in size, feeding habits, freedom from predators and disease it may seem odd that Peruvian boobies do not far outnumber red-foots or at least increase until occupying all possible breeding stations within the zoogeographical area to which they are adapted. However, the Peruvian booby suffers periodic disasters that eclipse practically the whole population. These catastrophes do not recur with predictable frequency and severity, but traditionally occur around seven to ten or twelve years apart, which is also the periodicity of heavy rain years; the two events are connected. Hence the Peruvian booby has repeatedly to repair an extraordinarily heavy population drain not suffered by the red-foot. Such enormous catastrophes are rare, 1891, 1911/12, 1925/26, 1932, 1939 and 1957/58 being the only severe recorded ones, though minor crashes have occured between, very roughly at the frequency mentioned earlier. The last minor one occurred in 1963. When we were on the islands in December 1964 everything was obviously flourishing and there was no indication that the following year would see a disastrous crash. This latest in the line is of special interest for several reasons, but before considering it let a reconstruction of Murphy's account of the 1925 catastrophe furnish the dramatic background to these fantastic happenings.

It all starts with an event which hardly seems catastrophic. A warm-water and nutritively poor current, El Niño (called after the Christ child because it comes around Christmas), from the Panamanian region sweeps too far south and invades the region of the cold water Humboldt, destroying, driving south or banishing to deeper layers the cold-loving anchovies. Surface temperatures may rise as high as 27°C., which is considerably higher than the warmest Galapagos waters. Bereft of their main food, the sea-birds are reduced to desperate straits. Breeding grounds are largely or entirely deserted, leaving eggs to rot and chicks to starve. Adults erupt from their normal areas into Chile and Ecuador, searching for food in the most improbable places, including, by report, among cattle and in the streets and markets of Lima, before dying in hundreds of thousands. Corpses litter the shores and pile up on the beaches. Meanwhile the climatic effects of the warmer water-vapour laden air meeting the colder air further south releases deluges of rain which, under a north-westerly wind, scour the slopes of the Andes and the guano islands and wash enormous quantities of mineral salts into the sea. A dramatic growth of plankton, stimulated by the increased mineral content, in turn nourishes a red crustacean which becomes so profuse that the sea looks blood-stained. The death and decomposition of these animals and the countless sea-bird corpses charge the water with hydrogen sulphide, which reaches such a concentration that it converts the lead in the paint covering the bottom of ships into black lead sulphide, so the ships turn black in Callao harbour, the mark of the so-called 'Callao painter'.

The latest (1965) population decline of serious proportions is of particular interest for one very good reason. As mentioned earlier, the recent increase in the *anchoveta* fishing industry of Peru has been so vast, the catch reaching almost ten million tons in one year, that the possibility of over-fishing began to exercise interested parties, not least those concerned with the future of the guano birds. This is by no means a new problem for the Peruvians; the scientific advisors to the Corporacion de Fertilisantes have been eyeing it warily for at least twenty-five years, Ing. Gamarra told me, but the phenomenal growth of the fishing industry spotlighted the issue. How long can the anchovy population withstand annual cropping of the seven to ten million tons by man plus several million tons by the guano birds? Once the anchovies are depleted what will happen to the birds?

When the 1965 crash began, the total population of guano birds was about seventeen millions (this figure, based on actual censuses, is not likely to be precise but is valid for comparison with previous estimates similarly calculated) and by early 1966 it had dropped to about half a million.* However, many birds were then away at sea and could not be counted. A mere two months or so later there were apparently some three million back on the islands. (The 1956/57 crash was from about twenty-six to six and a half million.) The over-all population level of guano birds has risen substantially since about 1935 as a result of artificially produced mainland nesting areas (the guano authorities transformed mainland roosting areas into nesting ones by protecting selected spots with concrete walls ten feet high). Therefore, when the 1965 crash came the population was quite high, though by no means at its highest within recent years (1955, twenty-eight million). So the axe fell heavily, and undoubtedly the axe was the familiar Niño. Whatever else is made of the situation, 1965 was a Niño year, with the usual dramatic rise in sea temperatures – discernible, incidentally, even in the Galapagos Islands. It is interesting to note that the peak number of deaths occurred in June and that, not only in absolute numbers but also proportionally, more guanay cormorants died than did boobies or pelicans. The percentage mortality of these three species in the total was about 70, 20 and less than 10 per cent whereas guanays form a higher proportion of the living population.

The terrific crash, therefore, coincided with the Niño and in the ordinary way would not have aroused furious debate. It did so because the decline was suggestively linked with a temporary (as it now seems) drop in the *anchoveta* catches, which dropped by about 2·4 million *toneladas* between 1963/64 and 1964/65. Obviously there was the possibility that the anchovies had been over-fished and that this had aggravated the Niño effect. However it should be recalled how massive was the 1957 disaster, which occurred *before* commercial fishing had really started. Apparently the valid suggestion by the Guano Administration that over-fishing might be a contributory factor was taken up by the press and inflated and distorted so that

* *Las Poblaciones de Aves Guaneras . . .*

fishermen versus birds became an emotional issue and facts irrelevant. Then the allegation gained ground that fishermen were actively clubbing adult birds to death in order to prevent them spoiling their nets or interfering with their catch. Figures as high as more than 43,000 birds clubbed in eight days were responsibly circulated, as well as more irresponsible accounts of roosts wiped out with dynamite and fishermen invading colonies and breaking non-existent eggs. El Niño completely receded as a factor in the situation. These disturbing stories probably have a considerable basis in fact, but it is absurd to suggest that direct killing by fishermen could have been materially responsible for the population crash. Nevertheless, it seems that destruction of the birds has been publicly advocated in some quarters, a purely dismaying and scandalous possibility.

The Peruvian Government has apparently submitted its facts and figures to the Food and Agriculture Organisation and elsewhere for advice on whether the anchovies are being overfished and if so what to do about it. The F.A.O. thought, and later emphatically re-affirmed, that there was as yet no evidence for over-fishing, but the Americans thought otherwise and recommended, as conservation

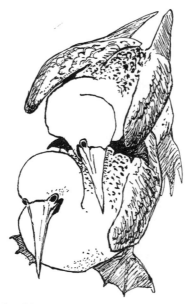

*Figure 55* Peruvian boobies mating

measures, a closure of fishing during the supposed breeding season from June to August, a ceiling of seven million tons for the annual catch and a limit on the number of fishing licences.

Whether there has been and still is over-fishing and whether this affected the 1965 crash, remains to some extent unsolved, but the Instituto del Mar reports, on the basis of experimental fishing, that after the Niño ended in February 1966, *anchovetas* were back in their usual numbers and sizes. However, the 1966 recommended ceiling of seven million tons was reached by May, but fishing continues until June. So far as the birds are concerned, they are apparently enthusiastically tackling the job of climbing back to their usual figures. Their population growth following a crash is explosive, reaching about twenty-five per cent per annum. Clutches are larger and breeding seasons begin six months earlier than usual and follow each other in quick succession, so that in a very few years these resilient birds recoup their losses; a biological feat as amazing as the dramatic crash itself.

# Some Conclusions 17

The view that characters, behavioral or structural, of
which a function cannot be seen at a glance, might well
be 'neutral', has in the past led to a more or less
defeatist attitude. But the justification of such a
hasty conclusion is now being seriously questioned . . .
and the need for more systematic studies of survival
value begins to be more widely felt.

N. Tinbergen

A simple but testing question will measure the extent to which I
have succeeded in relating our findings on the biology of these sea-
birds to wider issues. How well do the features here described form
a coherent and consistent picture of the birds' overall adaptedness,
and how satisfactory are known biological principles in explaining
the nature and origin of this adaptedness? This chapter is my last
chance to integrate the several aspects of morphology, distribution,
ecology and behaviour, introduced under the species described
earlier. This involves some repetition, but I refer to the relevant
chapters for details.

## COMPARATIVE MORPHOLOGY IN THE *Sulidae*

Within the family there are both strong physical similarities and
marked differences between species. All members of the family fall
within a fairly narrow range of overall size, shape and weight. The
proportions of body parts; certain broad plumage characters,
namely white underparts and bright feet and/or faces, are common
to nearly all (Table 1). The differences lie mainly in the colours of
plumage and bill, face, legs and feet.

*Shape and Structure*

Long narrow wings, streamlined cigar-shaped body, typical beak (long, strong, serrated and pointed) and webbed feet are clearly adaptations to their common way of life, involving extensive foraging flights, powerful plunging for fish – requiring minimum frictional resistance to aid penetration – the ability to hold and even spear fish, and to swim under water. The uniformity within the group in these respects is a convincing testimony to the over-riding importance of the sulid feeding method. Similarly, the absence of a brood patch is connected with their habit of incubating eggs underfoot. Within other fairly homogeneous sea-bird groups we find a greater range of size and structure than in the *Sulidae*, though it is difficult to know how much of this is due simply to the larger number of species in these groups. Despite the similarities, however, there are differences inviting an explanation, among which the following seem to me to sustain fairly convincing interpretation.

The gannet's greater size, weight and strength when compared with the rest of the family may be partly an expression of Bergmann's rule (that among the forms of a polytypic species body size tends to be larger in the cooler areas within the geographical range. This conserves body heat.) However, I feel that another and perhaps more important function of its greater size has to do with the greater size of its main prey and the depth to which it must penetrate in diving for them. This is partly a function of weight and it is significant that the gannet is hardly bigger than the white booby but weighs almost twice as much. Weight, too, has other correlates, here, perhaps, the value of a thick layer of insulating fat under severe winter conditions. Also, more abundant food may encourage greater weight than in a species needing vastly more foraging effort per fish.

The blue-foot's long tail is in both sexes an aid to diving in relatively shallow water. However, the marked sexual dimorphism adapts the male particularly well for this since he is both extremely light and has an even longer tail than the female in relation to overall size. I am not sure how the small size of the male red-foot should be interpreted, but I wonder if it might be linked with greater specialisation for feeding on flying fish in the air, where agility might be especially useful.

TABLE 1  Comparative morphology in the *Sulidae*

| | | Gannet North Atlantic | Boobies | | | | |
|---|---|---|---|---|---|---|---|
| | | | Red-foot | White | Blue-foot | Peruvian | Brown |
| Weight (gm) | M | 3,130 | 940 | 1,630 | 1,280 | 1,300 | 950 |
| | F | 3,090 | 1,070 | 1,880 | 1,800 | 1,520 | 1,290 |
| Beak length (mm) | M | 100 | 85 | 107 | 106 | 94 | 96 |
| | F | 99 | 90 | 109 | 114 | 99 | 102 |
| Wing length (mm) (approx.) | M | 505 | white form 372 brown-tailed form | 460 | 440 | 390 | 406 |
| | F | 515 | 393 white form 389 brown-tailed form | 480 | 460 | 410 | 432 |
| Tail length (mm) (approx.) | M | 250 | 205 | 198 | 236 | 175 | 218 |
| | F | | 204 | 201 | 237 | 185 | 215 |
| Upperparts | M | white with black wing-tips | white or brown | white | brown | brown | brown |
| | F | | | | | | |
| Underparts | M | white | white or brown | white | white | white | white |
| | F | | | | | | |
| Bill | M | blue | blue | orange | slaty blue | dark bluish | yellow |
| Face | | black | red | black | black | blackish | greenish |
| Feet | F | black with lines green | red | slaty to greenish | ultramarine blue | blackish-blue blue | greenish |

The red-foot's short tarsi are linked with its tree and bush nesting habits and its almost total avoidance of the ground. Certainly its ability to walk on the ground has been vastly reduced, but it may also be that twig-hopping is facilitated by tarsi shorter than those found in the rest of the family. Its prehensile feet are also an adaptation to this habitat.

The remainder of the inter-specific differences in structure are doubtless adaptive, but they are either less extreme than the cases given above or probably involve more compromises. The size and shape of the bill, for instance, varies widely in the family and is certain to be linked with different food preferences and methods of hunting, but these differences are still entirely obscure.

### Broad conclusions

Gannets are far the heaviest, but both white and blue-footed boobies have longer beaks, though, in fact, not as deep. Red-foots have the smallest beaks; it, and especially the brown booby, have relatively long wings. Blue-foots have the longest tails (although the table does not show this the male's tail as a proportion of body length is longer than the female's to a greater extent than in any other species). These factors represent important adaptations for modes of fishing, some of which have been suggested in the text, but most are yet to be worked out.

### Colour

Turning now to plumage and colour, the most striking similarity is the possession in the adults of all species of white underparts. The brown form of the red-foot is a partial exception to this, but its almost wholly white form, overall the more common, upholds the rule. The juveniles, too, conform pretty well as shown in figure 56. Only the juvenile gannet, in particular the North Atlantic gannet, is both dark all over and different from the adult. The juvenile red-foot is brown all over, but so is the brown form of the adult. I have already quoted Phillips's investigation which gave experimental evidence for the view that white underparts are adaptive for plunge-diving birds by making them harder to see from below, and that seems to me the most convincing interpretation of white underparts in the *Sulidae*. What about the exceptions – the brown form of the red-foot and the juvenile gannet? Nothing is known about the adaptiveness of brownness in the red-foot, but I have tentatively suggested a tendency for this form to specialise in semi-nocturnal or nocturnal hunting. However, it could be that the explanation is physiological, brownness being linked with some capacity not amenable to field observation. I suppose whiteness to be the special case in this species and brownness the phylogenetically, as it is also the ontogenetically, primitive condition. The function of black plumage in the juvenile gannet may be interpreted as making the juvenile less likely to elicit attack from the adult, particularly the male. As the time for fledging approaches, the adult male gannet becomes considerably more aggressive than he was when the chick was small, and this aggression shows in his increased attacks on his mate. If the chick possessed adult plumage it would tend to draw attack from the male and might easily be dislodged from the cliff ledge with fatal results. So the black plumage, by making the juvenile as unlike the adult as possible, will reduce its attack-releasing properties. Thus, even though dark underparts are less helpful to the juvenile than white ones would be, and may considerably handicap it during its hard struggle to learn the skills of fishing, it is presumably even more important that it should inhibit adult attack. In fact, we find that it acquires white underparts as the very first plumage change, years before it acquires white upperparts, so reversing the handicap as soon as it can do so.

So much for plumage similarities. Moving on to the differences and having paid so much attention to white underparts, it is worth looking at the *upperparts*; what differences are there and can any of them be explained?

Adult sulids are basically divisible into those with white upperparts (gannet, white booby, and the white form of the red-foot) and those with dark upperparts (brown form of red-foot, blue-foot, Peruvian and brown). I think one may immediately dispose of the possibility that white has no special significance but is just a neutral lack of colour, since all forms specially acquire it from a quite different juvenile plumage.

The gannet's conspicuous white upperparts attract others to fishing birds. It is less certain that the attraction *benefits* the birds that do the attracting, but in the absence of any other function specifically for the white upperparts, it seems fair to assume that its main function is in helping fishing flocks to form. The way(s) in which fishing in flocks benefits the individuals remains to be shown (see pp. 48–49). Juvenile gannets are also led to fish shoals by going where the conspicuous adults are fishing.

There is also the subsidiary point that by pinpointing flying individuals white upperparts help form the typical skeins in which gannets fly from the fishing grounds back to their nesting colonies. However, Peruvian boobies form similar skeins and they have brown upperparts. Still, Peruvian boobies fish in a more restricted area and at a much greater concentration than gannets and are thus far more likely to fall in with others on their journey. The white plumage of the red-foot and white booby is likely to act similarly to the gannet's in attracting others.

The interpretation of the advantage of dark upper-parts is entirely speculative. With the exception of the brown form of the red-foot, all species brown above are, either mainly or in good part, inshore feeders and not as likely to benefit from attracting conspecifics to form a fishing flock. Also, the brown, blue-footed, red-footed, Peruvian and Abbott's boobies are all subject to more or less intense persecution from frigates and skuas, and since countershading is an effective form of simple camouflage and moreover fits in with the advantage of white underparts described above, it may be that one advantage of dark upperparts lies in enhanced protection from such persecution. Unfortunately white boobies are also parasitised! All such characters are compromises and more may emerge if we knew the extent to which the various boobies are parasitised and the value to them of all-whiteness rather than countershading. This balance can be expected to vary from species to species.

The remaining differences in appearance, brightly coloured bills, faces, irises and feet, can be more convincingly dismissed. They are obvious morphological 'markers', enhancing movements of head and feet used in display. The precise significance of each particular colour and combination of colours in the different species is, and is likely to remain, unknown. It is not even certain that there *is* a significance in a particular colour rather than colour or brightness in general, since it is not certain that boobies have colour vision.

Metabolic waste products may inevitably produce colour and colour in general can be used as a marker. Or it may have evolved under specific selection pressure as a specific adaptation.

## FEATURES OF BREEDING ENVIRONMENT IN THE SULIDAE

### Habitat

Each sulid breeds in colonies of its own typical size and density, set in a typical kind of habitat. As I hope to make clear, these features are all important determinants of the species' behaviour. First, however, the facts. Gannets breed mainly on cliffs; cliffs were apparently the habitat in which their behaviour evolved and are still the preferred habitat, although there are several colonies on fairly flat ground. Peruvian boobies are also largely cliff-nesters, though again without being tied to that habitat. White and blue-footed boobies, on the other hand, are quite happy on slopes or flat ground and virtually never breed on cliffs. The blue-foot, especially, can use extremely flat ground, without even take-off points or breeze, as in the crater on Daphne. Brown boobies apparently like steep slopes and broken ground on scarps or near cliff-edges. The red-foot is a tree and bush nester; it and the rare Abbott's booby of the Indian Ocean Christmas Island are the only boobies adapted to an arboreal habitat. So habitats are varied and broadly distinctive for each species.

### Colony Size

Colony size is also fairly distinctive for each species. The largest sulid colonies in the world are probably those of the Peruvian booby. One island may hold hundreds of thousands of boobies. The second largest colonies are undoubtedly those of the South African or Cape gannet, whose main colony on Malagos Island probably numbers about twenty-five thousand* pairs (vastly higher figures are quoted – Speight estimated six million birds on Ichabo – but I find these hard to accept). Not only are gannet colonies of all three races (North Atlantic, South African and Australian) occasionally of spectacular size, but the average size is very large. In the case of the

* Rand.

2nd year

juvenile

North Atlantic gannet
*Morus bassana*

Australian gannet
*Morus serrator*

juvenile

Brown booby
*Sula lencogaster*

Cape gannet
*Morus capensis*

292

white form

dark form

juvenile

Red-footed booby
*Sula sula*

Abbott's booby
*Sula abbotti*

juvenile

Blue-footed booby
*Sula nebouxii*

juvenile

White booby
*Sula dactylatra*

juvenile

Peruvian booby
*Sula variegata*

re *56* Identification of the world's *Sulidae*

British population of the North Atlantic gannet the average colony size, if we exclude recently established colonies and call St Kilda one colony, is around eight to ten thousand pairs. The situation is quite different amongst the rest of the boobies. The largest white booby colony numbers probably not more than five-thousand pairs, the big majority are less than two thousand pairs and a very large number hold only a few hundred pairs. Much the same is true of the blue-footed booby, whose colonies are almost to be numbered in hundreds of pairs rather than thousands. The red-footed booby colony on Tower was very large, at an estimated 140,000 pairs, but this seems unusually if not uniquely big and records for other parts of the world show colonies mainly of hundreds or a few thousand pairs. For the sake of completeness, although this book does not deal in any detail with the two other boobies, Abbott's booby is confined to one small and relatively scattered colony on Christmas Island numbering about 2,000 pairs,* and the brown booby breeds in colonies comparable to or smaller than those of the white booby.

## Colony Density

Colony density can theoretically vary independently of colony size, though in fact really dense nesters also form large colonies. Here again there are valid generalisations. Where topography permits the gannet nests at a density of about 2·3 pairs per square yard and the Peruvian booby up to about two pairs per square yard. This is pretty thick on the ground, allowing little more than space in which to turn round. White, brown and blue-footed boobies never approach this figure. At their densest white boobies average around one pair in four to ten square yards and usually breed much more widely spaced as small, scattered groups or even semi-solitary pairs. This situation applies also to the blue-foot. Red-foots vary considerably; in favoured areas when the bushes are a fairly even height, with good perches and plenty of interlacing twigs to support nests, they reach a density of one pair in nineteen square yards, but over a wide area of less favourable trees a much lower density is probably normal.

The factors discussed above – habitat type, colony size and density

* My population figures for Abbott's booby are not yet worked out, but 2,000 is probably a conservative number.

– will figure largely in the attempt to interpret the species total behaviour in broad outline. Before that, however, we should look at some possible causal factors underlying distribution, habitat and colony characteristics. Social and pair behaviour is greatly influenced by the breeding habitat, but what dictates colony characteristics? Again, the best one can do is to suggest correlations.

In the case of the Peruvian booby the correlation between abundant food, limited breeding sites and large dense colonies amounts almost to a direct cause and effect relationship, but this is not true for the North Atlantic gannet. Here, as I described at some length in Chapter 4, the most convincing interpretation, at least to me, is that, in an area of seasonally abundant food and seasonally predictable weather, particularly autumn gales, it is an advantage for breeding to be so ordered that the young grow up, fledge and undergo the transition to independence at the most favourable times, which, moreover, are constant from year to year. This requires seasonally synchronised breeding, which is helped by the social stimulation derived from nesting in large dense colonies. This is certainly not the whole explanation; some degree of coloniality is forced on the gannet by the relatively limited number of suitable breeding stacks, but the extent of the density and size of the colony certainly cannot be fully explained in terms of shortage of breeding stacks.

Perhaps the simplest explanation fitting the few known facts concerning the red-footed, brown and white boobies is that extremely large colonies would seriously over-populate the hunting area (the area within which hunting trips for food for their young are practicable). This view may be particularly valid since to some extent the different species take the same kind of prey. We saw how serious was the food shortage facing breeding red-footed and white boobies on Tower; in 1964 92 per cent of all red-footed booby eggs laid in the observation colony failed to produce fledged young. We may doubt whether either the year or the area were typical of the species' normal breeding success, but it is almost certainly true that over their world range the red-footed, white and brown boobies, all predominantly warm water species, sometimes find it difficult to feed their young. Extremely large colonies would seem biologically undesirable and since there is normally no shortage of oceanic

TABLE 2 Colony size and density in the *Sulidae*

| Species | Colony size Max. pairs (in world) | approx. av. | Examples of colony density yards per pair | Locality (of colony density) |
|---|---|---|---|---|
| North Atlantic gannet | 17,000 | 8–10,000 | 0·43 | Bass Rock |
| Cape gannet | 40,000 | c.10,000 | 0·4 | Cape colony |
| Red-footed booby | 140,000 | 1,000 | 10·0 37·0 | Tower (Galapagos) British Honduras |
| White booby | probably c.5,000 | 1,000 | 50·0 10·0 | Tower (Galapagos) Ascension Island |
| Brown booby | probably c.3,000 | 1,000 | 10·0 | Ascension Island |
| Blue-footed booby | 10,000 | 2,000 | 7·0 | Daphne (Galapagos) |
| Peruvian booby | 250,000 | 50,000 | 0·5 | Guañape N. (Peru) |
| Abbott's booby | one colony only c.2,000 pairs | | scattered | Christmas Island (Indian Ocean) |

*Note:* Some of these figures are approximations only and there is considerable variation between localities. However, the general trends are clear.

islands in the areas which have any at all, there is no good reason for dense nesting either. This may be particularly true where weather is not markedly seasonal and any effect of social stimulation in synchronising breeding is relatively unimportant or even detrimental (see Chapter 4).

There are, of course, good reasons why the birds should be colonial at all. The Galapagos archipelago, for instance, is virtually the only group of islands in hundreds of thousands of square miles of flying-fish populated sea. Obviously there is a vast hunting ground here. But owing to the complex ocean currents very few of the Galapagos islands are in warm seas (or, probably, within practicable foraging distances of enough warm sea) and also with the right kind of cover. So Tower and Wenman are the only islands with large red-foot populations; the population of Tower is unusually large for the species – perhaps the largest in the world.

The blue-foot is a somewhat special case. Its distribution, though quite extensive, is markedly discontinuous. By far the largest numbers (many thousands) occur on the Lobos Islands of Peru and this species is largely cold water loving. However, even in the Galapagos its numbers are nothing like so great as suitable nesting space would allow; the Punta Suarez colony on Hood numbers a mere five hundred pairs whereas that and the adjacent areas could hold many thousands. One is tempted to correlate this with relatively poor food, since the Peruvian colony is so much larger and food there is so much more abundant.

Many of the points made above will be referred to again when discussing related topics, both ecological (for example, clutch size) and behavioural (for example, the effects of dense nesting on social behaviour) but, first, there is more background information to consider.

FEATURES OF FEEDING ENVIRONMENT

I have already suggested that many of the boobies' *breeding* habits, such as size and density of colonies, may be basically related to the features of their feeding habitat and I instanced the Peruvian booby, gannet and red-footed booby as good cases in point. Before pursuing further ecological comparisons in the *Sulidae* I want to bring together some of the main characteristics of their *feeding* habitats. The following account is too simplified for complete accuracy but the main points are probably valid. The distribution limits are for the breeding range of the species; the areas in which they feed may extend these limits according to how oceanic they are. However, in the breeding cycle no boobies forage more than a hundred or two miles as a rule and it is the location and characteristics of their feeding area insofar as it affects breeding, that will be mainly of interest in our comparison.

Boobies are mainly pan-tropical. The white booby occurs widely in the Indian, Pacific and South Atlantic oceans from between about 30°S. to 25°46' N. and 171°44' W. to 154° E. – in other words a broad belt around the warmer waters of the world. Its largest colonies (probably Clipperton and Melpelo) lie 10°17' N. and 3°59' N. respectively and its centre of distribution is possibly the middle area of the Pacific. The white booby is probably mainly an offshore feeder.

The red-footed booby overlaps with the white for much of its range, but is typically even more restricted to sub-tropical waters, with its centre of distribution probably just north of the equator in the Pacific and in the Caribbean. It is mainly an offshore forager, avoiding inlets and coastal waters and hunting well out to sea.

The brown booby, like the white and red-footed, is very much a wide-ranging tropical species, with breeding stations in the South Atlantic, Pacific and Indian Oceans, but not in the Galapagos archipelago. It is often sympatric with either or both the red-footed and white boobies and in the Gulf of California with the blue-foot. It seems somewhat intermediate between inshore and offshore feeders; it frequently fished close inshore on Ascension, but is also met with well offshore and is probably not so specialised for inshore feeding as the blue-foot.

The range of the blue-footed booby is more easily defined as southwards from the Gulf of California to the northern Peruvian islands. However, the middle third of this range is practically devoid of blue-foots, which are effectively confined to three main areas – islands in the Gulf of California, the Galapagos and the western seaboard of Central America, southwards along the north-west coast of South America to Peru. Unlike white and red-footed boobies, it feeds mainly inshore and is relatively rarely encountered more than a few miles offshore.

The Peruvian booby is even more limited in its range, occurring only on the Peruvian and some north Chilean guano islands and on a few mainland Peruvian *puntas*. It feeds in the belt of the Humboldt from very close inshore (but still usually in deep water) outwards to the western limits of the current.

Turning now to the gannets, which are perhaps better separated into the genus *Morus*, there is a clearly demarcated distribution of each of the three species or races (probably better treated as races). The main stronghold of the North Atlantic gannet is the west coast of Britain, though there is a large colony on Bonaventure in the St Lawrence. The South African gannet breeds on six islands, five on the west coast of South Africa. The Australasian gannet ranges from Tasmania along the south coast of Australia to about as far north as south-eastern Queensland on the east and Fremantle on the west. Thus there are three cleanly separated breeding populations of gannets in the world. The North Atlantic gannet, at least, seems a typically offshore feeder, though it also feeds close inshore.

What, then, are the distribution patterns shown by the sulids? First, the really big concentrations nearly all occur in particularly productive areas, either in cool, temperate or cold-water regions or in areas with upwelling water rich in minerals and the lower forms of life and thus fish. The classical Humboldt situation, supporting the large Peruvian booby colonies, has already been discussed at length. The vast South African gannetries are in the region of the Benguela current – in many respects a situation closely resembling the Peruvian islands and the adjacent Humboldt. Indeed, as Hutchinson points out, there are even four species (the gannet, a cormorant *Phalacrocorax capensis*, a pelican *Pelecanus rufescens* and the Cape penguin) filling the niches occupied on the Peruvian islands by the analogous Peruvian booby, guanay cormorant, Chilean pelican and Humboldt penguin. The South African birds feed extensively on the pilchards, maas-bankers, anchovies and cephalopods (Rand). Then the Australasian and North Atlantic gannetries are in cool water, rich in fish. The northern gannet preys on the vast shoals of herring, mackerel and saithe in the North Sea and North Atlantic and shows every sign of enjoying abundant food.

In addition to the relative abundance of prey species in the areas occupied by the various members of the *Sulidae*, one must also consider the important relationship between food supply and season. I have instanced the Peruvian booby and the three gannet races as examples of vast colonies in food-rich areas. They are all, also, to a marked extent seasonal breeders, consistently producing their young at certain times of the year rather than all the year round. Young Peruvian boobies are mostly reared at the time of the greatest abundance of *anchovetas*, between November and May. The South African gannet, laying mainly in September and October, rears its young from December to February – or at least that is the period of their greatest demands. It is also the period when the abundance of its main prey species is, overall, at its highest – squids reach peak

W

abundance in November/December, pilchards in February/March and maas-bankers reach their second highest peak in December (their peak is reached in April).* The northern gannet breeds at the opposite end of the year, but again its production of young coincides with the main abundance of herring and mackerel and the latter in particular are extremely important at this time. Finally, the Australasian gannet, laying in September/October in the other hemisphere, turns the gannet's year upside-down, and probably, like the northern gannet, coincides with the best time for feeding its young, though I don't know of any good evidence for this.

One ought also to remember that the availability of food to the newly fledged young is an important factor in their survival. The Peruvian booby resembles other boobies in feeding its young after they become free flying, but the gannets do not. The South African gannet young fledge when food seems reasonably plentiful – at least the time of year when all the main prey species reach their lowest level is June/July/August and by this time the young should be well and truly self-supporting. The North Atlantic gannet fledges when there is also a vast herring movement into the waters through which it migrates, at least on the east side of Britain. It is not known how important, if at all, this is to their survival, but the correlation is suggestive.

Turning now to the rest of the boobies, their colonies (except the Peruvian) are usually relatively small. The distribution of the red-footed, brown and white boobies is usually reckoned broadly to follow that of their important or even principal food item, the flying fish. This happens also to be a distribution over vast stretches of uniformly warm, uniformly food-rich (or poor, depending how you view it) seas. There are scores, probably hundreds, of minor upwellings in this world-wide belt and if details were known, these may indeed explain many of the preferred feeding areas of these boobies, as Bailey has suggested. Generalising widely (I hope not wildly), however, it seems basically true that the main zoogeographical, large (though local) areas of these boobies do not embrace areas as rich in food as those of the Peruvian booby and the gannets. When clutch size is discussed, it will be evident that, in fact, all these boobies rear one chick, often with great difficulty, whilst the

* Rand

Peruvian booby rears three or four and the gannets one, but with great ease, quickly and giving it large fat reserves.

The blue-footed booby stands a little aloof, for reasons which were described in Chapter 11. It is often basically in the same position as the red-footed, white and brown boobies, with all of which it is sympatric but with two significantly extenuating circumstances – a tendency to inhabit colder waters (as in the south of the Galapagos Archipelago) and a particular ability to fish close inshore. Hence, it can rear two or three young by the mechanism described in Chapter 11.

Finally, in the correlation between zoogeographical distribution and breeding characteristics, there is the question of seasonal variation in weather. The northern gannet, as already mentioned, produces young which fledge in August/September and thus have a good chance of fair weather during that critical two or three weeks after fledging. In the Galapagos, on the other hand, there is no marked difference in weather from month to month, and no young red-footed boobies are liable to suffer from this factor. It is known that the red-foot varies from region to region in its laying season, but no attempt has been made to link this with the survival value of producing young at the best time for weather. In the Galapagos the red-foot lays in most months, as does the blue-foot. The white booby shows a clear tendency towards more seasonal breeding, despite the large spread in any one year. Why this should be so, even in the Galapagos, is unknown.

In this somewhat breathless survey I have ignored many relevant problems and omitted much important detail. The aim has been to paint a broad picture of the feeding environment of the family to place alongside the account of their breeding characteristics. Now it remains to fit some further ecological details into this framework.

## Clutch Size

Clutch size in the *Sulidae*\* varies from one in the gannet and the red-foot; one or two in the brown booby; one, often two in the white booby; one, usually two but often three in the blue-foot; to two, three or four in the Peruvian booby. In sea-birds in general,

\* See Nelson, 'Clutch Size . . .'

clutch size is low in offshore feeders and higher in inshore feeders. The *Sulidae* are essentially offshore feeders and five out of seven of them rear but a single chick, whether by limiting the clutch to one or by reducing the brood to one as in the white booby. This is quite clearly a response to the food situation just described. The white, red-footed and brown boobies all make heavy weather of rearing their young, quite a lot of which starve. The exceptions, the Peruvian booby with its two, three or four young and the blue-foot with its two or three, have already been explained in their respective chapters. The blue-foot, it will be recalled, has evolved an inshore fishing ability and with it a sexual dimorphism in form and behaviour which facilitates the rearing of two or three young rather than the single one of the other species. The Peruvian's situation, with its relatively near and very abundant food, has been invoked so often in this book that no more need be said.

The gannets all seem anomalous at first sight. I have argued that they enjoy a much more reliable and abundant food supply than most boobies, yet they manage to rear only one chick (Nelson, 1964). However, the one chick is equivalent to two or three in its food consumption and in the large fat deposits laid down. Whereas the boobies have opted to feed their young for, in the most extreme case we knew, over three hundred days (red-foot), the northern gannets do so for ninety days. The very fact that it can compress its feeding period so drastically and yet produce such heavy young is alone evidence enough of the abundance of its food at this time, and surely suggests, though it does not prove, that since food is so seasonally plentiful, it is advantageous to use it to the full. Thus, one supposes, has evolved the gannet's departure from the rest of the family in dropping a long period of feeding the young, followed by post-fledging feeding; instead the gannet has acquired the new regime of rapid, extensive feeding, coupled with seasonal breeding. All would probably be well in this argument if it were true that the gannet's one chick is, in fact, equivalent to two or three booby chicks, and hence in accord with the food situation and the most the gannet could rear. Chapter 4 showed that this is not the case, at least for the northern gannet. It is unsatisfactory to explain exceptions by special pleading, but a possible answer is that the gannet evolved its regime under different conditions from the ones now

TABLE 3 Comparative breeding biology in the *Sulidae*

| Species | Clutch size | Egg wt (gm) | Incubation period (days) | Fledging period (days) | Period of post fledging feeding | Period between beginnings of successive successful breeding cycles (months) |
|---|---|---|---|---|---|---|
| North Atlantic gannet | 1 | 104·5 | 43·6 | 90 | 0 | 12 |
| Red-footed booby | 1 | 54 | 45 | 130 | 90+ | 12+ |
| White booby | 2 (1–2) | 70 | c.43 | 115 | 60+ | 12 |
| Brown booby | 1 (1–2) | 60 | c.43 | 105–120 | 50+ | 10–12? |
| Blue-footed booby | 2 (1–3) | 65 | 41 | 102 | 50+ | 9–10 |
| Peruvian booby | 3 (2–4) | c.60 | prob. 40–3 | c.100+ | some weeks | 12 |

obtaining and is too slow a breeder to have made the necessary adaptive changes since conditions became apparently more favourable. Summing up this entire section, I suggest that in sulids, large, dense colonies occur in relatively food-rich areas and benefit from relatively well synchronised, seasonal breeding. Smaller, sparser colonies benefit species in areas in which food is not locally, nor overall, rich, and where there is also no seasonal abundance of food and therefore no advantage in seasonal breeding. Sulid clutch size is low overall, as befitting an offshore feeding family, and particularly fitting those species which experience periods of serious food shortage. The exceptions to low clutch size are explicable on evidence of special food situations and/or special habits.

COMPARATIVE BEHAVIOUR IN THE *Sulidae*

Perhaps the stage is now well enough set for an attempt to make some useful comparative points about behaviour in the family. Whether or not you accept my suggestions concerning the *reasons* for nesting densely and in huge colonies as against more thinly and in smaller ones, you can at least accept the *facts* of this situation and assess the rest of the chapter from this point on. Basically, the gannets and boobies are all colonial breeders. Every species has striking coloured parts and also, in every case, some striking displays in the breeding season. The rest of their behaviour is fairly straightforward and has either been mentioned already or is common to all members and of no special comparative behavioural interest. This is perhaps not quite true, since small differences, say, in preening or defaecating behaviour, in breathing rates, in precise flying rhythms, etc. may all exist and be significant in the biology of the species. However, they are all extremely subtle differences, if they do exist, difficult to interpret and probably irrelevant to the main comparative story. This story concerns mainly reproductive behaviour, particularly the displays and other large units of behaviour involved in getting a territory, getting a mate, maintaining the pair relations and also the wider social relations within the colony; in other words, mainly communication behaviour. All the time, however, I want to refer back to the ecological features of the species – whether of habitat, fishing methods, colony density or whatever – in an attempt to relate their behaviour and ecology. As I have said, they all possess striking displays, but the emphases are different in each species and we are interested to know where the emphasis is placed and why.

First, one may list three important features in which all sulids differ from each other; then it is possible to see the pattern of their display repertoire and why it is that they have this feature and not that, exaggerate one and underplay another. This is the list:

All sulids vary in weight, size, proportions and aerial agility; also in colours and patterns. Some of these differences have already been related to fishing behaviour but they evolved in balance with display behaviour as well.

All sulids vary in habitat type.

They also vary in territory size (i.e. density). This, too, has been tied in with ecological factors. Together with variations in locomotory ability, territory size greatly affects the extent of their contacts and interactions with neighbours and in the case of a mated pair with each other and their young.

Taking the first point, the male blue-foot, red-foot or brown booby weighs less than a third as much as the male gannet, yet it is more than three-quarters as big. Whatever led to the evolution of these size differences, a higher proportion of aerial displays occur in these three boobies than in the gannet. Blue-foots have a very well developed flight circuiting, in which the male circles his territory, and pair circuiting in which mates do so together. Also, both sexes, but particularly the athletic males, show the agile aerial 'saluting' display. Brown boobies also flight and pair circuit and the male frequently performs the advertising display in full flight. Red-foots flight circuit as territorial behaviour and also as part of the advertising display, though they do not advertise in flight. Gannets, on the other hand, have no pair circuiting and no aerial advertising, though the male does flight circuit when establishing or re-establishing his territory; this is readily allowed by the cliff habitat, which facilitates take-off in this heavy bird.

Other factors inevitably complicate the picture. Thus, red-foots cannot get around in their tree and bush territories as well as brown and blue-footed boobies can walk around in their territories. So they would seem even more dependent on aerial displays; however, they have made do with fewer displays rather than evolved new aerial ones; their repertoire is the smallest of all boobies. The blue-foot, on the other hand, is agile on the ground as well as in the air and can get around its flat territory better than the brown can move around its steeper slopes and cliff edges. So we find considerable ground interaction between pair members and between neighbours in the blue-foot, more than in the brown. Although the gannet shows flight circuiting, its cliff habitat and dense nesting prevents it walking around – it has no territory other than the actual nest – so locomotory displays are reduced, though pair and neighbour contacts are inevitably maximal. These points will be developed later.

The second difference between sulids, that of habitat type, really acts in conjunction with other factors, particularly habitat size. Together, these two factors help determine the degree of aerial and territorial mobility and, as a result, the development of the appropriate signal behaviour to communicate the intention of walking or flying as the case may be. The type of nest-building behaviour (functional or symbolic) is also affected.

The habitat features which, in my opinion, interact with density effects in determining the species behaviour repertoire, are for the red-foot the arboreal habit, limiting movement (and hence contacts and social interactions between neighbours) and requiring functional nest-building; for the gannet and Peruvian the cliff habitat, limiting locomotion and facilitating take-off and requiring functional nest-building; for the blue-foot, the flat ground habitat encouraging locomotion and social behaviour (take-off is no problem because of the species' lightness) and freeing the bird from functional nest-building. The brown and white boobies are somewhat intermediate; the white is clearly less aerial than the brown, probably because it is larger and heavier rather than because of the habitat. In fact, the white booby may prefer rather flatter ground than the brown, but normally with some eminences from which it can take flight. Both species have a fair amount of contact with neighbours and hence social behaviour. The brown booby seems to make a somewhat functional nest in contrast to the blue-foot and white boobies, in which nest-building is purely symbolic. There seems no obvious reason for this, except perhaps, the brown booby's stronger tendency to nest on steep slopes and cliff edges.

Summing up so far, all the family show some degree of aerial and territorial display behaviour, though the relative extent of the two varies with the species; nest-building, whether functional or symbolic, is also correlated with habitat type. All species also have associated displays communicating the intention of flight and locomotion. Again, some species place more emphasis on the pre-flight signals and others on the pre-locomotory signals. However, other factors influence the extent to which pre-flight and pre-locomotory signals are developed and these, and other factors, are the subject of the next section.

The third and perhaps most important difference between boobies, affecting their displays, concerns the density at which they nest. The smaller the territory, the more the owner is pushed into contact with mate, neighbours and eventually offspring. Colonial birds depend for the attainment of suitable spacing out on a balance of fear and aggression – assertion and withdrawal. The balanced nature of this has been fully recognised for a long time, due in large part to Tinbergen (1954). I hope I showed in Chapters 5, 7, 11 and 16 that in sulids, there is aggression and fear not only between rivals (neighbours) but between mates and between parent and offspring. The question of why there should be competition for sites, and hence aggression, has already been discussed in an earlier part of this chapter and in other chapters. The aggression, at least, is roughly measurable if one accepts the validity of a measure involving the frequency and extent of overt acts of aggression and displays derived from them, and if one agrees that a bite or a jab delivered to one's mate is aggressive, as it is when delivered to one's rival. The territory size is also measurable; the figures are in Table 2, so we reach a situation in which, though all sulids are colonial and aggressive, some species are more aggressive and more densely colonial, or more aggressive and less densely colonial than others, and so on. These two facets constantly interact. At one end of the scale there is the gannet, the densest nester and showing the highest frequency of fights and threatening behaviour. Contrast the blue-foot, which nests quite widely spaced and virtually never fights. As usual, the issue is complicated by other factors – mobility, for instance, which affects the frequency with which the individual meets neighbours and to some extent mates.

The most adequate treatment, having defined the general relation between aggression and dense nesting, is to relate it to the species one by one, beginning with the gannet. Chapter 5 has already provided the details. Male gannets fight fiercely and frequently, often inflicting significant damage, when establishing and maintaining territory. Similarly, females fight for possession of males, if a triangular situation arises. Males also attack their females whenever the pair meet at the nest, which they do hundreds of times in a season. Furthermore, besides fighting and threat behaviour, they have evolved a conspicuous aggressive display by which they defend the site in ritual. This catalogue of aggressive acts handsomely exceeds anything the boobies show, and it is not surprising to find that it has strongly influenced other aspects of gannet social behaviour. The female cannot get away, since there is no territory except the nest, and there are hostile neighbours on most sides. She could, of course, flee every time the male arrived but their co-operation as a pair would not get very far.

Consequently, she has developed appeasement behaviour and the

307

pair have evolved a complex meeting ceremony by which they can express aggression and fear whilst simultaneously strengthening their relationship rather than destroying it. The pair also preen each other simultaneously, again probably a sublimated expression of aggression. One of the striking features of the gannet's domestic routine is that on no occasion do they leave nest, egg or chick unguarded. Yet to accomplish the change-over or nest relief without misunderstandings apparently involves prolonged and conspicuous posturing on the part of the bird about to leave, so that the message gets across. This, at least, is my interpretation of the sky-pointing posture, which typically precedes movement from the nest. Gannets sky-point prior to walking from the nest, and this posture is the precursor of locomotion rather than immediate flight. The gannet has other highly ritualised postures or movements, for example the posture resembling a pelican's resting position and used in ambivalent aggression/fear encounters to express some aspect of the balance between them (exactly what the pelican posture means is still unclear), and a ritualised version of the comfort movement by which plumage is shaken and settled. Overall, it is a very active species in display, with a large repertoire of distinctive displays which it performs at a high frequency throughout the entire breeding cycle.

One could conveniently consider one of several boobies next, all for different reasons. However, the Peruvian most resembles the gannet in its dense, cliff nesting habits. Next to the gannet it fights most, and has a ritualised form of jabbing and threat behaviour comparable to, though not so highly developed as the gannet's. So far as pair relations are concerned, the male is not unilaterally aggressive to his female as is the male gannet, but the pair have a ritualised meeting ceremony derived from aggressive jabbing. It should be recalled that they, too, are prevented from withdrawing into a quiet corner of the territory, which is almost as small as the gannet's. They perform symbolic nest-building and (like blue-foots) 'show' or 'present' nest material to each other by an upward arc of the head, with nest material in the bill. They, too, have displays which precede and communicate the intention of movement from the nest. However, they are not the same as the gannet's. For one thing, like all boobies, the Peruvian has converted the sky-pointing display into a sexual advertising display. Now it uses a form of goose-stepping or parading on the spot to indicate departure (usually initially on foot) and moves off with its head held upwards and backwards. A quick rattle of its wings communicates the intention of flight.

The Peruvian leads to the blue-foot because these two are closely related. I have mentioned the blue-foot's liking for flat ground and its tendency to move around, and also stressed its aerial displays. Territories are relatively large, and this combination gives rise to several displays involving locomotion and pre-movement postures. Exaggerated parading is a form of ritualised locomotion; wing-rattle and wing-flick are flight precursors and bill-up-face-away is a display performed by a bird about to leave or actually leaving its mate, and is probably derived from the intention movement of locomotion. Sexual advertising is the sky-pointing display and is performed by both sexes, thus probably reinforcing the relatively simple meeting ceremony as a pair bond strengthening display. This species is relatively unaggressive, intraspecific fights are rare and the threat behaviour little developed, though there is a ritualised aggressive site-ownership display. Symbolic nest-building is incorporated into pair interactions, so that by a combination of primitive meeting ceremony, mutual advertising and symbolic nest-building, the blue-foot achieves considerable interaction between mates. Several of its displays use the extraordinarily brightly coloured feet. The Peruvian booby so much resembles the blue-foot that I would consider it to be derived from it and to have reduced some of the blue-foot's displays (such as saluting and parading) as a result of the limitations of cliff-nesting, whilst exaggerating others (such as the meeting ceremony) perhaps because of the proximity enforced by cliff-nesting with its associated loss of some locomotory pair interactions.

The white booby is much akin to the blue-foot so far as territory size is concerned, though perhaps it never reaches quite the density of the densest blue-foot groups. Basically, it is a sloping or flat-ground species, fairly well spaced, given to locomotion and rather less to aerial displays. It is more inclined to overt fighting at territorial boundaries, and between pair members there is about the same order of aggressive behaviour as between blue-foot pair members. The greeting ceremony is a hostile-looking jabbing, but it is ritualised in so far as there is no actual biting. Like blue-foots, white boobies also show a ritualised bill-touching. Parading and symbolic nest-building are well marked features of pair interactions but the former is much less exaggerated than in the blue-foot and the latter lacks the special movement by which blue-foots 'show' the material to their partner. The intention movements of locomotion, signalling impending departure from the mate, take the form of the bill-up-face-away much as in the blue-foot and the wing rattle, preceding flight, is also shown. A significant difference between the two species is that the white booby lacks mutual advertising, the male alone performing the sky-pointing display.

The brown booby has hardly figured in this book because it breeds neither on the Galapagos Islands nor in Peru and at the time of writing I had not seen it elsewhere. Since then, I have studied it on Christmas Island and to make this comparative chapter more complete, a brief summary of its behaviour follows. It is not extremely close to any other booby, or at least not as similar as the Peruvian is to the blue-foot, though it shows many of the family features.

It is more aerial than the white booby and the male advertises in flight; as in the blue-foot, the pair advertise to each other. Like the white, it has a vigorous, though relatively undifferentiated meeting ceremony, called mutual jabbing. It performs ritualised bill-touching and has head-waving – motivationally aggressive and functionally declaring site-ownership. Although tending to nest on steeper ground and perhaps less given to territorial locomotion than the blue-foot or white, it nevertheless parades and shows ritualised intention movements of locomotion (bill-up-face-away) and of flight (wing-rattle). The nest is perhaps functional, and nest-building movements are much used in pair interactions.

Finally, the red-footed booby in many ways falls at the opposite end of the scale to the gannet. Its aerial agility was described earlier and I also suggested that large territory size and arboreal habit allowed withdrawal but hindered free movement around the territory in an aggression/fear situation, either between rivals or pair members. Unlike the white booby, blue-foot, and probably the brown booby, in their relatively large territories, the red-foot does not move around much, even though the space is available. For all practical purposes, its territory is merely the nest and a few nearby perches. It usually lands on one of the latter and hops to the nest. Unlike the gannet or Peruvian booby which are cheek by jowl with neighbours and virtually unable to move, or the white, brown and blue-footed boobies which parade around in their territories, the red-foot reduces its contacts to a minimum and the pair spend much time apart from each other. When the mates do meet and interact, it is often in a relatively hostile manner; their meeting ceremony is extremely difficult to distinguish from hostile jabbing between rival males. The advertising display forms a striking exception, being very well developed and performed as a mutual display. It seems that it makes up to some extent for the virtual lack of a meeting ceremony in the red-foot. Nevertheless, it seems that the pair bond is much less intimate in the red-foot than in some boobies and particularly the gannet. It is only for a short period before egg-laying that red-foots are at all intimately involved with each other, either in sharing nest building, mutual displays, copulation or preening each other. Obviously co-operation is essential at this time, but later they come and go with the minimum of contact and when both are simultaneously present in the territory, they usually sit well apart. This may explain why it is that several of the displays common to other members of the family are missing or much reduced in the red-foot. The elaborate parading and bill-up-face-away by which blue-foots communicate their intentions of moving in the territory are missing, because red-foots do not move much; when they do, it is usually to fly, and this is signalled by a wing-flick, which is the immediate precursor of flight. The interesting point here is that in the chain of preparatory actions, wing-flicking is a step nearer to actual flight than is wing-rattle; wing-rattle is the signal used by the boobies that usually parade around before taking off, wing-flicking is used by the red-foot, which takes off *without* prior parading. Looking at its behaviour from a different angle, the red-foot lacks mutually appeasing behaviour analogous to the mutual fencing of the gannet, or appeasing behaviour of the female equivalent to gannet facing-away, because complete withdrawal is practicable and is used. Females *do* face-away, but in a very fleeting way compared to the gannet's exaggerated posture.

Looking back over this part of the chapter, it seems that the

# TABLE 4 Comparative behaviour in the *Sulidae*

*Species arranged in approximate order of density of nests in colonies*

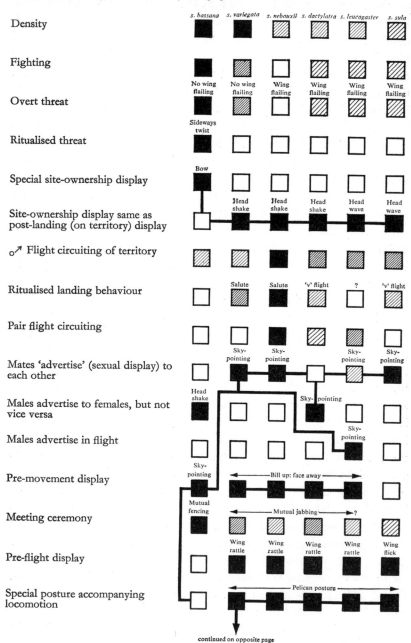

Density

Fighting

Overt threat

Ritualised threat

Special site-ownership display

Site-ownership display same as post-landing (on territory) display

♂ Flight circuiting of territory

Ritualised landing behaviour

Pair flight circuiting

Mates 'advertise' (sexual display) to each other

Males advertise to females, but not vice versa

Males advertise in flight

Pre-movement display

Meeting ceremony

Pre-flight display

Special posture accompanying locomotion

s. bassana · s. variegata · s. nebouxii · s. dactylatra · s. leucogaster · s. sula

continued on opposite page

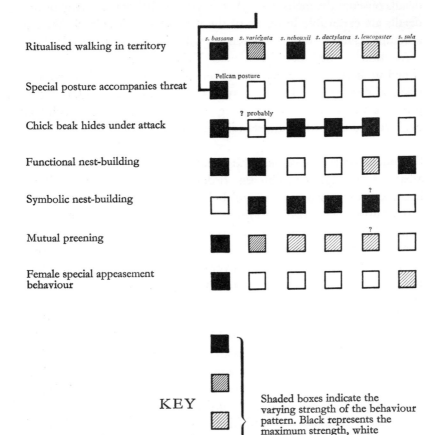

| | s. bassana | s. variegata | s. nebouxii | s. dactylatra | s. leucogaster | s. sula |

Ritualised walking in territory

Special posture accompanies threat — Pelican posture

Chick beak hides under attack — ? probably

Functional nest-building

Symbolic nest-building

Mutual preening

Female special appeasement behaviour

KEY — Shaded boxes indicate the varying strength of the behaviour pattern. Black represents the maximum strength, white represents none at all

**NOTES**

1 The presence or absence of particular behaviour patterns can be related to the main features of the habitat (density of nests, cliff, ground or tree nesting, etc.). The predominance of certain types of behaviour in a species' repertoire indicates their particular importance – e.g. aggression and its associated behaviour patterns (female appeasement, meeting ceremony, etc.) in the gannet.

2 Boxes joined by lines indicate homologous behaviour patterns.

details obscure the main story. Yet it is precisely because many of the details are explicable in terms of the main factors involved that the account achieves some coherence; without them, it would lack conviction by default of evidence. This comparative section has aimed to show how, given the observed factors of habitat, colony size and density and the anatomy of the species concerned, one can go some way towards interpreting the behaviour patterns each has evolved and towards understanding the differences.

So much for the boobies. The great frigate-bird and the waved albatross, belonging to different orders, seem to me worth pairing because a comparison of some of their main biological characteristics throws up some interesting points. To begin with, they are both very large sea-birds living at any rate to a fair extent on squids and fish; they are sympatric (on Hood) and both are magnificent fliers. Both lay single egg clutches and take a very long time to rear their young, and in consequence cannot breed every year, but probably breed once in two years if their attempts are successful. The adults of both species are long-lived. This seems an impressive list of similarities, but there are some equally formidable differences. Frigates probably do not pair for life as albatrosses do and so their reproductive behaviour repertoires are fundamentally different; their feeding regime and with it their method of rearing young are basically different and their population dynamics are very dissimilar in detail.

The fact that albatrosses and frigates both breed on Hood is itself worthy of note, since albatrosses are typically birds of high Antarctic latitudes and frigates belong mainly to the hot tropical seas. Hood Island shares equatorial heat with Antarctic water and it is probably via the Humboldt that the albatross reached the island, just as the penguin reached the Galapagos.

Much of this book has played around the topic of food and its great influence in determining so many of the biological features of the sea-birds it portrays; colony size, density, and behaviour have been related to it, and again it provides a point of departure.

The chief difficulties apparently facing the red-footed boobies of the Galapagos – periodic but unpredictable scarcity of food – also hit the frigate hard. These great birds, which, though there is no such thing, have been called the finest fliers in the world, are highly specialised hunters and have evolved a higher wing area to body weight ratio than any other sea-bird. An albatross (and in this chapter I mean only the waved albatross) supports seven to nine pounds on its eight-foot wing spread, but a frigate with wings as long and significantly broader than that supports a mere two-and-a-half to three pounds. This specialisation enables it practically to live on the wing, flying down other sea-birds by superior speed and agility, and cruising relatively vast distances without rest, unable to settle on the surface of the sea. It may be even more dependent on flying fish than is the red-foot so far as its direct hunting goes, though it certainly frequently takes squids.

Several features of frigate breeding biology reflect its offshore feeding habits. The one egg clutch, for instance, and the slow growth of the young. These, however, apply also to the albatross, yet there are big differences between the two. The frigate's egg weighs 5·1 per cent of the average female body weight. The albatross's egg, though it weighs twice as much as the frigate's, is still only 7·5 per cent of the female's weight, and this despite the very important fact that the frigate is a nidicolous species in which the young hatch blind, naked and helpless, whilst the albatross chick hatches thickly clothed in down, with open eyes and is active from the first. The Procellariformes lay notoriously large eggs and the notable fact is that the frigate should produce one almost as large in terms of its cost to the female, despite the basically different method of producing the young, in the one case favouring advanced development within the egg (and therefore necessarily having to provide more yolk) and in the other producing a far less developed chick. As in the case of the red-footed booby, whose egg is proportionately larger than in most boobies, the frigate seems to have gone as far as other factors allow in producing a relatively large egg. This favours the survival of the chick, which often is unlucky enough to emerge when food is scarce and is hard pressed to survive at all. The ability to hang on for an extra day or two could well be crucial to it and this in turn depends partly on the reserves with which it hatches.

The growth patterns of albatross and frigate chicks are widely dissimilar. The frigate follows the red-foot pattern of slow growth, frequent recessions and a large number of chick deaths directly or indirectly through food shortage. Then, and most staggering of all,

x

for the almost incredibly long period of several months' (perhaps more than six) free-flying juveniles are wholly or partly dependent on their parents. It must be remembered, too, that the young frigate, as a result of these protracted efforts on the part of its parents, reaches only the meagre weight of perhaps two-and-a-quarter pounds. The albatross chick, on the other hand, grows rapidly from the very beginning. It takes as long as the frigate to grow to the free-flying stage but on the way it registers up to ten pounds in weight. In terms of absolute weight gained, it grows several times faster than the frigate and starvation is rarely encountered. Like the frigate, it has recessions in growth, but as with the egg comparison, these reflect basically different biological situations. The frigate, like the red-foot, may suffer stunted growth for relatively long periods. In any bird, the weight attained immediately after a feed soon drops as the food is assimilated, metabolised and the waste products excreted. Frigates and red-foots, however, often continue dropping until they weigh less than before the feed and over a period this may continue until a substantial weight loss has occurred. Albatross chicks, on the other hand, lose weight massively after a feed because the feed is so huge, but they usually maintain a steady growth.

In both albatross and frigate, the far-ranging hunting regime means relatively infrequent feeds but whereas the frigate may return with 200–300 gm of food, the albatross returns with up to 2,000 gm. As I said in Chapter 9, the albatross's mechanism of manufacturing oil means that it can range widely, feeding as it goes, and the longer, within reason, that it stays away, the more it can bring back; it can be turning fresh food into oil even as it returns. The frigate is not in this happy position and the utmost it can do is to return with a full crop and perhaps part of the stomach contents. If it has far to travel, much of its food will have been digested by the time it gets back. Yet, apparently, judging from the long spells a hunting frigate requires, it needs to stay at sea for some time before it can find enough for itself and to bring back. So the young have to wait, during which they are losing weight all the time, without the compensating weight of food at the end.

The young albatross does not return to be fed once it has fledged. The long wait over, it takes off when it is fully able to fly and goes to sea. There are no figures whatever for their mortality rate, but it must be substantial, since the adults live so long and the population does not increase significantly. The juvenile frigate on the other hand returns for food for months after fledging and its mortality is correspondingly reduced, though by no means eliminated. This, of course, is exactly parallel to the differences between the gannet and the boobies – the former producing fledged young from seventy-three per cent of eggs laid but showing no post-fledging care of the young and losing seventy-five per cent of juveniles in their first few months of independence, whilst the red-foot, for instance, loses well over three-quarters of its eggs or young before they fledge (on Tower in 1964, ninety-two per cent of eggs laid failed to produce fledged young) but its post-fledging mortality is certainly much lower than the gannet's.

Despite superficial similarities, therefore, there are large differences in the breeding biology of the frigate and albatross. One of the most intriguing and least explicable is the fact that whilst the great frigate has a very wide distribution and is numerically a successful species, the waved albatross is confined to a paltry three thousand on Hood. The theory of natural regulation of animal numbers that in so many cases successfully explains things in terms of density-dependent competition for food at some stage in the animal's life (not necessarily the one in which it is feeding its young) and rejects the idea that animal populations fluctuate randomly in response to fortuitous environmental changes, has limitations here. As in other small closed populations, like the Galapagos hawk, with apparently abundant food and nest sites and no obvious source of mortality capable of keeping the population down, it is hard to see what prevents an increase (but see Chapter 9).

Turning to the comparison of behaviour in the albatross and frigate, another interesting series of linked differences emerges. Again, food is the ultimate causal factor. Because frigates take so long to complete a full reproductive cycle, they cannot breed every year. There is not time, even if the adults could stand the strain of plunging from one breeding to the next without recuperation. In Chapter 13, I described how puzzling we found the frigate's territorial behaviour. The male did not establish a territory and then stick to it – that was obvious enough from the way in which a

317

displaying male moved from one area to another if he had been unsuccessful in attracting a mate. At that time, we had very few facts of frigate biology at our disposal, so it seemed possible that the mobile males were young birds that had no breeding territory anyway. Even at that, it would have been a notably different situation from that of the boobies in which the male establishes his territory before attracting a female and does not move around trying out different spots. But when it became clear that the mobile birds included adult experienced males, the implications went deeper. Obviously, even birds that had bred did not necessarily return to their old site to pair up with their old mate. In fact, as I described, unless one postulates that the female goes around looking for her last year's mate and singles him out from the five, ten or even twenty among whom he may be displaying, it seems that the chances of permanent pairings are very slight; quite different from the typical situation in a long-lived seabird. Indeed, both territorial behaviour and the interactions between mates seemed much reduced. The principal male display by which he attracted a female was certainly exotic – far more so than any booby display – but that was all. Territorial displays were virtually non-existent, in the sense of special ritualised displays maintaining ownership of territories, and pair relations were minimal. Everything was put into the effort of getting a female and then once the pair bond had been sufficiently formed, the extremely long business of incubation and chick-rearing went on virtually as though two strangers were sharing the job. All this, with its several important side effects (see Chapter 13), stemmed from the once in two years breeding cycle. This apparently made permanent territories impracticable because, since the population was not 'in phase' – some bred one year and others the next – the nests (if any remained) or perhaps the site, of one pair could be taken over the next year by another.

The albatross falls much more conventionally into line. It has a very strong tendency to mate for life and the pair interactions are, to put it mildly, extensive, complex and ecstatic. The nest site hardly exists as such and territory is not hotly defended because once the chick hatches, the territory tends to move slightly, being the area around the chick, though with a tendency to centre around the actual nest site. However, it seems precise enough for the pair to re-unite with each new cycle. It seems that the frigate has had to put up with the disruption of the type of courtship and pair behaviour commonest among sea-birds in order to come to terms with the exacting demands of its feeding environment. The albatross has not been moulded by the same kinds of selection pressure and has maintained the traditional permanent pair bond, even though its territorial behaviour is not as highly developed as, for instance, in the *Sulidae*.

This chapter cannot have failed to give the reader indigestion, but maybe it has unified the separate accounts and put some finer details into perspective. When working in the field, one usually hopes that something new and exciting will turn up. Important discoveries are rare, but the piecing together of the thousand and one smaller bits of biological information can eventually fill a big canvas. The more penetrating and perceptive biological thinkers have put the rest of us in their debt by creating the wide vistas, enunciating the general principles. We who follow after, prove the depth of their insight by recognising, in a thousand and one detailed instances, the working of these laws. It is appropriate that the finer details in these chapters, if they testify to anything, testify to the all-powerful influence of natural selection, in the neo-Darwinian sense, in producing the wonderfully adapted forms that live lives, often far from enchanting, in the enchanted islands.

# *Food for one Year*     *Appendix 1*

4 sacks flour
2 sacks sugar
12 packs icing sugar
24 packets cornflakes
24 tins oats
7 lb oats
30 lb spaghetti
30 lb rice
7 lb dried peas
21 lb dried beans
6 large packets dried vegetables
Countless lbs candied fruit sent in mistake for dried
100 tins corned beef (bad, thrown away on arrival)
12 tins chitterling (sent by mistake and bad)
24 tins stew ⎫
4 tins chicken ⎬ stolen *en route*
1 tin turkey ⎭
50 tins spam
24 tins salmon
50 tins tuna
50 tins sardines
24 tins sausages
4 tins ham
24 tins bacon
100 tins butter
100 tins margarine
50 tins lard

2 tins cheese
12 cheeses
60 tins milk
24 tins cream
10 5-lb tins dried milk
7 lb tea
24 tins coffee
2 tins cocoa
Hundreds of tins of fruit juice sent in mistake for fruit
14 lb dried egg (ghastly mistake)
2 gal. corn oil
1 gal. honey
24 jars jam
24 tins tomato puree
12 jars pickle
2 jars salad cream stock cubes
36 jellies
24 lb biscuits
12 lb chocolate
24 packets mints
1 crate lemons
200 tins fruit
Misc. yeast, spices, etc.
1 large sack salt

Many desirable items were just not available in Ecuador.

BIRDS

| | |
|---|---|
| Albatross, black-browed | *Diomedea melanophris* |
| black-footed | *nigripes* |
| Buller's | *bulleri* |
| grey-headed | *chrysostoma* |
| Laysan | *immutablis* |
| royal | *epomophora* |
| sooty | *Phoebetria fusca* |
| wandering | *Diomedea exulans* |
| waved | *irrorata* |
| Blackbird | *Turdus merula* |
| Black noddy | *Anous stolidus* |
| Booby, Abbott's | *Sula abbotti* |
| blue-footed | *nebouxii* |
| brown | *leucogaster* |
| Peruvian | *variegata* |
| red-footed | *sula* |
| white | *dactylatra* |
| Brambling | *Fringilla montifringilla* |
| Budgerigar | *Melopsittacus undulatus* |
| Buzzard | *Buteo buteo* |
| Chaffinch | *Fringilla coelebs* |
| Condor | *Vultur gryphus* |
| Cormorant, cape | *Phalacrocorax capensis* |
| guanay | *bougainvillei* |
| Crow | *Corvus corone* |
| Cuckoo | *Cuculus canorus* |
| Dove, Galapagos ground | *Nesopelia galapagoensis* |
| Duck, eider | *Somateria mollissima* |
| Eagle, golden | *Aquila chrysaetos* |
| Falcon, Greenland | *Falco rusticolus* |
| peregrine | *peregrinus* |

| | |
|---|---|
| Finch, Darwin's cactus | *Geospiza conirostris* |
| large-billed ground | *magnirostris* |
| mangrove | *Camarhynchus heliobates* |
| warbler | *Certhidea olivacea* |
| woodpecker | *Camarhynchus pallidus* |
| Flamingo | *Phoenicopterus ruber* |
| Flycatcher | *Mycarchus magnirostris* |
| Frigate bird, great | *Fregata minor* |
| magnificent | *magnificens* |
| Fulmar | *Fulmarus glacialis* |
| Gannet, Australasian | *Morus serrator* |
| Cape | *capensis* |
| North Atlantic | *bassana* |
| Goose, greylag | *Anser anser* |
| Guillemot | *Uria aalge* |
| Gull, Andean | *Larus serranus* |
| black-headed | *ridibundus* |
| Californian | *californicus* |
| Dominican | *dominicanus* |
| dusky | *fuliginosus* |
| Franklin's | *pipixcan* |
| glaucous | *hyperboreus* |
| great black-backed | *marinus* |
| herring | *argentatus* |
| Iceland | *leucopterus* |
| ivory | *Pagophila eburnea* |
| kittiwake | *Rissa tridactyla* |
| laughing | *Larus atricilla* |
| Ross's | *Rhodostethia rosea* |
| Sabine's | *Xema sabini* |
| swallow-tailed | *Creagrus furcatus* |
| Hawk, Galapagos | *Buteo galapagoensis* |
| red-tailed | *jamaicensis* |
| sparrow | *Accipiter nisus* |
| Swainson's | *Buteo swainsoni* |
| zone-tailed | *albonotatus* |
| Hen | *Gallus domesticus* |
| Heron, Galapagos purple | *Ardea herodias* |
| yellow-crowned night | *Nyctanassa violacea* |
| Mocking bird | *Nesomimus* sp. |
| Osprey | *Pandion haliaetus* |

BIRDS (*continued*)

| | |
|---|---|
| Owl, Galapagos barn owl | *Tyto alba punctassima* |
| short-eared | *Asio flammeus galapagoensis* |
| snowy | *Nyctea scandiaca* |
| tawny | *Strix aluco* |
| Peacock | *Pavo* spp. |
| Pelican, brown | *Pelecanus occidentalis* |
| Chilean | *thagus* |
| pink-backed | *rufescens* |
| white | *erythrorhynchus* |
| Penguin, Cape | *Spheniscus demersus* |
| Galapagos | *mendiculus* |
| Humboldt | *humboldti* |
| Petrel, diving (burrowing) | *Pelecanoides gamotii* |
| Galapagos storm | *Oceanodroma tethys* |
| Hawaiian storm | *Pterodroma phaeopygia* |
| Madeiran storm | *Oceanodroma castro* |
| Phalarope, grey | *Phalaropus fulicarius* |
| Pintail, Galapagos | *Poecilonetta galapagoensis* |
| Pipit, meadow | *Anthus pratensis* |
| rock | *spinoletta petrosus* |
| Ptarmigan | *Lagopus mutus* |
| Puffin | *Fratercula arctica* |
| Raven | *Corvus corax* |
| Razorbill | *Alca torda* |
| Red grouse | *Lagopus scoticus* |
| Robin | *Erithacus rubecula* |
| Rook | *Corvus frugilegus* |
| Shag | *Phalacrocorax aristotelis* |
| Shearwater, Audubon's | *Puffinus lherminieri* |
| sooty | *griseus* |
| Skua, great | *Catharacta skua* |
| Arctic | *Stercorarius parasiticus* |
| Tern, fairy | *Sterna nereis* |
| Inca | *Larosterna inca* |
| little | *Sterna albifrons* |
| Tropicbird, red-billed | *Phaethon aethereus* |
| Turnstone | *Arenaria interpres interpres* |
| Vulture, black | *Coragyps atratus* |
| king | *Sarcoranphus bafa* |
| Turkey | *Cathartes aura* |

| | |
|---|---|
| Wandering tattler | *Heteroscelus incanus* |
| Warbler, Galapagos yellow | *Dendroica petechia aureolo* |

OTHER ANIMALS

| | |
|---|---|
| Albacore | *Seriola lalandi* |
| Anchovy | *Engraulis* spp. |
| Bear | *Ursus* spp. |
| Butterfly, meadow brown | *Maniola jurtina* |
| Centipede, giant | *Scolopendra galapagoensis* |
| Cod | *Gadus morrhua* |
| Crab, fiddler | *Uca leptochelia eibli* |
| red | *Grapsus grapsus* |
| Crayfish | *Panulirus penicillatus* |
| Deer | *Cervus elaphus* |
| Dolphin | *Delphinus* spp. |
| Elephant | *Loxodonta* spp. |
| Fox | *Vulpes vulpes* |
| Goat | *Capra* spp. |
| Hare | *Lepus europaeus* |
| Herring | *Clupea harengus* |
| Iguana, land | *Conolophus subcristatus* |
| marine | *Amblyrhynchus cristatus* |
| Kangaroo | *Macropus giganteus* |
| Lizard, lava | *Tropidurus* spp. |
| Maas banker | *Trachurus trachurus* |
| Mackerel | *Scomber scomber* |
| Manta, giant | *Manta* spp. |
| Marlin | *Makaira herscheli* |
| Mouse, house | *Mus musculus* |
| Newt, crested | *Cristatus cristatus* |
| Octopus | *Cephalopoda* |
| Parrot fish | *Scaridae* |
| Pilchard | *Sardinops ocellata* |
| Porpoise | *Phocaena* spp. |
| Puffer fish | *Tetraodon annulatus* |
| Rabbit | *Oryctolagus cuniculus* |
| Rat, black | *Rattus rattus* |
| brown | *Rattus norvegicus* |
| Galapagos | *Oryzomys* spp. |
| Saithe | *Gadus virens* |

OTHER ANIMALS (*continued*)

| | |
|---|---|
| Sand eel | *Ammodytes* spp. |
| Seal, atlantic | *Haliehoerus grypus* |
| elephant | *Macrorhinus angustirostris* |
| Galapagos fur | *Arctocephalus galapagoensis* |
| grey | See 'atlantic' |
| Sea-lion, Galapagos | *Zalophus wollebacki* |
| Sea trout | *Salmo fario* var. *trutta* |
| Shark, black | *Carcharinus melanopterus* |
| white tipped | *Carcharinus longimanus* |
| Snake, Galapagos | *Dromicus* spp. |
| Squid | *Cephalopoda, Decapoda* |
| Squirrel | *Sciurus* spp. |
| Stickleback, three-spined | *Gasterosteus aculeatus* |
| Tortoise, Galapagos giant | *Testudo elephantopus* |
| Tuna | *Thunnus* spp. |
| Turtle | *Caretta caretta* |

# Glossary of Scientific Terms

*Adaptive* A character, whether behavioural, physiological, anatomical, etc., is adaptive if it confers survival value on its possessor. Most (some would say all) biological characters are adaptive, though the ways in which they are so may be extremely difficult to understand.

*Allelomorph* Genes occupying corresponding loci on a pair of chromosomes.

*Allopatric* See *Sympatric*.

*Altruistic Behaviour* This idea has become better known in recent years as an important concept in social behaviour, perhaps particularly with respect to reproduction. It really implies doing something which benefits the group at large but without benefiting the pair concerned, to whose interests in the conventional sense (i.e. production of more young) it may in fact be inimical. Thus, a pair of animals voluntarily refraining from breeding whilst other members of the group reproduce may in fact be acting in the interests of group survival if the food situation is such that all-out breeding by the whole group would lead to over-exploitation, to the detriment of the whole population. The refraining pairs would be behaving altruistically.

*Ambivalent Motivation* When an animal simultaneously experiences two differing 'drives' or motivations, it is ambivalently motivated. The result may be conflict behaviour or displacement reactions, typical for each species in given circumstances, but widely differing between different species and in different circumstances.

*Analogous* If structures or behaviour patterns, for example, serve similar ends in different species but are not derived from the same source, they are analogous; wings of butterflies and birds are analogous. If they share the same source, they are homologous; the foreflipper of a whale and the arms of a man are homologous, as are two behaviour patterns that stem from the same ancestral source.

*Breeding Cycle* The sequence of events taking place during reproduction, including everything necessary to bring about successful breeding.

*Breeding Season* Sometimes used loosely as synonymous with breeding cycle; should refer to the actual period of year during which breeding activities take place. Can be predictable in some species and non-seasonal (i.e. not occurring every year at the same season) in others.

*Carboniferous* A geological epoch lasting from 270 to 210 million years ago.

*Collective Territory* An area defended by a group of individuals (more than a family) against others of the same species. Most territories, by contrast, are defended by one bird, a pair, or, in some cases, a family.

*Crèche* A system in which the care of young is not confined to the parents or even to individuals that have recently bred. 'Aunts' take charge, indiscriminately, of pooled broods or part broods belonging to other females. Eiders and emperor penguins are good examples because in the former the young are dependent on the crèche females for protection and guidance, whilst in the emperor penguin the young must actually be fed by crèche adults.

*Deferred Maturity* Some large, long-lived birds may go several years before they breed for the first time. This may or may not be also the period which it takes them to develop fully adult plumage, etc. In a strict sense maturity can only be said to be 'deferred' if it is somehow put off beyond the minimal time necessary. Thus, several species do not usually breed until they are one or more years older than the age at which breeding is physiologically possible.

*Dominance* See *Homozygous Recessive*.

*Ecology* The biological discipline that has to do with an organism's relationship to its external environment, including other organisms. Covers a vast field of inter-relationships. The mechanisms by which ecological adjustments are made are in the last analysis behavioural, and this book has given many examples of the relationship between ecology and behaviour.

*Ecological Niche* That part of the total environment to which an organism is particularly well adapted. A niche may be relatively broad or highly specialised.

*Endemic* Applied to a species or other group (genus, family, etc.) in relation to its restriction to a stated area (which may be a tiny island or a whole continent, thus introducing practical difficulties in application).

*Fledging Period* The time the young bird spends in the nest between hatching and (usually) making its first sustained flight or otherwise leaving the nest, usually not to return. In nidifugous species cannot be so reckoned, but is still the period between hatching and becoming capable of flight. This may or may not also be the time at which the young bird has achieved its full complement of true feathers and/or the full growth of these.

*Gene* A unit of inherited material, recognised by its constant effect on the development of an individual bearing it.

*Genotype* See *Phenotype*.

*Gonads* The organs (male testes, female ovaries) responsible for producing sex hormones which, interacting with external stimuli, greatly influence sexual and aggressive behaviour.

*Gonyx* (or gonys) The ridge formed by the two rami of the lower mandible near its tip; particularly evident as a flat bottom edge to part of the lower mandible of gulls.

*Heterozygote* (see *Homozygous*) Having different allelomorphs on the two corresponding loci of a pair of chromosomes. Typically one gene is then dominant and the other recessive; the character contained by the dominant gene appears in the phenotype.

*Homologous* See *Analogous*.

*Homozygous Recessive* Homozygous means having identical genes (that is, not different allelomorphs) in the two corresponding loci of a pair of chromosomes. The allelomorph which is ineffective in the heterozygote is said to be 'recessive' in contrast to the dominant allelomorph which produces its effect in the phenotype regardless of whether it is present in single dose (masking a recessive) or in double dose (in a homozygote).

*Innate* Strictly, only inborn behaviour which does not need to be learned is innate. However, the once hard and fast line between innate and learned is now extremely blurred. Many behaviour patterns, though basically innate, are partly learned (e.g. a species may inherit the general type of its song pattern, but is affected by the particular features of the song it hears around it whilst still a helpless chick in the nest (possibly, who knows, in the egg!). Also, maturation of many behaviour patterns (such as snail smashing in thrushes) affects its expression, and maturation is difficult to separate, entirely, from learning.

*Intention Movement* Certain behaviour patterns, for instance fledging in birds, are typically preceded by movements which, in preparing the animal for the behaviour in question, also convey its 'intentions'.

*Juvenile* The first fully-feathered and free-flying stage in a bird's life, until the next moult (whole or part).

*Littoral* A zone on the sea shore between high and low water marks.

*Mesozoic* A geological era compounding the (successive) Triassic, Jurassic and Cretaceous periods which together lasted from 180 to 60 million years ago. The so-called 'middle' period dominated by reptiles.

*Natural Selection* The environmental (in the broadest sense) forces which act on an organisms' attributes, so that the biologically fittest (taking all characters as an interacting whole) survive best, together comprise natural selection.

*Nidicolous* Birds whose young are born in a relatively helpless condition, virtually naked and largely blind, as are passerines and gannets and boobies.

*Nidifugous* Birds whose young are born active, with a thick downy plumage and eyes open.

*Oligogene* A 'large' gene responsible in an all or none way for a single character in the phenotype, as against polygenes, whose effect is additive, leading to graded intermediates in the phenotypes.

*Ontogeny* The process of development in an individual.

*Pentadactyl Limb* The basic type of mammalian limb having certain parts in fives (five fingers, wrist bones, toes, ankle bones, etc.).

*Phenotype* Genes express their effects in the living organism or phenotype, the genetic construction of which is the genotype.

*Phylogeny* The evolution and relationship of taxonomic groups. 'Ontogeny recapitulates phylogeny' in the sense that during development the individual human, for instance, goes through the main stages that the species went through during its evolution.

*Post-fledging Feeding* Species in which parents continue to feed their young after these have become free-flying (or whatever definition of fledging one accepts – see *Fledging*) may be said to show post-fledging feeding. All boobies do so, but gannets do not. The frigate-bird may continue post-fledging feeding for as long as six months.

*Proximate Factors* See *Ultimate Factors*.

*Ritualised Displays* Stereotyped behaviour patterns of a more or less conspicuous and exaggerated kind, with signal value, usually, but not always, to individuals of the same species. Often show off a brightly coloured part or a conspicuous structure.

*Social Stimulation* (or facilitation) Is the sum of the external stimuli, perhaps mainly behavioural in the sense of interactions involving seeing, hearing and reacting by overt behaviour to other members of the group. This social stimulation 'facilitates' breeding in the sense of bringing about its onset earlier, and synchronising it to a degree higher (though variable) than it would otherwise have been. Actual proof of this effect is still rare.

*Sympatric* Two or more species with overlapping distribution are sympatric in the areas of overlap. Two or more species whose distributions do not overlap are allopatric. Two species may be sympatric in part of the range and allopatric in the rest, or totally one or the other.

*Synchronisation in Breeding* A measure of the period over which laying (in birds) or parturition is spread, usually as a proportion of an ordinary unit (week, month, year). Highly synchronised breeding is that in which a high proportion or all of the population produces eggs or young within a relatively short period rather than spread out over a long one.

*Teleological* In attempting to answer the question 'why?' in relation to ends or final causes, teleology deals with design or purpose especially in natural phenomena. Particularly associated with a religico-natural historical view implying either conscious knowledge of end results by animals, or control by God. Unfairly applied sometimes as a criticism of perfectly valid investigations of function and adaptation in animals.

*Ultimate Factors* are usually contrasted with proximate factors, following an old definition by Baker. Ultimate factors are those, for example the availability of food, to which a species' reproductive activities may be geared. If food, or lack of it, is going to be a major factor causing mortality in a population, breeding will be geared so that the species, on the whole, copes adequately with the situation. This may mean laying a certain number of eggs rather than more or less, breeding at a certain time of year, etc. This breeding regime, however, will be initiated and controlled by mechanisms depending on proximate factors, such as light, temperature, etc. The bird responds to these before the ultimate factors have had any chance to come into play; nevertheless by so doing it behaves adaptively.

*Zoogeographical* The world is divisible into several geographical areas in each of which the fauna share affinities, but are definably distinct from those of other zoogeographical areas.

# Bibliography

ABS, M., CURIO, E., KRAMER, P., and NIETHAMMER, J. (1965), 'Zur Ernährungsweise der Eulen auf Galapagos'. *J. für Orn.*, **106**, 49–57.

ALEXANDER, W. B. (1928), *Birds of the Ocean*. New York.

BAILEY, R. S. (1964), 'Cruise of R.R.S. *Discovery* in the Indian Ocean'. *The Sea Swallow*, **17**, 52–6.

BEEBE, W. (1924), *Galapagos: World's End*. New York.

COKER, R. E. (1919), 'Habits and economic relations of the guano birds of Peru'. *Proc. U.S. Natl Mus.*, **56**, 449–511.

COLNETT, J. (1798), *A Cruising Voyage Around the World*. London.

CURIO, E. (1964), 'Zur geographischen Variation des Feinderkennens einiger Darwinfinken (Geospizidae)'. *Verh. Dtsch. Zool. Ges. Kiel*, 466–492.

CURIO, E., and KRAMER, P. (1964), 'Vom Mangrovefinken (*Cactospiza heliobates*, Snodgrass und Heller)'. *Z. Tierpsychol.*, **21**, 223–34.

DARLING, F. F. (1938), *Bird Flocks and the Breeding Cycle*. Cambridge.

(1939), *A Naturalist on Rona*. Oxford.

(1947), *Natural History in the Highlands and Islands*. London.

DARWIN, C. (1874), *The Descent of Man*. 2nd edn. London.

(1890), *A Naturalist's Voyage Around the World*. New York.

DORWARD, D. F. (1962), 'Comparative biology of the White Booby and the Brown Booby *Sula* spp. at Ascension'. *Ibis*, **103**b, 174–220.

DROWNE, F. P. *See* HARRIS, C. M.

EIBL-EIBESFELDT, I. (1960), *Galapagos*. London.

FOSBERG, F. R. (1965), 'Natural Bird Refuges in the Galapagos'. *The Elepaio*, **25**, 60–7.

GIBSON-HILL, C. A. (1947), 'Notes on the birds of Christmas Island'. *Bull. Raffles Mus.*, **18**, 87–165.

GIFFORD, E. W. (1913), 'The birds of the Galapagos Islands . . . (Columbiformes to Pelecaniformes)'. *Proc. Calif. Acad. Sc.* **2**, 1–132.

HAILMAN, J. P. (1963), 'Why is the Galapagos Lava Gull the colour of lava?' *Condor*, **65**, 528.

HARRIS, C M., and DROWNE, F. P. (1899), 'Diaries of the Webster-Harris Expedition 1897'. *Novitates Zoologicae*, **6**, 86–135.

HEYERDAHL, T., and SKJOLSVOLD, A. (1956), 'Archaeological evidence of pre-Spanish visits to the Galapagos Islands'. *Amer. Antiquity*, **22**.

HOBSON, E. S. (1965), 'Observations on diving in the Galapagos Marine Iguana *Amblyrhynchus cristatus* (Bell)'. *Copeia*, **2**, 249–50.

HOWARD, L. (1952), *Birds as Individuals*. London.

HOWELL, T. R., and BARTHOLOMEW, G. A. (1962), 'Temperature regulation in the Red-tailed Tropic Bird and the Red-footed Booby'. *Condor*, **64**, 6–18.

HUTCHINSON, G. E. (1950), 'The biogeochemistry of vertebrate excretion'. *Bull. Am. Mus. Nat. Hist.*, **96**.

KRUUK, H. (1966), 'The competition for food between some East African vultures (Falconidae, Aegypiinae)' in *Abstracts 14th Int. Orn. Coug.* Oxford. p. 78.

LACK, D. (1946), *The Life of the Robin*. London.

(1947), *Darwin's Finches*. Cambridge.

(1954), *The Natural Regulation of Animal Numbers*. Oxford.

'Las Poblaciones de Aves Guaneras y su Situacion Actual'. (1966), Instituto del Mar del Peru. *Informe*, **10**.

LORENZ, K. (1966), *On Aggression*. London.

MARKHAM, C. R. (1892), 'Discovery of the Galapagos Islands'. *Proc. of Royal Geographical Soc.* London.

MEIKLEJOHN, M. F. M. (1951), 'The Naturalist's Early Morning Walk'. *Bird Notes*, **25**, 13–15.

MURPHY, R. C. (1936), *Oceanic Birds of South America*. New York.

NELSON, J. B. (1964), 'Factors influencing clutch size and chick growth in the North Atlantic Gannet *Sula bassana*'. *Ibis*, **106**, 63–77.

(1966), 'The behaviour of the young Gannet'. *Brit. Birds*.

(1966), 'The breeding biology of the Gannet *Sula bassana* on the Bass Rock, Scotland'. *Ibis*, **108**, 584–626.

(1966), 'Clutch size in the *Sulidae*'. *Nature*, **210**, 435–6.

(1966), 'Flighting behaviour of Galapagos Storm Petrels'. *Ibis*, **108**, 430–2.

(1966) 'Population dynamics of the Gannet (*Sula bassana*) at the Bass Rock, with comparative information from other *Sulidae*'. *J. Anim. Ecol.*, **35**, 443–70.

NIETHAMMER, J. (1964), 'Contribution à la connaissance des mammifères terrestres de l'île Indefatigable [= Santa Cruz] Galapagos'. Extrait de *Mammalia*, **28**, 593–606.

PALMER, R. S. (1962), *Handbook of North American Birds*. New York.

PARKER, E. (1943), *Oddities of Natural History*. London.

PECK, G. W. (1854), *Melbourne and the Chincha Islands; with sketches of Lima and a Voyage Round the World*. New York.

PHILLIPS, G. C. (1962), *Survival value of the white colouration of gulls and other sea-birds*. D. Phil. Thesis. Oxford.

PIKE, O. G. (*c.* 1920), *Bird Biographies*. London.

PUMPHREY, R. J. (1952), in *Biology and comparative physiology of birds*, ed. A. J. Marshall. New York.

RAND, R. W. (1959), 'The biology of guano-producing sea-birds'. *Commerce*, **39**.

RICE, D. W., and KENYON, K. W. (1962), 'Breeding cycles and behavior of Laysan and Black-footed Albatrosses'. *Auk*, **79**, 517–67.

SNOW, D. W. and B. K. (1967), 'The breeding cycle of the Swallow-tailed Gull *Creagrus furcatus*'. *Ibis*, **109**, 14–24.

SPEIGHT, W. L. (1940), 'The South African Guano Islands'. *The Fertiliser, Feeding Stuffs and Farm Supplies Jour.*, **25**.

THORPE, W. H. (1956), *Learning and Instinct in Animals*. London.

TINBERGEN, N. (1954), 'The origin and evolution of courtship and threat display' in *Evolution as a Process*, ed. J. Huxley. London.

TINBERGEN, N., BROEKHUYSEN, G. J., FEEKES, F., HOUGHTON, J. C. W., KRUUK, H., SZULC, E. (1962), 'Eggshell removal by the Black-headed Gull, *Larus ridibundus* L.; a behaviour component of camouflage'. *Behav.*, **19**, 74–117.

VAN DEN ASSEM, J. (1965), 'Territory size as a factor in reproductive competition in the three-spined stickleback'. *Summaries 9th Int. Ethol. Conf. Zurich*, 3.

VERNER, J. (1961), 'Nesting activities of the Red-footed Booby in British Honduras'. *Auk*, **78**, 573–94.

VERRILL, G. E. (1923), 'Rough notes on the avifauna of Paita, Peru'. *Auk*, **40**, 303–12.

WYNNE-EDWARDS, V. C. (1962), *Animal Dispersion in Relation to Social Behaviour*. Edinburgh.

# Index